To Work in the Vineyard of Surgery

To Work in the Vineyard of Surgery

The Reminiscences of J. COLLINS WARREN (1842–1927)

" . . . to labour commendably, and with a good
conscience to work in the Vineyard of Surgery."

WILLIAM CLOWES (1544–1604),
Maister in Chirurgerie and
Chirurgeon to the Queen.

Edited, with Appendices,
Notes, and Comments, by
EDWARD D. CHURCHILL, M.D.

HARVARD UNIVERSITY PRESS
Cambridge, Massachusetts
1958

Preface

A few years ago Dr. Richard Warren gave me an opportunity to read the reminiscences of his grandfather, Dr. J. Collins Warren. I found certain parts quite exciting and other passages dull and tedious; the entire manuscript cried for radical editing, a task on which Dr. Warren had worked but had not been able to make headway before his death. Dr. Richard Warren generously accepted the bold suggestion that I try my hand as editor and annotator.

Dr. Warren lived in intimate association with two institutions, the Medical School of Harvard University and the Massachusetts General Hospital. He was a participant in the joint endeavor to educate doctors, advance medical knowledge, and care for the sick. This joint undertaking of Harvard and the Hospital has been going on for a hundred and fifty years, and is pursued more energetically today than ever before.

I did not know Dr. J. Collins Warren, although I recall seeing him once or twice when he made a visit to the Hospital on some special occasion. My acquaintance with the two institutions is more than a passing one because I too have spent years of my professional life immersed in their joint endeavor. These institutions are my real bond with Dr. Warren — and, of course, the conviction held in common about the ascending importance of surgery as the ancient healing art gains the strength of a science.

Many editorial liberties have been taken with the manuscript of the Reminiscences, and new material has been bonded in from Dr. Warren's scattered writings. Those who fear mutilation may check by reference to the copies preserved in the archives of the Massachusetts Historical Society. The typescripts are there with undisturbed patina for anyone to examine.

As for the Appendices, the first started out to be a collection of supplementary biographical material, but here, as in the notes, the editor-author could not resist following through some thoughts of his own. Appendix II is a somewhat ponderous but documentary record of the beginning of Harvard's attempt to reduce the citadel Cancer, a siege which is going on some fifty years later with echoes of the same trumpet calls to action. In Appendix III the editor-author takes over completely and not only offers interpretations but indulges in extrapolation that renders him completely vulnerable.

Of course it must be obvious that my prime interest did not become fixed on Dr. Warren as a person but lay in the events which surrounded him. While careful effort has been made to keep the little he reveals of himself, I still feel that I can claim no more than a superficial acquaintance. Indeed, the Warren Reminiscences have afforded an opportunity to look upon the Vineyard in which we both have worked from two vantage points separated by a half century. The reader is reminded that at the best two points can determine only a straight line, and under such circumstances the interpretation of events, particularly recent ones, becomes deceptively and perilously simple.

Identification of sources within the text or accompanying footnotes stands as acknowledgment to numerous authors and publishers. The Houghton Mifflin Company, which now occupies the site of the former Warren house on Park Street, courteously gave permission to interweave material, without quotation marks, from a published essay by Dr. Warren entitled "Reminiscences of Park Street" with the text of his narrative. Without blanket permission from *The New England Journal of Medicine* to draw freely upon its pages and those of its titular predecessor, *The Boston Medical and Surgical Journal,* adequate annotation would have been impossible. I am also indebted to the Massachusetts Historical Society, to various Harvard University publications, and to the Archives and the Records of the Massachusetts General Hospital. The editorial counsel of the Harvard University Press has been offered and accepted. The painstaking and patient help of Mr. George H. Jacobsen in uncovering historical material, checking and rechecking references, correcting and rephrasing the text, proofreading, and preparing the index made my projected task feasible. I can only hope that my colleague Dr. Richard Warren will be pleased rather than disappointed by this interpretation of the manuscript of his grandfather.

E. D. C.

CONTENTS

ILLUSTRATIONS

The Warren Family

Members of the Warren family have made many contributions to the medicine and surgery of the New World. From 1782 to the present, with scarcely an interval, Warrens have been teachers at Harvard and, since its opening in 1821, staff surgeons of the Massachusetts General Hospital.

JOSEPH WARREN (1741 — 1775)

Medical practitioner and patriot, who gave his life on Bunker Hill as a general officer of the Revolutionary army at the head of his troops.

JOHN WARREN (1753 — 1815)

Brother of Joseph; a leader in the establishment of the Medical Institution of Harvard College, and first professor of anatomy and surgery; a founder of the Massachusetts Medical Society; director of a military hospital in Boston during the Revolution.

JOHN COLLINS WARREN (1778 — 1856)

Son of John; professor of anatomy and surgery at Harvard, and first surgeon of the Massachusetts General Hospital; joined with James Jackson in the founding of the Hospital, where he performed the historic operation under ether on October 16, 1846.

JONATHAN MASON WARREN (1811 — 1867)

Son of John Collins; visiting surgeon at the Massachusetts General Hospital; introduced the art of plastic surgery from Europe to America, and first performed a free transplant of human skin.

JOHN COLLINS WARREN (1842 — 1927)

Son of J. Mason; professor of surgery at Harvard, and visiting surgeon at the Hospital; pioneered in bringing to America Lister's technique of surgical healing without infection; performed in 1889 the first operation in a new surgical building designed to protect patients from operative infections; with Henry P. Bowditch, brought the great undertaking of a new Harvard Medical School to completion in 1906.

JOHN WARREN (1874 — 1928)

Son of John Collins; associate professor of anatomy at Harvard; expounder of the architecture of the human body, the foundation on which all modern medicine and surgery is based.

RICHARD WARREN

Nephew of John; clinical professor of surgery at the Harvard Medical School.

To Work in the Vineyard of Surgery

Two Discoveries
Awaken an Ancient Art

It seems worth while to make a record of some of my personal recollections because I have been so situated as to be more or less intimately in contact with the prime movers in that great change which was brought about in surgery by the introduction of anesthesia. Although I was only four years of age at the time of this historic event, my relations to many of the parties concerned were such that I have always felt that I had more or less personal knowledge of an epoch in medicine and surgery which marked the beginning of a new and great era.

Surgery had made but few advances during that portion of the nineteenth century which preceded the public demonstration of anesthesia at the Massachusetts General Hospital on October 16th, 1846.[1] The wars of the early part of the century had no doubt improved greatly the technique of surgical operations which the master minds

[1] As is so often the case with major "discoveries," there were many claimants to the honor of having been "first" in the formulation of the concept, the development of the method, or the selection of the particular drug for the abolition of pain during a surgical operation. Dr. Warren (hereafter referred to as J. C. W.) lived in decades torn by the angry dispute known as the "ether controversy." Actually, the control of pain had been "in the air" for several decades prior to 1846, and the time was ripe for the conjunction of an imaginative and bold inventor, a mature and responsible surgeon, and a willing patient. This conjunction took place in the operating room of the Bulfinch Building on the 16th of October 1846. In an attempt to preserve the significance of the event and raise it out of the acrid waters of contention, President Charles W. Eliot and Dr. Henry P. Walcott wrote the familiar words inscribed on the north wall of the Ether Dome:

> On October 16, 1846 in this room, then the operating theatre of the Hospital, was given the first public demonstration of anaesthesia to the extent of producing insensibility to pain during a serious surgical operation. Sulphuric ether was administered by William Thomas Green Morton, a Boston dentist. The patient was Gilbert Abbott. The operation was the removal of a tumor under the jaw. The surgeon was John Collins Warren. The patient declared that he had felt no pain during the operation and was discharged well December 7. Knowledge of this discovery spread from this room throughout the civilized world, and a new era for surgery began.

This inscription gave origin to the term "public demonstration," and to this day the Hospital in a self-conscious way avoids reference to a "discovery" of ether anesthesia.

of Baron Larrey in France, Sir Astley Cooper in England, and others
had done so much to design. The operation of lithotrity [2] introduced
by Jean Civiale was beginning to displace the time-honored cutting
for stone, but it stood out as rather a brilliant exception to what was
otherwise a persistence of old methods.

Surgery was responding, of course, to the stimulus given by a
more intimate knowledge of anatomy and pathology, but innovations even at the great medical centers were few and far between.
Surgical operations in civil practice were rarely operations of choice,
for it was only dire necessity that forced a patient to submit to the
knife. The number of operations performed was extremely small,
except in war time. The surgical service at a hospital could not
absorb a great deal of the surgeon's time, and there were few
men indeed who undertook to limit their practice to surgery alone,
as can be seen by a study of the lives of the prominent physicians
of that period. The number of operations was so small that when
an opportunity to demonstrate the advantages of sulphuric ether
as an anesthetic agent was sought by Dr. Morton at the Massachusetts General Hospital, it was necessary to wait a fortnight before
a suitable patient turned up.

The historic event of the discovery of anesthesia marks the close
of the first of three great eras. The second era, from Morton to
Lister, was distinguished by only a moderate increase in the scope
of surgery. During this period, owing to the abolition of pain, operations increased tenfold in number, although there were no corresponding improvements either in the technique of the operations
or in the management of wounds. Surgeons were equipped neither
by skill nor by scientific knowledge to keep pace with the changes
ushered in by the great discovery. So the second era, during which
my medical career began, was replete with the dangers and com-

[2] Lithotrity, or lithothripsy, is an ancient procedure, attempted by the Byzan-
tines and the Arabs, and revived sporadically many times. Its perfection required
the forging of a precise and well-tempered instrument that could be passed
through the natural passages into the urinary bladder, there to seize and crush
a stone into tiny fragments. In the hands of the adept this procedure was safer
and less subject to complications than cutting for stone (lithotomy). One technical difficulty of the operation was ridding the bladder of the bits of stone, for if
a fragment remained it became a nucleus for the formation of a new stone. An
efficient apparatus for washing the fragments out of the bladder was invented by
Dr. Henry J. Bigelow, who christened the procedure litholapaxy (see Chapter
XVI).

Jean Civiale is usually credited with the introduction of lithotrity in the nineteenth century. He was well known to John C. and J. Mason Warren. The latter,
writing to his father from Paris in 1854, said: "Among the medical men here the
principal attention I have received has been from Civiale, whose kindness has
been unbounded . . . He has asked much about you, and says you are a wonder;
that he never saw so active a person."

plications which inevitably arose from the crowding together of numbers of surgical patients. Civil surgery came to have as high a mortality as that which marked the campaigns of the Napoleonic wars. It was not until two decades after the introducion of anesthesia that the pioneer work of Louis Pasteur paved the way for Joseph Lister's first studies on the causes of wound infection. This made it possible to contend with hospital infection, at first by means of chemical disinfectants. The second era may fairly be said to have covered three decades, for it was not until after another ten years that antiseptic surgery began to be replaced by aseptic surgery [3]

[3] The terms *antisepsis* and *asepsis* will be found with considerable frequency particularly in the latter part of this volume. It is worth while at this point to consider the ways in which these terms are used. In the surgical writings of German and American authors it is conventional to identify a period during which antiseptic surgery flourished and a subsequent period of aseptic surgery. The latter extends to the present time. The transition from one period to the other is usually dated by the introduction of sterilization of instruments and materials by heat, with at least partial elimination of chemical disinfectants. This development took place from 1872, when Richard von Volkmann, professor of surgery at Halle, began his experiments, to 1891, when the results of the aseptic system as developed in the service of Ernst von Bergmann were published by Schimmelbusch.

In both the so-called antiseptic and aseptic periods the goal was the same — to obtain healing without suppuration — and Lister was primarily interested in this achievement. "In using the expression 'dressed antiseptically,'" he wrote in 1869 (*Lancet 1,* 451), "I do not mean merely 'dressed with an antiseptic,' but 'dressed so as to ensure absence of putrefaction.'" Aseptic surgery, however, came to mean surgery in which sterilization by chemical antiseptics had been abandoned, and antiseptic surgery, that carried out with the aid of chemical agents — a confused meaning not conveyed by the two terms. This popular usage is the one employed by J. C. W.

Sir William Watson Cheyne, who knew Lister intimately and was closely associated with him in his surgery, presented the case for a more logical usage of the two terms in the First Lister Memorial Lecture given on May 14, 1925: (*Lister and his Achievement* (London, 1925). Lister, he said, called his method of treatment "the antiseptic treatment of wounds" and the results that he hoped to obtain "aseptic results." In other words, antiseptic methods (against sepsis) are utilized to achieve aseptic results (free from sepsis). Antiseptic methods, thus defined, include all systematic techniques employed to prevent the entrance of bacteria into an incision or wound. Lister, despite his liberal use of carbolic acid, was not tied to any particular method or technique of disinfection. He envisioned healing without suppuration, and so long as a method produced this aseptic result he was satisfied.

The identification of an aseptic period distinct from an antiseptic period has the earmarks of a product of German chauvinism uncritically accepted by American surgery in the closing decades of the last century. The violence of the reaction of a Scotsman to the idea can be illustrated by a brief quotation from the Lister Oration of Sir James Learmonth delivered on April 4, 1952. Sir James occupies the chair of clinical surgery in the University of Edinburgh held by Lister from 1869 to 1877.

I give no weight to the rather tawdry attempts which have been made to separate the "antiseptic" from the "aseptic" era. Those who try to do so

and anything like the modern standards of operating room techniques and care of wounds was approached.

The third era, or the modern one in which the present generation rejoices, was eventually established on a firm basis. It is safe to say that no other generation of physicians in the history of medicine has seen such extraordinary changes in the practice of medicine and surgery as have been witnessed by the generation of which I have been a member.

---

have not studied Lister's papers: for example, his statement that "The part to be operated upon, then, being in an *antiseptic* atmosphere, if the finger is to be introduced into the wound . . . you must take special care that it is an *aseptic* finger."

See also Douglas Guthrie, *Lord Lister: His Life and Doctrine* (Edinburgh: E. & S. Livingstone, 1949), chap. V; and note 4, Chapter XVI.

꙳ II

An Old New England Surgeon

On November 21, 1900 Dr. J. Collins Warren addressed the Book and
Journal Club of the Medical and Chirurgical Faculty of Maryland, the
chairman having requested him to talk on some subject connected with
the early history of Boston medicine. The title of the address, "Reminiscences of an Old New England Surgeon," referred to his grandfather, Dr.
John C. Warren, one of the pioneer surgeons of New England. The address
was published in the February 1901 issue of the *Maryland Medical Journal,*
and in edited form is inserted here.

My remarks will consist of some biographical notes from the life
of Dr. John Collins Warren, one of the pioneer surgeons of New England. He was the son of Dr. John Warren, who was a brother of
the General Joseph Warren killed at the battle of Bunker Hill.[1]

---

[1] The *History of the Bunker Hill Monument Association,* published in 1877, is
dedicated "To the Memory of Daniel Webster, Edward Everett, Thomas Handa-
syd Perkins, John Collins Warren, and William Tudor, the Principal Originators of
the Bunker Hill Monument . . . and Solomon Willard, the Devoted Architect."
It was Dr. John C. Warren who secured the three acres on top of Bunker (Breed's)
Hill for the Association in 1823. He also served on the Board of Directors and as
vice-president. The cornerstone of the Monument was laid by General Lafayette
in 1825, and the dedication exercises took place in 1843, the orator on both
occasions being Daniel Webster.

Dr. J. Mason Warren served as a director of the organization. J.C.W. was
elected a director in 1868 and later became president. The 1915 *Proceedings* of
the Association noted the following resolution:

> *Resolved,* That the Bunker Hill Monument Association has learned with
> great regret that its President, Dr. John Collins Warren, has declined to be
> again a candidate for reëlection, and while it feels compelled to accede to his
> wishes, it desires to express to him its deep appreciation of the value of
> his services. The presidency of this Association was his almost by hereditary
> right, and through a long membership, and constant interest in its welfare,
> he was thoroughly familiar with its purposes and needs. With unfailing tact
> and courtesy he has presided over its meetings for ten years, and has added
> to their attraction by his presence and his wise counsel. Largely through his
> efforts, the Association is today free from debt; its Lodge at Bunker Hill has
> been improved and adorned; and the Society has increased in public favor
> and influence. In his retirement from office Dr. Warren will take with him
> the cordial regard and confidence of this Association, and an earnest ex-
> pression of its hope that for years to come it may have the pleasure of his
> presence at its meetings and the benefit of his sound judgment in the
> conduct of its affairs.

A statue of Joseph Warren by Henry Dexter was placed near the base of the
Monument and dedicated on June 17, 1857.

Many of you may not be aware that General Warren was a member of the medical profession. John and Joseph were intimately associated with one another; their father was Joseph Warren, an old Roxbury farmer, whose homestead remains in the possession of the family at the present time.[2]

It was as early as the year 1630 that John Warren, a fellow-passenger of Governor Winthrop on the *Arbella*, arrived in Salem. A brother of this John Warren, Richard Warren, was one of the Pilgrim Fathers who came over in the *Mayflower*. John was said to have resided in Ashburton, a little town in Devonshire in England. On a recent visit to England, I made a pilgrimage to this spot and saw the old homestead, a modest farmhouse, still standing as it was built in the early seventeenth century. Interesting in connection with this visit to the old English homestead was the discovery of a place nearby labeled upon a map as "Bunker Hill." It seems probable that the immigrants who named the famous battleground came from this part of England, as did many others who settled in the colony of Massachusetts.

Joseph Warren was a physician in active practice in Boston[3] at the breaking out of the Revolutionary War, and he continued to treat his patients till the eve of the battle of Lexington. A private ledger and a daybook are preserved, and show that his practice included a number of distinguished families in the town of Boston and its vicinity. Joseph Warren was an ardent patriot, and devoted what time he could spare from his practice to the cause of his country. He was an orator of no mean ability, and his oration delivered in the Old South Meeting-House on the fifth anniversary of the so-called Boston massacre of March 5, 1770, when several citizens were fired

---

[2] The birthplace of Joseph and John Warren was a wooden house built in 1720 by their grandfather. Stark's *Antique Views of ye Towne of Boston* (1882) reproduces an engraving of this building, and the accompanying description was written by J.C.W. A model of the house made from the wood and moss of the original structure is on permanent display at the Old South Meeting-House.

In 1846 Dr. John C. Warren had the old house replaced by a stone cottage, which is still standing as No. 130 Warren Street, Roxbury. He placed two memorial tablets on the front wall, one for his uncle Joseph and the other for his father John. A statue of Joseph Warren by Paul Bartlett was placed in the nearby square by the City of Boston in 1904. The inscription it bears was composed by Charles W. Eliot. A view of the cottage was reproduced in the March 28, 1940 issue of the *New England Journal of Medicine*.

[3] Joseph Warren graduated from Harvard College in 1759 and then served an apprenticeship under Dr. James Lloyd of Boston. He began his medical practice in 1764, the year of his marriage to Elizabeth Hooton. Six years later he leased a house on Hanover Street nearly opposite the head of Elm Street. This lot became the site of the American House in 1835, during the excavation for which several wired skulls, evidence of Warren's interest in anatomy, were found by the workmen. An illustration of the Joseph Warren house appears in Stark's *Antique Views*.

at and killed by British troops on State Street, although of an old-
fashioned style of eloquence, recalls vividly those stirring events.
Warren was unable to reach the pulpit, owing to the crowding of
the aisle and doorway by British officers, there to prevent his entrance.
Climbing a ladder on the rear of the church and crawling through
a window, he appeared suddenly in the pulpit with his manuscript
in hand. During the progress of his oration it is said that a British
officer laid some bullets on the reading-desk beside the speaker.
Warren carelessly dropped his pocket handkerchief upon them and
continued his address undisturbed by the incident.

The closing paragraphs of this address are worth giving to you:

You, then, who nobly have espoused your country's cause; who generously
have sacrificed wealth and ease; who have despised the pomp and show of
tinselled greatness; refused the summons to the festive board; been deaf to
the alluring calls of luxury and mirth; who have forsaken the downy pillow
to keep your vigils by the midnight lamp for the salvation of your invaded
country, that you may break the fowler's snare and disappoint the vulture
of his prey, you then will reap that harvest of renown which you so justly
have deserved. Your country shall pay her grateful tribute of applause.
Even the children of your most inveterate enemies, ashamed to tell from
whom they sprang, while they in secret curse their stupid, cruel parents, shall
join the general voice of gratitude to those who broke the fetters which
their fathers forged.

Having redeemed your country, and secured the blessing to future generations, who, fired by your example, shall emulate your virtues, and learn
from you the heavenly art of making millions happy, with heartfelt joy, with
transports all your own, you cry, "The glorious work is done!" Then drop
the mantle to some young Elisha, and take your seats with kindred spirits
in your native skies.[4]

Joseph Warren was still a young man at the time of his death,
being but thirty-four years of age. Among the most interesting relics
that relate to him is the prayer book he carried at the battle of
Bunker Hill, taken by a British soldier from his pocket after the
engagement and carried to England, where it was purchased by
the Reverend Samuel Wilton, "who gave at least ten times the
value of it in order that it might not be shown as a spoil taken from
a Presbyterian rebel, and sent it to this country to his next of
kin to be preserved as a relic in memory of its former owner."[5]

John Warren, some twelve years younger than Joseph, was born
in 1753. He was his brother's pupil, and had already begun practice

[4] As quoted in Richard Frothingham, *Life and Times of Joseph Warren*
(Boston, 1865). The original manuscript of the address may be seen in the
museum room of the Massachusetts Historical Society.

[5] This prayer book may also be seen at the Massachusetts Historical Society.
The vest worn by Joseph Warren at the battle of Bunker Hill may be seen in the
armory of the Ancient and Honorable Artillery Company in Faneuil Hall.

in the town of Salem at the time of the battle of Bunker Hill. There was no medical school in Boston at this period, and education in medicine was obtained by serving an apprenticeship with some leading practitioner. During the early part of the war John Warren served as a surgeon in the Revolutionary army, and in that capacity came in contact with Dr. John Morgan, who was appointed director-general of the army hospitals by Washington soon after his arrival at Cambridge to take command of the forces. The friendship formed with Morgan seems to have been continued in after life, for I have in my possession one of the earliest works on a medical subject published in this country, *A Disquisition Upon the Medical Schools of America,* delivered at a public anniversary commencement held at the College of Philadelphia in 1765. This copy was presented to Dr. John Warren and is inscribed by his "respectful and affectionate friend, John Morgan."

John Warren had a large general practice, and also devoted himself to surgery, having been well fitted for that specialty by his military experience. He was one of the founders of the "Medical Institution of Harvard College" [6] in the year 1782, and his reputation as an eloquent lecturer has been handed down to the present through generations of physicians.

He married a daughter of John Collins, a governor of Rhode Island; she became the happy mother of many children, of whom John C. Warren was the eldest. John Warren had settled in Salem, not wishing to compete with his brother's practice, and thinking that he might finally succeed to the practice of Dr. Edward A. Holyoke, his preceptor and a leading practitioner of that time, who was getting old. But the changes of the Revolution brought him back to Boston,[7] and it was fortunate that he did not remain in Salem, for he died in 1815 at the

[6] The institution popularly known as the "Harvard Medical School" has had a number of titles: Medical Institution of Harvard College (1782–1816), Massachusetts Medical College of Harvard University (1816–1858), Medical Department of Harvard University (1858–1867), Medical School (Boston) of Harvard University (1867–1896), and Harvard University, The Medical School (from 1896). [Thomas Francis Harrington, *The Harvard Medical School: A History, Narrative and Documentary* (New York, 1905), II, 513–516.]

The *Memorial History of Boston,* edited by Justin Winsor, Librarian of Harvard University (Boston, 1880–81), IV, 544, states: "Occasionally it is mentioned in the newspapers as the Boston Medical School . . . It is only in recent times, — perhaps within twenty-five years, — that the institution has been called the Harvard Medical School. This name has grown up gradually, and now we seldom or never hear any other given to it."

[7] When Dr. John Warren began private practice in 1777, his residence was situated on what is now the site of the Jordan Marsh Company, and here his first son, John C. Warren, was born. In 1785 he bought a large house on School Street just east of what is now City Hall Avenue, where he pursued his avocation of fruit culture. A chamber in this house was fitted up as a "medicine room" or "apothecary's shop in miniature, where the medical students sat and studied, or

age of sixty-one, whereas Dr. Holyoke some twelve years later celebrated his one-hundredth anniversary.

John C. Warren was born in 1778. He was the first Franklin Medal scholar [8] in the town of Boston, and graduated in good standing from

---

put up medicines," according to Edward Warren, his youngest son and biographer [*The Life of John Warren, M.D.* (Boston, 1874)]. "At an early period . . . the back windows of the house were occupied with drying preparations of legs and arms, and other anatomical and morbid specimens, prepared by Dr. Warren, and forming the basis of the Warren Museum, afterwards in the Medical College." In an upper chamber, "on awaking at sunrise in the morning, the eye rested upon the brilliant reflection of the sun on the gilded Indian on the Province House."

Edward Warren also records the following incident:

> I remember a festive meeting held at my father's residence, in one of the last years of his life. The ample house, with its large dining-hall, opening into the garden, furnished ample space for the society to range at will, and the shaded walks afforded the luxury of a rural residence within the very heart of the town. I do not know how many members were present. To my childish eyes the number seemed immense. [*Life of John Warren*, p. 235.]

The occasion was a meeting of the Humane Society of the Commonwealth of Massachusetts, of which John Warren was president from 1799 to 1813. Their broad humanitarian and scientific interests led the Warrens to be numbered among the early supporters of the Humane Society, and this allegiance was passed down from father to son. Dr. John C. Warren was a trustee from 1821 to 1828, and second vice-president from 1829 to 1831. He persuaded the Society to endow free beds at the MGH. Dr. J. Mason Warren served as trustee for sixteen years beginning with 1850.

J.C.W. became a trustee in 1878, and served as second vice-president from 1892 to 1893, as first vice-president from 1894 to 1897, and president from 1898 to 1921. Upon his resignation the Society passed a resolution in which it was stated that "the service rendered by Dr. Warren as President of the Society for twenty-three years is without a parallel in its history."

In 1895 the Humane Society, seeking more adequate measures of resuscitation of the apparently drowned, appointed J.C.W. and George B. Shattuck a special committee to study the problem. Their exhaustive report on the history and methods of artificial respiration was printed in the biennial publication of the Society for 1895–96, seven years before Schäfer announced his prone pressure method. It is appropriate to record that in 1873 the Humane Society awarded Dr. J. Collins Warren its Silver Medal for saving a boy from drowning.

[8] Benjamin Franklin's will (1790) provided a fund the interest of which was to "be laid out in silver medals, and given as honorary rewards annually by the directors of the said free schools [in Boston], for the encouragement of scholarship." In the first year of the awards (1792) twenty-one boys received medals, three at each of seven schools. John C. Warren was a medalist at the Latin School. For many years no official list of medalists was kept, but in 1856 Charles Colburn compiled such a list, and the name of John Collins Warren appeared first on this roster. The Annual Report of the Boston School Committee for 1857–58 contained the list and also a series of cuts illustrating the various designs of the medals through the years. The first cut shows on one side the inscription "Adjudged by the School Committee as A Reward of Merit to John Collins Warren. 1792" and on the other side, "The Gift of Franklin."

Dr. Warren initiated a movement in 1827 to erect a monument over the tomb of the parents of Benjamin Franklin in the Granary Burying Ground. In 1856 he presided over two meetings of medalists that led to the formation of the Association of Franklin Medal Scholars.

Harvard College in the class of 1797. On leaving college he did not at first enter upon the study of medicine, as his father had hoped that he would take up some mercantile pursuit. Society in Boston was feeling the influence of the great social changes that were going on at this period. The severity of Puritan manners had yielded somewhat to the softening influence and the polished bearing of the French officers whom their King had permitted to serve in the American Revolutionary war. In his autobiographical notes [9] Dr. Warren gives an interesting picture of life in Boston at the close of the 18th century:

At the period when I left college, and became an inhabitant of Boston, it was thought necessary to undergo the operation of a barber half an hour every day . . . the average time lost in this way was little short of an hour, besides the horrid consequences of being obliged to carry on one's head a quantity of curls, flour, pomatum, and a long cue or a heavy club.
. . . The dress, at that time, was a colored coat; metal buttons, usually yellow; colored and figured waistcoat; short breeches, buttoning at the knees; long boots, with white tops; and, when riding on horseback, a pair of leather breeches, instead of pantaloons of drab cloth. These leather breeches were daily cleaned with yellow clay, which required that the coat should never be brought in contact with them. Then a shirt, ruffled at the breast and about the wrists; a white cravat, filled in with what was called a pudding, the use of which, from the effect of habit, could not be dispensed with for some years. Cocked hats were very much worn at that time, but not by the young: and gentlemen of a certain age wore wigs, which were sent to the barbers once a week to be fresh dressed; so that, on Saturday night, we saw the barbers' boys carrying home immense piles of wig-boxes, as a preparation for going to church on Sunday . . .
Physicians who had much business, in those days, rode on horseback. Riding in a chaise was very rare, and in a four-wheeled carriage still more so. My father rode on horseback till within a few years before his death . . . [10]
Dr. Lloyd generally drove a very fine horse; and Drs. Jarvis and Whipple were famous for beautiful saddle-horses, and the elegance with which they rode . . .
Large parties opened at seven or eight o'clock in the evening, and were much more formal than at present . . . Dances were usually, at the opening of the ball or assembly, one or two minuets. A friend of mine told me . . . that he saw me dance a minuet in 1806, or thereabouts; and that this was the last time he had witnessed this dance in Boston. After the minuets, contra dances and cotillons were in fashion . . .
. . . Persons of a certain age were treated with a degree of deference now wholly disused. In fact, one of the great traits in the manners of the present day is the want of respect with which young persons are accustomed to treat those older than themselves . . .

[9] These autobiographical notes were assembled and edited by Edward Warren in *The Life of John Collins Warren, M.D.* (Boston, 1860).
[10] Dr. John C. Warren wrote in his autobiographical notes: "As soon as I got into practice, I purchased a horse for saddle and harness, and visited my patients in town on horseback, as my father did the greater part of his life . . . I have owned more horses than I can enumerate."

. . . Gentlemen's dinner-parties began early, and ended late . . . The great care on the part of the host was to present to the guests as much ordinary wine as they could be made to drink, and then to bring forward, in succession, a variety of old wines, each having a character a little better than that which preceded. All of these had some remarkable history connected with them; the detail and discussion of which constituted an important part of social conversation.

. . . On the whole, the dinner-parties of those times must be looked on with disgust: for not only was the quantity of wine sufficient to make irreparable inroads on the physical organization, but these potations led to the greatest extravagance of language and thought; and the conversation at a dinner-party, if taken down by a stenographer, and presented to the party on the morning following, would have filled them with shame and regret.

In later life, it may be well to remark, Dr. Warren became president of the Massachusetts Temperance Society, and on accession to that office felt obliged to give away a cellar of fine wine. At some of his later dinner parties the old Negro butler used to carry around two fine silver pitchers in his hands, inquiring of each guest in turn whether he would have rain water or Cochituate water.

An idea of Dr. Warren's somewhat stern bent of mind may be gathered from the following note of his:

My father was so very much occupied in professional business, giving lectures, attending societies, etc., that punctuality and method were indispensable to the accomplishment of these numerous objects. I therefore learned very early to apportion out my time for definite objects; and . . . formed a habit of occupation which . . . compelled me to fly from indolence and repose by something like an instinctive movement. For the same reason, I have been led to avoid all those amusements which are resorted to merely to pass away time, without contributing any thing to the stock of intellectual, moral, or physical improvement.[11]

After one year spent in the study of medicine at home he embarked for London in June 1799, on the ship *Minerva*. Our country being at that time at war with France, the ship had an armament of 26-pounders. The passengers immediately enrolled themselves and took charge

[11] Dr. Warren's habit of making productive use of leisure time led him to organize the Thursday Evening Club (first called the Warren Club). This included men of varied professions and accomplishments who met informally at their homes in rotation for "scientific conversation." The first meeting was held in Warren's house at No. 2 Park Street on October 27, 1846. Half a century later the club was described in *The Life and Letters of William Barton Rogers* (Boston, 1896) as "one of the best features of Boston life."

J.C.W. became secretary of the organization in the 1870's, and later its president. The Thursday Evening Club should not be confused with the "Warren Club" organized in 1890 "for the fuller and freer discussion of medical subjects than is possible in the larger societies." Of this latter group Dr. James G. Mumford served for a time as president, and J.C.W. was an honorary member.

of some of the guns, and in the course of the voyage became quite proficient in gunnery practice. In a letter to his father Dr. Warren wrote:

One night the captain, determined to try our alacrity, and presence of mind, ordered the mate and boatswain to call all hands to quarters at midnight, when we were buried in profound sleep. In five minutes we were all at our stations, and had every gun prepared for action. We cried to the captain to point out the enemy, that we might fire; and were not unpleasantly disappointed at hearing it was merely an experiment. So, after all hands had a drink of grog, we retired quietly to our berths.

On landing at Dover the travelers found a fine British regiment and a body of artillery. Warren wrote in his notes:

One of the officers, seeing us there, spoke to one of our party; and, finding we were Americans, immediately told us that he had been in America in the late war, and was, if I recollect rightly, in the Battle of Bunker Hill. His name was Captain Parker. He attended to us through the review, and afterwards took us to his quarters to tea.

Traveling through the south of England, Dr. Warren chanced to meet General Arnold, "the traitor, so called."

He was there with his family. I recollect a son, very handsome; and a daughter. Arnold was rather a stout man, broad-shouldered, large black eyes. He walked lame, from a wound received at the attack of Quebec, I think.

On arriving in London Dr. Warren made an arrangement with Mr. William Cooper, surgeon of Guy's Hospital, to be his dresser for a year, for which he paid the fee of fifty guineas. Mr. Cooper was the senior surgeon, and Warren was immediately put in charge of about forty patients. Quite a large number of these patients required daily dressing, which he practiced for a year faithfully. During his week he slept in the hospital. As Mr. Cooper was well advanced in life, he left matters pretty much to his dressers. He came to the hospital only twice a week, and walked around with them in a very quiet way, making amusing and instructive remarks. He had no great respect for America, considering her as having separated from the British Empire before maturity. He was pleased, however, to find Americans so white-complexioned and so little contaminated with Indian blood.

This gentleman was succeeded by his nephew, Mr. Astley Cooper, who was then quite a young man and very promising. Warren says of him: "He was one of the handsomest men I ever saw; was always very kind to me through his life." Of his work in London at this time, Warren wrote in his notes:

In the morning, I went through my dressings; at noon, attended Cline and Cooper's lectures; dissected in the afternoon; and wrote off my notes at night. This last I did with great regularity; and got a fair copy, in epitome, of the lectures above mentioned; and also of Sir Astley Cooper's lectures on surgery, in the evening. At the same time, I attended a complete course of midwifery by Dr. Haighton, and a course of physiology by the same gentleman. We had also a good course of lectures on the teeth, by Mr. Fox . . . The most distinguished medical men of that time were Dr. Saunders, Ralph, and Babington, in Guy's Hospital. At St. Thomas's was Dr. Fordyce; at St. Bartholomew's, Mr. Abernethy; and at St. George's, Sir Everard Home.

In one of his letters to his father at this time he writes:

Once, I remember, you asked whether I intended to become a surgeon. The question remains unanswered. At that time, I had seen enough to have an idea of the difficulties of an operation, but none of its pleasures: now I see a good operation with the pleasure I used to feel at the successful solution of Euclid's problems, — a pleasure greater than almost any I know. I have acquired that taste, that high relish, for these, without which no man can exert himself for the attainment of any art; and am only surprised that I was so long blind. There are operations almost every day, — the stone, hydrocele, cataract, and amputations innumerable; but Mr. Cline's operations for aneurism or hernia are grand. It is a pleasure to see him take up or turn his knife . . . Dissection is carried on in style: twelve or fifteen bodies in a room; the young men at work on them in different ways. The people called resurrection-men supply us abundantly. An odd circumstance happened some time since. A hungry beggar had got some bread, and ate with so much avidity as to suffocate himself and fall down in the street. One of the resurrection-men, passing, immediately claimed the man as his brother, took him to the dissecting theatre of St. Thomas, and secured a good price. The man's trachea is now made into a preparation.

You are all familiar with the difficulties which surrounded the early teachers of anatomy, and it is not necessary for me to allude more to this subject here, except to say in this connection that Dr. Warren, who later experienced the great difficulties in the study of anatomy that had been the lot of his predecessors, left directions that after his death his body should be dissected, his skeleton prepared and articulated and deposited in the Warren Museum at the Harvard Medical School, and it still hangs there today.

In the autumn of 1800 Warren left London for Edinburgh in company with his friend Jones, the author of the well-known treatise on the "Hemorrhage of Divided Arteries." Warren said of him:

Jones was a West Indian, a native of Barbadoes. He resided much in England; but ultimately returned to his native island, and died there at an early period . . . We left London together in a post-chaise, — a very expensive but delightful mode of conveyance, as it enables one to stop at any moment to examine an interesting spot . . . We took about a month to go to Edinburgh; stopping, of course, at all interesting spots.

Dr. Warren remained a year in Edinburgh, and obtained a medical degree from that university.

My course at Edinburgh was to rise at eight in the morning; and, having breakfasted, to go to Dr. Gregory's lecture at nine, Dr. Hope's chemistry at ten, John and Charles Bell at eleven, infirmary at twelve, Monro's anatomy and surgery at one. I got home about three, and dined; then passed the afternoon and evening in writing off lectures.

We see in this tabular view of closely crowded exercises the operation of a system which was followed so assiduously by our teachers under the old system of medical education prevailing in this country during the first half of the century.

In June 1801, Dr. Warren left Edinburgh to go to the Continent. As an example of the slowness of travel in those days it may be mentioned that the voyage across the North Sea on a Dutch vessel occupied a week, the travelers being obliged to live upon salt pork, beef, and cabbage. The following winter was passed in Paris in the household of the celebrated Dubois, his clinical studies being conducted chiefly at La Charité, the Hôtel Dieu being in too bad a condition at that time to be attended with advantage. Warren says:

The French students with whom I mingled were green from the French Revolution. They were, for the most part, a rude and vulgar set of people. Sometimes they behaved in such a way that I resented it, and got into some pretty serious quarrels.

Dr. Warren returned to America in the autumn of 1802 and began at once the practice of his profession. During the following summer he was left in charge of his father's practice, medical and surgical. "At that period, I made sometimes fifty visits a day." He succeeded his father as professor of anatomy and surgery, and continued to hold that position until 1847, covering a period of life as a teacher of forty years. The "Medical Institution of Harvard College" had been situated at first in Cambridge, but owing to the difficulty of professors in active practice reaching that locality, it was moved in 1810 to the town of Boston. It was about this time that it was proposed to establish a hospital in Boston, and Drs. James Jackson and John C. Warren, two leading practitioners in the community at that time, addressed a circular letter to some of the wealthiest and most influential citizens for the purpose of awakening in their minds an interest in the subject. In this letter they said:

A hospital is an institution absolutely essential to a medical school, and one which would afford relief and comfort to thousands of the sick and miserable. On what other objects can the superfluities of the rich be so well bestowed?

They made the mistake of placing this hospital in the hands of an independent board of trustees, instead of uniting it intimately with the medical school.[12]

[12]This remark, made in 1900, reflects the growing annoyance felt by J.C.W. and a group of Harvard faculty members who were pressing for much-needed reforms in medical education. From about 1870 significant changes had been made in the preclinical years of the curriculum, but the road toward more effective clinical instruction was blocked by the presence of physicians and surgeons who had gained vested rights to hospital ward services by donating professional care to the medically indigent. Staff appointments in the hospitals customarily were made without consultation with the University, and promotions were traditionally based on seniority.

Actually, J.C.W.'s statement as it stands is not a very realistic one. The sponsorship of the Medical Faculty by Harvard was a matter of loose and nominal association from 1783 to the presidency of Charles W. Eliot. Not until 1898 was the Medical School recognized as an integral part of the University by the assignment of unrestricted university funds to medical purposes. An intimate identification of the Medical Faculty with a hospital before the University was ready to participate in medical education in a wholehearted way might well have led to the emergence of a hospital-school after the British pattern.

In London the decay of the private medical schools in the mid-decades of the nineteenth century led to the rise of the hospital-schools. These introduced much-needed supervision of and rules of conduct for their students, after the pattern of the colleges in Oxford and Cambridge. As the major emphasis in medical education lay in preparation for practice, it was inevitable that the vocational training of doctors came to center in the great London hospitals.

In this country the inadequacy of the proprietary medical schools — and the Harvard enterprise must be classed as such — first attracted attention when viewed against the background of a developing medical science. The examples of the Vienna and Berlin schools outweighed the tradition of the followers of Sydenham, which shaped events in England, and medical education came into the orbit of the university. The University of Michigan Medical School, which opened in 1850, was from the beginning an integral part of the University. At Harvard the integration of University and Medical School beginning with Eliot is described in these reminiscences. The Johns Hopkins adopted a university pattern along German lines, placing clinical training within the framework of research and thus bringing a new emphasis to the teaching of medicine.

So it was largely the impact of medical science on medicine as a useful art that led to the union of medical schools and universities in the United States. Hospitals, immersed in the task of caring for the sick by traditional methods and struggling to keep abreast of the need for more and more beds for the medically indigent among growing urban populations, gave little thought to the potential tools which science held for medicine; hospital-schools, if they had been formed in any great number, could only have promoted clinical training largely by apprenticeship methods.

It can be asked in a broad sense whether medicine is making the most of its university association or whether, like some individual students, it is so preoccupied with the pursuit of science on the one hand, or with practice on the other, that it is becoming deaf to the expectations and needs of society. It is said that the medical student should derive from the university community the help required to make of himself all that he is capable of being and that the university community in turn should represent a way of life which develops the power to

It may be of interest that after the death of Caspar Wistar of Philadelphia, the distinguished professor of anatomy in the University of Pennsylvania, in 1818, Dr. Warren was asked to become a candidate for that position. Years later he received an invitation from the Regents of the University of New York to take the office of professor of anatomy in that institution. He wrote:

The same reasons which had operated on my mind in regard to Philadelphia, influenced me in respect to that from New York; and, with the expression of my thanks for the high honor conferred upon me, I respectfully declined the invitation.

Dr. Warren was one of the founders of the *Boston Medical and Surgical Journal,*[13] which was established in 1828 by merger of the *New England Journal of Medicine and Surgery* and the *Medical Intelligencer.* At this time Dr. Warren occupied the mansion-house

distinguish clever and plausible workmanship from mature scholarship. What the university can offer to the individual it can do for the art as a whole — but only if medicine will look at its own limitations and seek a more complete expression of its powers by closer integration with the university community.

It is true that many decades ago voluntary hospitals dragged their heels when asked to coöperate in reform of medical education; at best they followed university leadership at an excessively leisurely pace. Nevertheless, they contributed to a joint undertaking other values that should not be overlooked. These institutions, of which the Pennsylvania Hospital (1751), the New York Hospital (1771), and the Massachusetts General Hospital (1811) are noteworthy examples, were inspired by the eighteenth-century British voluntary hospitals. Guy's Hospital (1723) in London was the first. They were a product of the Christian ethics and philanthropy of the so-called age of enlightenment and imprinted lasting qualities on British and American medicine that might not have been generated by universities. Certainly the humanitarian traditions of these hospitals were found lacking in the sphere of German medicine, the rapid development of which took place within universities. These influences were also lacking in Parisian surgery in the early decades of the nineteenth century. J. Mason Warren, writing from Paris in 1832, observed: "It seems to be rather an object to study the natural history of disease, and to perform an operation beautifully, than to save the life of the patient."

In a vein of impatience similar to that shown by J.C.W., Abraham Flexner referred to the voluntary hospital as weighed down by "conservatism, vested interests, absence of true university ideals, lack of resources, lack of leadership and excessive dependence on tedious committee procedure." Flexner, at the time of his writing, was trying to "abridge the evolutionary process by setting up summarily the conditions necessary to scientific development on the clinical side," and likewise had encountered resistance.

The editor has commented on the history of university-hospital relation in other notes and again in Appendix III. See also his paper, "The Development of the Hospital" in the Lowell Lectures of 1948, *The Hospital in Contemporary Life,* edited by N. W. Faxon (Harvard University Press, Cambridge, 1949), and the presidential address to the American Surgical Association entitled "Science and Humanism in Surgery," *Ann. Surgery 126,* 381 (1947).

[13] J.C.W. was editor of the *Boston Medical and Surgical Journal* from 1873 to 1879.

at No. 2 Park Street, which not only accommodated the members of his family but served as a place of study for a considerable body of medical students, to whom one room with a sanded floor was assigned. The system of medical apprenticeship was evidently at that time in its highest stage of development.

At the age of fifty-nine Dr. Warren sought relaxation for the first time by a visit to Europe, returning to the scenes of his youthful studies, fortunate in being able to find many of his old friends and teachers still alive. On the voyage across the Atlantic in the good ship *George Washington,* it may be of interest to mention that his family had as a fellow passenger Louis Napoleon. This was after his first attempt to incite a revolution in France, following which he had to come to America; he was now returning to his mother, who was quite ill at Geneva. Warren says of the Prince:

> He was versed in classic literature and fond of it; quite a proficient in mathematics, and showed me a thick octavo volume he had composed on the sciences of artillery and engineering. He was also versed in the simple accomplishments which make a part of French education — comic acting, tricks with cards, etc., some of which were very remarkable. All these things he did with imperturbable gravity, never looking as though he enjoyed them, but doing them for the amusement of others. He never talked politics.

Dr. Warren was fortunate in the friendship of so distinguished a surgeon as Sir Astley Cooper throughout his life, and it was with great pleasure that he was enabled to meet him again on his return to London. He says of him at that time:

> Sir Astley Cooper continues to be one of the most zealous and successful cultivators of anatomical and pathological science. Having acquired an ample fortune, he has no occasion to submit to the laborious and responsible duties of the profession; but he is ready at stated hours to give advice to those who apply, both at his own house and in the town. He rises early, and employs two or three hours in anatomical and surgical investigations before breakfast; afterwards he receives patients at his house till two; then visits till six or seven, — the common hour of dinner.

During this visit to London a very beautiful daughter of Dr. Warren was so unfortunate as to contract smallpox. She was supposed to have been exposed to the disease during the review of one of the regiments of the Guards in London, when she was escorted along the line on the arm of a British officer. She was attended during her whole illness by no less a person than the Queen's own physician, Sir James Clark. Dr. Warren says of him:

> Dr. Clark is the author of the best treatise on consumption which we have in the language . . . Dr. Clark is a person whose character and

manners excite extraordinary interest in those who meet him . . . He is now physician to the Queen, and has reposed in him a high degree of confidence by distinguished persons.

His patient, Emily Warren, now a very old lady [1900], writes to me as follows:

On looking over my mother's journal I find the following entries: "Sir James Clark called to bid adieu, and brought Dr. Warren the Queen's autograph, written expressly for him, which I had framed. Sir James has been very kind, visiting Emily every day since her illness."

Through the courtesy of Sir James Reed, Her Majesty's physician today, the writer has been able to obtain a duplicate autograph from the Queen written over sixty years later.

The crowning event of Dr. Warren's surgical career came late in life, many years after his second return from Europe. The details of the first introduction of surgical anesthesia at the Massachusetts General Hospital in 1846 need not to be gone into here. Dr. Warren was then the senior surgeon of the Hospital, of which he had been one of the founders. He had left upon it the impress of his strong personality, and established an *esprit de corps* which has pervaded the staff of the Hospital from its foundation until the present time. Of what he had to do with the great discovery I will myself make no mention, but will be content with giving an extract from the obituary address given by Dr. Oliver Wendell Holmes at a special meeting of the Suffolk District Medical Society on May 5th, 1856:

He had reached the age when men have long ceased to be called on for military duty; when those who have labored during their days of strength are expected to repose; and when the mind is thought to have lost its aptitude for innovating knowledge, and to live on its accumulated stores. Yet nothing could surpass the eagerness with which he watched and assisted in the development of the newly discovered powers of etherization. It is much for any name to be associated with the triumphs of that beneficent discovery; but when we remember the reproach cast upon Harvey's contemporaries, that none of them past middle age would accept his new doctrine of the circulation, we confess it to have been a noble sight when an old man was found among the foremost to proclaim the great fact, — strangely unwelcome, as well as improbable, to some who should have been foremost to accept it, — that pain was no longer the master, but the servant, of the body.

III

Nineteenth-Century Boston
and Its Surgery

My earliest recollections of Boston go back to a period when the residential quarter was in a very different locality from the Back Bay with which we are familiar at the present time. Soon after my parents married, they moved to a house in Pemberton Square, facing the foot of the approach from Somerset Street.[1] The Square was then filled by family residences, and the same class of dwellings continued on through Somerset to Beacon Street, and down the Hill but a little distance below Charles Street, stopping opposite the Public Garden.[2] The dwelling farthest in that direction was on the corner of what now is Brimmer Street.

Park Street was then purely residential. At either end were dwellings dating back to the beginning of the century, the Ticknor mansion to the north and the block of four buildings adjacent to the Park Street Church on the south. The only evidence of its role as a thoroughfare was the passage of the old stagecoach in the early morning from the northern to the southern railway terminus and the not infrequent blocking of the road by flocks of sheep which were being driven across the city. Cab-stands were unknown, and a quiet

[1] Dr. Jonathan Mason Warren (1811–1867) and Anna Caspar Crowninshield (1815–1905) were married on April 30, 1839 in the Crowninshield residence at the corner of Beacon and Somerset Streets, Boston. They moved to No. 29 Pemberton Square in 1840, and it was here that J.C.W. was born on May 4, 1842. In the 1880's the street numbers were changed, and the bow-fronted, four story house now standing as No. 30–32 Pemberton Square is probably the former No. 29.

[2] The area of the Public Garden was originally a part of the Roxbury Flats, submerged at high tide except for a knoll (Fox Hill) on its eastern margin. It received consideration in 1813 as a site for the MGH, after its eastern portion had been filled in. In 1839 a civic-minded group headed by Horace Gray was incorporated as the "Proprietors of the Botanic Garden." They imported John Cadness from London as the first gardener, but, owing to the nature of the fill and the inroads of the Back Bay waters, little horticultural development was achieved during J.C.W.'s boyhood. Attempts by various city councilors to break up the Garden into building lots were defeated and in 1859, following a legislative act and its acceptance by the voters, the area was dedicated to the people "forever" as the Public Garden, and soon it was widened and laid out in its present design. The Ether Monument placed there in 1868 was the gift of Thomas Lee.

homelike atmosphere which also pervaded both Tremont and Winter Streets gave safe approach to the shopping district for pedestrians. The granite block still to be seen on Tremont Street [1914] was then comparatively new, and farther north on Tremont Row,[3] as it was called, was a fine old block built along lines with which one is so familiar today in many parts of London. The residential quarter of Boston at that time was largely in this locality, extending well beyond Washington Street through Summer Street and past Church Green.[4] Indeed, there was a close resemblance between the Boston of that time and many parts of old London, such as Piccadilly at Green Park. Many blocks of houses in that area are so strongly suggestive of Boston that in many a wandering through the residential quarter of London the native city of my youth has been brought back with startling clarity. London has often given me a strong homelike impression, as if it were the cradle of my race, and called back events indelibly associated with my boyhood.

This feeling is reawakened when I wander in memory down the Winter and Summer Streets of old Boston. The mansion-houses in that region with their columns and bowed fronts represented what was best in the architecture of the home of the old Anglo-Saxon family. On Bromfield Street was the Bromfield House, an old English type of inn with an archway through which the stagecoach might have passed. Hamilton Place and Temple Place were less ostentatious, the quiet abodes of many of our oldest families. Domestic Boston was then just beginning to trickle through Boston Neck and spread along the southern shore of the original Back Bay. But although a few valiant efforts were made to make this new region fashionable, as in the case of the Deacon House,[5] society showed

---

[3] "Tremont Row" formerly designated the west side of Tremont Street between Pemberton Square and Howard Street. Facing Tremont Row was a wedge-shaped row of buildings owned by William Scollay, the removal of which in the 1870's left the open area now known as Scollay Square. Court Street formerly extended along the east side of Scollay's buildings to Hanover Street.

[4] The following description of Summer Street is found in Samuel Adams Drake's *Old Landmarks and Historic Personages of Boston* (1872): "Fifty years gone by Summer Street was, beyond dispute, the most beautiful avenue in Boston. Magnificent trees then skirted its entire length, overarching the driveway with interlacing branches, so that you walked or rode as within a grove in a light softened by the leafy screen, and over the shadows of the big elms lying across the pavement." To this day the marker at the busy intersection of Summer and Bedford Streets reads "Church Green," although the Green and the graceful church designed by Bulfinch have long since vanished.

[5] The Deacon House, designed like a French château, was built in the late 1840's for Mr. and Mrs. Edward P. Deacon within the enclosure of West Concord, Washington, and Worcester Streets. It was an example of the best "French roof" style, built of brick, and surrounded by a high brick wall with entrance lodge and other accessories. The house and its contents were sold at auction in 1871, and

little inclination to drift in that direction, and remained faithful to the region of Beacon Hill. Only when modern enterprise paved the way for the development of Commonwealth Avenue and its tributaries after the Civil War did the real change come.[6]

When I was three years of age, our family moved from Pemberton

---

thousands admitted by ticket crowded the mansion to view its splendors. In 1881 it became the home of the Massachusetts Normal Art-School (1679 Washington Street). A drawing of the Deacon House, made when Roxbury Neck served as a horse-and-sleigh racing course, is reproduced in Mussey's *Old New England* (Wyn, New York, 1946, and a photograph appears in Allan Forbes's *Forty of Boston's Historic Houses* (State Street Trust Company, Boston, 1912).

[6] The "Back Bay" was originally part of the Charles River estuary. At high tide its eastern shore coincided roughly with the present Charles Street and extended southerly to the Neck, a narrow isthmus about a mile long connecting the towns of Boston and Roxbury. The highway along the Neck (now Washington Street in the South End) was sometimes inundated at high tide to the height of a horse's knee. Low tide turned the bay into an unsavory marsh known as Roxbury Flats.

The first great change was the Mill Dam, a project conceived by Uriah Cotting. This is described in Justin Winsor, ed., *Memorial History of Boston* (Boston, 1880–81) as the "event which more than any other determined the future of Boston." The Boston and Roxbury Mill Corporation was incorporated in 1814 to build a combined dam and toll road extending the line of Beacon Street from the foot of Beacon Hill westerly across the bay to Sewall's Point, Brookline (now Kenmore Square) and also to build a cross dam with a similar road (now Hemenway Street) from Gravelly Point, Roxbury to the main dam. In the 1930's the excavation for the underpass at Commonwealth and Massachusetts Avenues uncovered a portion of the cross dam. The old bay was thus divided into two enclosed areas, a "Full Basin" (Fens) on the west and a "Receiving Basin" (Back Bay) on the east. The incoming tide filled the western basin, and with the outgoing tide a controlled flow through gates into the Receiving Basin was utilized to operate machinery in two flour mills and an iron mill. The Receiving Basin emptied into the Charles River estuary at low tide.

The mills failed to prosper, however, and by the 1840's the basins functioned chiefly as receptacles for public sewage, which accumulated because basin level was usually lower than river level. The Back Bay of this period has been described as "a body of water so foul that even clams and eels cannot live there, and a place that no one will go within a half mile of in the summer time unless absolutely necessary, so great a stench was there" [Bostonian Society, *Proceedings* (January 18, 1938), p. 35]. It was universally believed that the basin emitted disease-bearing miasms. In 1849, when it was thought that an epidemic of cholera was approaching Boston by way of Philadelphia and New York, the Board of Health "directed the large tract of marshy land, constituting the Back Bay, to be flooded from the ocean" as a prophylactic measure (Boston City Document No. 66, 1849). Eventually public agitation led to the second great change — the conversion of the Back Bay and Fens into dry land by extensive filling.

This project, the real fruit of Uriah Cotting's original endeavor, was undertaken under the Tripartite Agreements of 1856 and 1864 on the part of the Commonwealth, the City, and the Boston Water Power Company, an affiliate of the original corporation. The City acquired the Back Bay district and over a period of three decades developed it in accord with the plan of Arthur Gilman. The first buildings west of the Public Garden appeared about 1860. The City acquired the Fens in 1878 and developed this area after the plan of Frederick Law Olmsted, the central feature of which was a greenbelt system of parkways that called for the coöperation of neighboring communities in the formation of the Metropolitan Park Commission.

Square to No. 6 Park Street.[7] The lot on which this house stood, nineteen feet in width, had been purchased by my grandfather, Dr. John C. Warren, in order that his son Mason might be near him; and the house which had already been planned by the architect, Mr. George M. Dexter, was built upon it. Provision was made for introducing gas, and my mother was responsible for a statement often dwelt upon by her that this was the first private house in Boston in which gas was used as a means of illumination. Several years later Cochituate water was introduced into the city, an occasion marked by a celebration which culminated in the turning on of the fountain in the Frog Pond and a speech by Daniel Webster.[8]

The installation of "fixed basins" in every bedroom was considered a great advance over the old type of washstand. There were two bathtubs, which for a house with less than twenty feet of frontage was considered a generous supply. Each was fitted with an apparatus for a shower-bath, which poured a feeble stream of cold water

---

[7] Nos. 4, 5, and 6 Park Street were demolished in 1956 to make way for a new building.

[8] The Cochituate Water Celebration on Boston Common was described with surprising eloquence in Boston City Document No. 50, 1848:

> The Mayor, addressing the assembly, asked if it were their pleasure, that the water should now be introduced. An immense number of voices responded "aye"; whereupon, on the signal of the Chief Engineer, the fountain gate was gradually opened, and the water began to rise, in a strong column, increasing rapidly in height, until it reached an elevation of about eighty feet . . . and fell gracefully on all sides in a regular form, exhibiting a power and beauty, which produced an evident surprise on the whole of the expectant multitude. After a moment of silence, shouts rent the air, emphatically attesting the universal joy, in witnessing this proof of the actual attainment of the object of so long cherished hopes. The profusion with which the desired treasure was poured out gave manifest satisfaction, as an earnest of the abundance of the future supply . . . The sun was just sinking below the horizon, and its last rays tinged the summit of the watery column. The bells began to ring — cannon were fired — and rockets streamed across the sky.

The official report made no mention of a speech by Daniel Webster, although Rowse's lithograph of the event depicts Webster with his dog, standing in the foreground of the throng around the Frog Pond. The celebration attracted the largest audience in the history of the city up to that time. It included a parade that required two hours to pass any given point, an "Ode to Water" written by James Russell Lowell and sung by the school children, and addresses by the Hon. Nathan Hale and Mayor Josiah Quincy, Jr.

Dr. John C. Warren was an interested spectator, for he had long been an agitator for the piping of pure water into Boston. In 1803 he made a chemical analysis of impurities in the town's well water, and about 1820 introduced a petition to the Legislature, signed by most of the physicians in Boston, calling for a pure-water project. Since 1795 Boston's water needs had been partly met by a log pipeline from Jamaica Pond, a branch from which had been extended to reach the MGH. The new Cochituate system carried fresh water over fourteen miles by aqueduct and tunnel to the Brookline Reservoir, and thence to the Beacon Hill Reservoir, a magnificent structure supported on massive granite arches.

upon the shoulders of those whose system could withstand the shock. The tonic effect of this mode of ablution was heralded abroad with much enthusiasm by the medical fraternity, and was administered indiscriminately to the young, the feeble, and the aged as a panacea for many ailments. The imperfections inseparable from the plumbing of those days soon gave rise to complications which were not always compatible with an ideal hygienic standard, and finally led to the abolishment of the "fixed basin" from the sleeping-apartment. It was in this house that the younger members of the family were born; and, although there were but four master's bedrooms, it was supposed at the time to give ample accommodations for a family of seven children.

I was sent to school at the Park Street Church at the age of five. This was in 1847. It was a girls' school, kept by Miss Dwight, and I was the only boy. The school-room was situated in the brick portion of the tower which supports the steeple, and was lighted by an arched window above the main entrance on Tremont Street. A door from the farther end led directly up into the wooden steeple, which served as a playground for the pupils. Miss Dwight's scholars varied in age from beginners to "big girls." I remained there about one year and then was transferred to Mr. D. B. Tower's School for Boys. This school occupied a large room on the ground floor of the church, running from Park Street to the rear of the building, facing directly upon the Granary Burying Ground. The entrance was, as at present, on Park Street. Thanksgiving Day was always observed by an annual gathering at the school. Each boy's desk was covered with a generous supply of apples, nuts, and raisins; and some of the older boys were expected to contribute to the day's entertainment by "speaking pieces." One of the older boys was the leading star, and always wound up the day's exercises with an oratorical effort which was greatly appreciated. Mr. Sullivan's school for boys was in the basement of the church, and was approached from Park Street corner by a steep flight of steps. This was also a popular school, but not so large as its neighbors. The three schools continued to occupy the church building for many years.

No. 5 Park Street was the site of the ancient Town Pound, and in the nineteenth century had passed through the hands of Thomas H. Perkins, John Gore, and Francis C. Gray. Josiah Quincy, who was President of Harvard from 1829 to 1845, purchased this property in 1857. I recall a visit which I made with my father to Mr. Quincy in his old age. He was suffering from an injury to his hip caused by a fall. He had been attended medically during his long life by three generations of the Warren family, and inasmuch as the first generation had yielded two members to his service (Joseph and

John), my father thought that the opportunity should not be missed of introducing to him a *fifth* Warren. I was still quite a lad and doubtless went with my father more or less by compulsion, but I recall vividly the scolding which my father got for not giving him a better leg. This threw me for the time being into the background, much to my satisfaction.

No. 8 Park Street was occupied by the Honorable Abbott Lawrence, whose dwelling has been preserved with comparatively little change by the Union Club. I recall an agreeable visit to Mr. Lawrence in my childhood; I was much entertained, while seated on his knee, by the exhibition of a bag of copper coins which had recently been discovered by workmen digging in his cellar. They were of more historical than monetary value, bearing the imprint of King George, and evidently buried there in Revolutionary times.

My grandfather's house at No. 2 Park Street, one of a block of four dwellings built by Charles Bulfinch in 1805,[9] was the birthplace of my father. It was also the resort of quite a number of medical students. The room on the ground floor which later became my father's office was then used by the students as a study room. The floor was covered with sand and the furnishings were of a corresponding degree of simplicity, in keeping with the rough lot of the young students. Their leisure moments were often spent in boisterous play on the adjoining Common.[10] They boarded, or at all events took their midday meal, in the house.[11] The Warren boys,

[9] Bulfinch's original plan for this block of four houses is one of the treasures of the Massachusetts Historical Society. Ogden Codman considered this plan to be the only existing one actually signed by Bulfinch (letter, Codman to J.C.W., March 25, 1920, Warren Papers, vol. 45, Massachusetts Historical Society). The front elevation is reproduced in *Prints, Maps and Drawings, 1677–1822*, a "Picture Book" published by the Historical Society in 1957. In design the four houses were similar to the Bulfinch dwelling now occupied by the Colonial Society of Massachusetts at No. 87 Mount Vernon Street on Beacon Hill.

[10] For a brief period Boston Common was a center for the game of cricket, in which J.C.W. was a participant. James D'Wolf Lovett wrote in *Old Boston Boys and the Games They Played* (Boston, 1907):

> In the late fifties the game of cricket tried hard to get a foothold in Boston and several clubs were formed, among which were the "Bostons," the "Bay States," "Star and Thistle," "Young Bostons," "Mount Vernon," and a few others. I belonged to the "Young Bostons," which numbered among its first eleven Collins Warren, George Mifflin, Horatio Curtis, Phil. Mason (afterwards killed in battle), Charlie and Jim Jackson, Frank Higginson, Nathan Appleton, Frank Loring, Harry Sturgis, and myself . . . but the Common was an impossible place for cricket, the hard baked ground making a good wicket or bowling crease out of the question . . . I with others drifted into baseball.

[11] The quartering of medical students in the houses of practitioners was a customary practice. Joseph Warren had studied in the home of Dr. James Lloyd, and in turn took into his own household William Eustis, Samuel Adams, Lemuel

Sullivan and Mason, were given places at the table, and took advantage of their association with companions of more mature years to play many childish pranks upon them. I recall the thrilling story of a fiery-headed youth, generally regarded as the "butt" of his comrades, who, after some more than usually impudent practical joke, pursued relentlessly young Sullivan out of the house and across the Common until the guilty urchin found sanctuary in the Frog Pond. This was before the day when that delightful old reminder of the mother country, the iron fence, was erected. Many other anecdotes of those days passed down to me give a vivid and lasting impression of the inadequacy and crudity of what was known as medical instruction in the early decades of the century.

The principal center of medicine was on the other side of Beacon Hill where the Massachusetts General Hospital had been placed on the bank of the Charles River — an admirable position not only for its proximity to the dwellings of the less prosperous members of the community but for its exposure to the fresh summer breezes floating across the waters. The Charles was not yet contaminated by the inevitable accompaniments of a rapidly increasing population on both sides of the river. The Hospital had been opened for patients about twenty-five years before.[12] At first it went through a quiet period of sleepy existence, with a small number of patients, and surgical operations were few and far between.[13] Each physician took

---

Hayward, David Townsend, his brother John Warren, and other graduates of Harvard College.

John Warren studied also in the house of Dr. Edward A. Holyoke of Salem. J.C.W.'s mother Annie Crowninshield, who lived until 1905, had a girlhood memory of Dr. Holyoke, whose house stood opposite the Crowninshield residence on Essex Street, Salem. Dr. Holyoke, who lived to the age of one hundred, is remembered as the first "graduate" of the Harvard Medical School (M.D. Hon. 1783).

John C. Warren studied medicine under his father for one year before sailing for the centers of European medicine. In later years his own pupils at No. 2 Park Street included such names as Reynolds, Storer, Flint, Willard Parker, Lewis, Otis, Barrett, Greene, Bemis, Tilton, and Fisher.

J. Mason Warren studied under his father for a short time before entering medical school at Harvard, after which he studied in Europe.

[12] The Hospital opened its doors in 1821. A patient was admitted for treatment on the service of Dr. James Jackson, Acting Physician, on the first day of September. The first patient on the service of Dr. John C. Warren, Acting Surgeon, entered on September 20 and was operated upon the following day. The case records of these two patients and of every patient thereafter are carefully preserved. In 1921 J.C.W. was a member of the Committee for the Observance of the Centennial Anniversary of the Admission of the First Patient to the Hospital.

[13] In the first twenty-five years the annual total in-patient admissions ranged from a low of 115 in 1822 to a high of 554 in 1826. The figure for 1845 was 453. The capacity of the Hospital was doubled by the erection of two new wings, and in 1848 the admissions rose to 804. (From 86th Annual Report of the Trustees, MGH, 1899.)

his turn at a service extending only a few months of the year.

Suddenly a time arrived when it seemed as though medical science had reached a point where new activities were in order.

A number of physicians then coming into practice had, like their fathers before them, studied in Paris and London. The pupils of Louis,[14] among whom may be mentioned Bowditch, Jackson, Shattuck, Holmes, Hooper, and Mason Warren, had come home with new ideas; new medical societies were being formed and enthusiasm for the advancement of medical science was in the ascendant.[15] The medical school of Harvard was moved to the head of North Grove Street, next to the Massachusetts General Hospital.[16] This was a most important event in the history of medical education, as full of significance for the future as the present great medical undertak-

[14] Pierre Alexandre Louis, a scholarly physician of Paris, exerted through his students a significant and lasting effect on Boston medicine. James Jackson, Jr., following an education at Harvard, studied under Louis on the wards of La Pitié in the years 1831–1833. His letters home described in detail the new art of physical diagnosis with the aid of the stethoscope and other developments in Parisian medicine. The young physician died in 1834 just as he was to start practice in Boston. Letters and case notes of the young Jackson were assembled by his father and added to *A Memoir of James Jackson, Jr., M.D.*, published in 1835.

Louis spent many years in hospital practice observing and recording clinical phenomena. Among other contributions to medicine, he introduced the "numerical method" as an instrument of precise clinical description. His portrait by Champmartin, a personal gift to James Jackson, Jr., became one of the treasured possessions of the MGH in 1867; it now hangs in the medical staff room.

[15] One of these new organizations was the Boston Society for Medical Observation, founded by Henry I. Bowditch and John Ware in 1835. This name was taken from that of a similar society in Paris presided over by Louis. The Boston group was suspended in 1838 but revived in 1846. A history of the society published in 1872 states:

> The object of the Society was to cultivate the taste for the accurate observation and the recording of cases while by the bedside of a patient. In this way it was thought that two useful ends would be gained: 1st — a collection of a number of accurately and minutely detailed observations, and 2d — the making of each member a skilful observer of disease, accurate in diagnosis and a rational practitioner of medicine.

J.C.W. and several other young doctors fresh from the schools of Vienna and Berlin joined this society about 1870, and the following year it was reorganized "in furtherance of the cause of Medical Science." In 1894 it was absorbed by the Boston Society for Medical Improvement.

[16] At a special meeting of the trustees of the MGH on Sunday, Feb. 22, 1846 it was:

> Voted on the communication made to this Board by Dr. J. C. Warren on behalf of the Professors of the Medical School of Harvard University that this Board are sensible of the courtesy which dictated the communication, but in regard to the subject of building a medical College in immediate proximity to the grounds of the Hospital they cannot perceive any advantage to this Institution to arise therefrom; but they think they can see that some disadvantages would be occasioned thereby. In stating however this opinion, the Board

ing [17] is to the medical profession of today. At about the same time the Bulfinch building of the Hospital was extended on either side by the construction of new wings.[18] These building activities of the school and the Hospital added to the medical plant of the day, foreshadowing, as it were, the new era in surgery which was to come into being.

The physicians of the earlier generation had enjoyed few advantages comparable even to the meager ones of the generation which succeeded them. Harvard's medical school, originally in Cambridge, had been moved into Boston early in the century and established in rooms over an apothecary store on what is now Washington Street; later it had erected a building of its own on Mason Street near the

---

> do not assume any right to object to the course suggested in the communication but intend simply to make an answer to the question proposed to them.

Dr. Frederic A. Washburn, in *The Massachusetts General Hospital: Its Development 1900–1935.* (Houghton Mifflin, Boston, 1939), recalls the indignation expressed by J.C.W. some eighty years later at this attitude of the trustees toward the communication of his grandfather regarding the Medical School. In fairness to the trustees of that period, however, it is well to bear in mind that medical students in the last century were notorious as an unruly and noisy lot. They were, for the most part, immature high school graduates turned loose in a heady environment. Although the Anatomy Act of 1831 had legalized the dissection of the human body in Massachusetts, stories about student "resurrectionists" were still in circulation. Doctors, because of their bold curiosity about natural phenomena, were commonly looked upon as "atheists" by the more pious members of the community.

In his Report for 1879–80 (p. 33) President Charles W. Eliot of Harvard wrote:

> An American physician or surgeon may be, and often is, a coarse and uncultivated person, devoid of intellectual interests outside of his calling, and quite unable to either speak or write his mother tongue with accuracy . . . In this University, until the reformation of the School in 1870–71, the medical students were noticeably inferior in bearing, manners, and discipline to the students of other departments; they are now indistinguishable from other students.

It is not surprising, therefore, that the Trustees were hesitant to welcome the Medical School with its students as neighbors for the sick patients in the Hospital. Even today, a student dormitory has on occasion proved to be an inconsiderate neighbor for a hospital.

The cost of the 1846 Medical School building was met partly by sale of the Mason Street building to the Boston Society of Natural History. Harvard University supplied the balance required, with the proviso that it be reimbursed with interest by the medical professors. Subsequently the donations of private citizens took much of this financial burden from the shoulders of the Medical Faculty. The new building was dedicated on November 4, 1846, the principal speaker being President Edward Everett.

[17] This undertaking was the relocation of the Harvard Medical School on the present Longwood Avenue site. It is considered at length in Chapter XXIII.

[18] The new west wing was opened in July 1846, and the east wing in July, 1847.

Common.[19] But this was somewhat distant from the site of the General Hospital, and in consequence medical instruction followed

[19] The earliest lectures on medicine started in the basement of Harvard Hall adjacent to the college kitchen and buttery. The exact location of the anatomical lectures by Dr. John Warren in the first years is still a matter of some speculation, but it is likely that the official place for lectures and dissections was or soon came to be the Holden Chapel, in competition with the college carpenter.

A number of causes brought the Medical Faculty to Boston in 1810, where they hired a hall above William B. White's apothecary shop at No. 49 old Marlborough Street, now Washington Street. This site is today occupied by William Filene's Sons Company. Mr. White was the South District Apothecary for the Boston Dispensary. The medical professors paid their yearly rental of $350 from fees collected from the students. The first circular ever issued by the Medical School appeared on September 5, 1810 and stated:

> The number of lectures will probably be about fifty, certainly not more than sixty, during the present season. This number will be gradually increased till it equals that given in the most respectable seminaries in the United States. The lectures will be delivered daily.
>
> The object of the new Professorship of clinical medicine [held by James Jackson] is, "to point out at the bedside of such sick persons, whose cases may be suitable for the purpose, the symptoms of the diseases under which they may labour, and to lecture upon the nature of such diseases and the indications of the cure and methods of treatment, which have by experience been found most successful in similar diseases."
>
> In addition to the lectures on surgery, the professors of that branch will exhibit to their students, at stated periods, the cases of surgical diseases in the hospital of the Alms House; also the operations in surgery, which may occur in publick or private practice, without any additional fee . . . Private pupils will be received by the professors on the usual terms . . . The subscribers have founded an expectation on these circumstances that students will resort to Boston from every part of the country; that thus they shall be enabled to enlarge the institution in various ways, so that this shall become, what it ultimately should be, THE MEDICAL SCHOOL OF NEW ENGLAND.

At an earlier date John C. Warren and John Gorham had rented rooms in Mr. White's building to give private demonstrations in "practical anatomy" (dissections) and in chemistry. The first Boston Medical Library, with Warren as librarian, the Boylston Medical Society, with Warren as president, and the Massachusetts Medical Society also moved into the same building along with the school.

Several years later Warren and Jackson busied themselves to obtain a more adequate school building. Private donations and a large financial grant from the Massachusetts Legislature brought success to the money-raising effort, and the building was erected in 1815–16. The architect was Jacob Guild, a "housewright" about whom little is known. The school is described in a circular attributed to John C. Warren and entitled *Some Account of the Medical School in Boston, and of the Massachusetts General Hospital* (1824):

> The Massachusetts Medical College is situated in Mason Street, near the Boston Common and Mall [just north of the present site of the Keith Memorial Theater]. This building is of brick, 88 feet in length, and 43 in breadth. Its figure is oblong, with a pediment in front, and an octagonal centre rising above the roof, and also forming a three-sided projection in the rear of the building. This is surmounted by a dome with a sky-light and balustrade, giving an air of elegance to the neatness and fit proportions of the building . . .
>
> In this building are contained the cabinet of anatomical preparations, con-

the traditional lines of apprenticeship to some prominent practitioner. A student was more or less intimately associated with the practice of his sponsor, which served as practically the only source of clinical instruction available to him.[20] While the advent of the General Hospital had improved these conditions materially, the old order of things still prevailed. This I have heard frequently from my father's lips.

In 1846 I was, of course, only four years of age and not sufficiently advanced to remember these interesting changes or the happenings which led to the discovery of anesthesia. My earliest medical recollections are confined to visits with my father to the Hospital in his one-horse chaise. While the visit was being made, I was left to amuse myself — to prowl about the garden in front of Bulfinch or wander along the beach at the foot of the bank on which the western end of the building stood. A small boat house gave accommodation to wherries for the students' use, and an arm of the river reached in beneath North Charles Street, which was then merely a bridge running from the jail to what is now Allen Street, to form an enclosed bay.[21] I remember little of the wards or the patients of those days, and my first glimpse of actual surgery must have been when, peeping through the half open door of the operating theatre, I saw Dr. George H. Gay in the act of severing the flesh with his

sisting of more than a thousand valuable specimens; the chemical apparatus, which is complete and costly; the apparatus and specimens used in the lectures on midwifery and materia medica; and the medical library, containing above 3000 volumes. An additional building is about to be erected adjacent to the College, to receive the *Linnaean cabinet*, an extensive collection of objects in natural history, which has lately become the property of Harvard University.

The new school was renamed the Massachusetts Medical College of Harvard University in appreciation of the grant from the Legislature. The library and the two societies that had been in Mr. White's building also moved into the Mason Street structure. In 1831 the Medical College was reorganized as a faculty separate from the mother institution in Cambridge.

[20] Prior to the opening of the MGH, clinical instruction of a sort had been given at the Boston Almshouse, the Boston Dispensary, the State Prison, and perhaps the Marine Hospital in Charlestown.

[21] Charles Street formerly ended at the Suffolk County Jail, and North Charles Street began at the line of Allen Street. The little bay between these two points was spanned by a pier bridge erected by the city in 1856. Several years later this bay was filled in, and the name of Charles Street was made to include the entire highway extending from Park Square to the old Canal Bridge at Leverett Street.

When the Hospital was first built, a sea wall was constructed along the eastern shore of the little bay. This is said to have been the point at which patients sometimes were landed by boat to be carried into the Hospital. A portion of the sea wall uncovered in 1937 when excavations were made for the George Robert White Building was preserved and left exposed adjacent to the new foundation.

knife and the blood flowing from a gaping wound. I was drawn
quickly away by my father, though somewhat reluctantly as I
recall. No other opportunity was given me to visit the operating
theatre [22] until I was fourteen years of age, when by special invitation arrangements were made for me to accompany my future
brother-in-law, Samuel Hammond,[23] and his friend, John T. Coolidge,
to an attendance on the regular operating day of the Hospital. For
this purpose I was given permission to leave Mr. Dixwell's School
at an early hour. This was not difficult to obtain, as Saturday morning from time immemorial had been known as "operating day" at
the Hospital.[24]

Operations were still performed in the old amphitheater made
memorable by the first public demonstration of the use of anesthesia.
The row of white wooden benches with iron rails on which to lean

[22] Dr. James C. White wrote in his *Sketches from My Life* (Cambridge, 1914)
under the heading of January 1854: "It is interesting to observe that on one occasion I saw present in the amphitheatre three generations of Warrens, John C.,
J. Mason, and J. Collins, the latter a boy." At that time J.C.W. was less than
twelve years old.

[23] J.C.W.'s oldest sister Mary was married to Samuel Hammond at No. 2 Park
Street on October 28, 1858. They settled in a new house at No. 116 Beacon
Street, on the site of the old Mill Dam.

[24] The display of operations at the Hospital on Saturday mornings continued
well into the 1920's. Unusual "cases" were assembled so that the senior surgeons
on duty could have an impressive list of operations scheduled for the amphitheater.
The two services, East and West, vied with each other in trying to stage the better
show. In the Surgical Building opened in 1900 the display reached major proportions. When the morning's list was a long one, an operation would be started in
a small room and then the entire outfit trundled like a troupe of gypsies into the
pit of the amphitheater, where the crucial phase of the procedure was demonstrated to visiting doctors, students, and nurses. The surgeon would be allotted,
say, fifteen minutes. Whether or no the operation had been completed, at the
expiration of the allotted time the tents were folded, the troupe moved off stage
to complete the operation elsewhere, and a new act took over.

The first decade of the twentieth century saw the heyday of showmanship in
operative surgery, for the procedures then undertaken were not of great magnitude, although the patients were often extremely ill. Great weight was placed on
the speed and daring of the operator. In cities where a single surgeon could gain
ascendancy over local colleagues, his operating theater became famous for
histrionic performances that might last the greater part of the day. Patient after
patient was wheeled into the amphitheater pit. In the somewhat more restrained
atmosphere of the MGH, where all men were equal and not one but eight visiting
surgeons ruled the roost by virtue of seniority, there developed this Saturday
morning performance which in the literal if not the idiomatic usage might be
called *surgery en passant.*

Even so, tensions mounted when some prima donna showed reluctance to with-
draw from the spotlight and overstayed his time to hold the audience spellbound
in an ad-lib recounting of his surgical prowess.

Since the opening of the George Robert White Building operations have been
performed so that a limited number of visiting doctors may observe suitable procedures from behind hermetically sealed glass windows.

during the operation surrounded half of the theatre. These were later removed altogether but have since been replaced, and the theatre at the present time resembles what it was on that historic occasion as nearly as care and memory can make it. Although the present instrument cases are new they closely resemble those of that period; the floor and ceiling, except for a coat of paint, remain unchanged.

The time at which I saw my first operation was just about one decade after the introduction of anesthesia. The method of administering sulphuric ether, as it was called (it was the only anesthetic used in the Hospital at that time), utilized a cone-shaped sea sponge unprotected by any covering. This method had been introduced shortly after the first operation under ether, and was employed for over twenty years at the Hospital. In the first few cases in which he administered anesthesia, Dr. Morton employed an apparatus invented by himself, which consisted of a glass chamber containing a sponge saturated with ether. A tube and mouth-piece with a valve arrangement was attached to the chamber, not unlike some of the inhalers of the present day which have supplanted the more simple forms of administration by the sponge and cone. I think the cone-shaped sponge was first employed by Dr. J. Mason Warren about two months after the operation which had taken place on October 16th. It is probable that the familiar daguerreotype was taken at this later date, for it shows that type of sponge being used. The operation depicted was nevertheless always referred to by my father as "the first operation under ether." [25]

To return now to my first experience. The number of spectators

[25] J.C.W.'s presidential address, "The Influence of Anaesthesia on the Surgery of the Nineteenth Century," in the 1897 *Transactions of the American Surgical Association (15, 25)* was illustrated by a reproduction of a daguerreotype with the following note:

> The illustration represents the operating-theatre of the Massachusetts General Hospital in the winter of 1847. The sponge used here is known as the first sponge with which ether was given. This method was adopted in February, 1847, by Dr. J. Mason Warren. The surgeons whose portraits appear in this picture are, on the patient's left, Dr. John C. Warren, Dr. Samuel Parkman; on the patient's right, Dr. J. Mason Warren and Dr. Townsend. The otherizer is probably Dr. Heywood. The daguerrotype from which the photogravure is taken has been in the possession of the writer's family since that time.

Contrary to popular belief, no daguerreotype was taken during the historic operation of October 16, 1846. According to an article entitled "Ether Day Observance" in the *Boston Transcript,* October 17, 1906, Josiah J. Hawes, a leading photographer of old Boston, "had come to the amphitheatre on that occasion to take a picture of the operation; but the sight of blood had so unnerved him that he was obliged to retire." The familiar daguerreotype of the "first" operation under ether was a reënactment taken by the firm of Southworth and Hawes at a later date.

was small as compared with the attendance of later dates. The operation was one for the removal of the upper jaw and was performed by my father. The cone-shaped sea sponge permitted a free evaporation of ether and its fumes saturated the atmosphere of the room. Attendance at a surgical operation in those days scented the person with the odor of ether, which clung for many hours afterwards. It was with some trepidation that I submitted myself to the ordeal of seeing a surgical operation, and I could not have had a more severe test, for, as any surgeon knows, the removal of the upper jaw bone is attended with bleeding and disfigurement and more mechanical difficulties than the usual operations of surgery. For such cases anesthesia was not pressed to its deepest form — and with good judgment, for insensibility of the vocal chords would permit aspiration of blood into the air passages that might give rise to serious complications. Death from asphyxiation under these circumstances has been known to occur when anesthesia was made more complete.

In the present case, although the patient expressed no suffering, there was more or less movement on his part with considerable vocal disturbance. A frightful gaping wound of the face, in which the tongue could be seen at times protruding, with occasional struggles during which more ether was applied, was sufficient to try the nerves of a youth of fourteen. I passed through the ordeal, however, entirely to my satisfaction and I thought my good father felt a certain degree of pride in my having gone through the "baptism of fire" successfully.

As I grew old enough to take an interest in medical affairs I found that the assumption that I was one day to become a doctor was gradually taken for granted.[26] I began to listen more attentively to

[26] At the age of eleven J.C.W. accompanied his parents to New York on the occasion of the American Medical Convention of 1853.
On their homeward journey, the morning of May 6, the train was wrecked in an appalling disaster at Norwalk. More than sixty persons were killed. J. Mason Warren recorded this episode in his private journal:

Just after passing the station at Norwalk, forty miles from New York, I suddenly felt a convulsive crack, immediately followed by the disruption of the train in front of us. Our carriage was at once lifted up from the rails and struck the one before it, the forward half being knocked into splinters. I expected instant death, as I saw everything in front of us, up to the very seats on which we were sitting — cars, passengers, and all — plunge headlong into the water and disappear. Having dragged Mrs. Warren and the children [J.C.W. and his cousin Benjamin Mifflin] up into the rear of the car which so happily for us had remained on the track, I made my escape with them on to the bridge behind, with the loss of nothing but my hat.

Through the recklessness of the engineer, the speed of the train had not been slackened on approaching the bridge; and as this was open for the

the conversation of those around me and to what my father saw fit to tell me of his share in the events which surrounded the introduction of anesthesia. I was too young at the time it had occurred to recall any of the actors excepting those related to my own family. The conversation often turned upon the "ether controversy," as it was called, and concerned itself with the relative merits of the claims of Jackson and Morton to the title of discoverer. Little was said of Horace Wells' employment of nitrous oxide, for no attempt had been made at that time to use gas in surgical operations, and I think it was not until some years later that it was employed in dentistry.[27] No mention whatever was made of Crawford W. Long's claim and I do not believe that either my father or grandfather had ever heard of him, for it was long after the death of both that I myself first heard of this claim through an article written by Marion Sims, published after I had been several years in practice.[28]

I recall well my father's account of a private operation under ether which he performed at the Bromfield House, an operation I think for a large fatty tumor. A number of members of the profession had been invited to witness the operation, and amongst them Dr. Charles T. Jackson.[29] Few of the surgeons of the Hospital espoused Jackson's

---

passage of a steamer, we were doomed to become the victims of his folly . . . Of all those who were plunged into the water with that part of the train which went down, the only person saved was Miss Griswold, daughter of the Rev. Dr. Griswold, of New York, who was resuscitated after two hours' constant exertion on my part. [In Howard Payson Arnold, *Memoir of Jonathan Mason Warren, M.D.* (privately printed, Boston, 1886), p. 234.]

Dr. John C. Warren had attended the convention but returned by an earlier train. Among the New England physicians who lost their lives in the disaster were Abel L. Peirson of Salem, and James M. Smith and James Harrison Gray of Springfield.

[27] The tragic story of Horace Wells, a dentist of Hartford, and his experiments with nitrous oxide as an anesthetic agent which preceded the spectacular demonstration of ether by Morton cannot be told in a brief note. It is recorded in detail in the voluminous writings that deal with the introduction of anesthesia.

[28] Dr. Crawford Long published his claim to priority in the use of ether anesthesia in the *Southern Medical and Surgical Journal* for December 1849. On April 11, 1861 the *Boston Medical and Surgical Journal* published a letter from Charles T. Jackson describing his visit to Long on March 8, 1854 in Athens, Georgia, and also a subsequent visit. Dr. Marion Sims's article on Long appeared in the *Virginia Medical Monthly* for May 1877.

[29] The operation took place on November 21, 1846 and was the second of two operations described by J. Mason Warren in his *Surgical Observations, with Cases and Operations* (Boston, 1867), p. 616:

On Nov. 12th, I performed the first successful operation under ether which was done in private practice, on a young woman, for a tumor of the arm . . . Nov. 21st, I did another operation in private practice, at which many of the profession were present, — the removal of a formidable tumor of the thigh, which is thus described by Dr. J. C. Warren: — "The patient

cause, and there was almost unanimous acceptance of Morton's claim as discoverer. Personally, I never saw Morton, the fact being that he had little to do with surgery at the Hospital after the first few operations under ether. The production of profound anesthesia was not easy to accomplish, particularly with the sponge method of administration, but dangerous complications were not commonly encountered. There was a sublime faith in the safety of ether as compared with chloroform, and it was the boast of the Hospital staff that the administration of ether might be entrusted to inexperienced students and any of the male ward-tenders if occasion demanded.[30]

It was not until after the Civil War that this method of giving ether underwent any important improvements. The large numbers

---

lying upon a bed, the vapor was administered by Dr. Morton, in the presence of Drs. C. T. Jackson, Reynolds, J. V. C. Smith, Flagg, Gould, Shurtleff, Lawrence, Parsons, Briggs, and others . . . The operation was completed in two or three minutes.

Nathaniel I. Bowditch's *History of the Massachusetts General Hospital* (Boston, 1851), p. 302, places the November 21st operation at the Bromfield House, a popular resort of business and professional men under the management of Selden Crockett.

J.C.W. wrote to President Woodward of the Carnegie Institution of Washington in a letter dated May 26, 1920:

My father . . . used to tell me that Dr. Jackson refused at first to have anything to do with the new discovery saying that "he" (Morton) "would kill somebody next." About this time my father performed the first [*sic*] operation in private practice at a hotel in Boston and invited a number of the profession to be present and witness it. He recalls seeing Dr. Jackson in the background peering over the heads of the other gentlemen present. Dr. Morton gave the ether and the operation was most successful as to the absence of any pain. The next day Dr. Jackson came out in the Daily Advertiser claiming a share in the new discovery. [Copy of letter in Warren Papers, vol. 24, Massachusetts Historical Society.]

[30] Ether experiments and "frolics" were popular among medical students prior to 1846. The following letter cited by J.C.W. in his 1897 presidential address is of interest:

Cambridge, February 15, 1877.

My dear Dr. Warren: Your note with regard to experiments with ether at the Massachusetts General Hospital in 1836 has reached me. I remember well our amusement with sulphuric ether; Dr. Samuel Parkman was the House-surgeon, I was House-physician, and Mr. C. K. Whipple House-apothecary. We were especially jubilant when Mr. Whipple ordered a fresh quantity of ether, for it was apt to deteriorate by keeping. Each tested it by breathing it from the bottle till it produced unconsciousness, the others watching the different effects upon each. We also experimented upon rats in a glass-globe until they were entirely motionless and often wondered that the treatment did them no harm. But with all our experiments we never thought of trying the sensibility under ether, even by pricking with a pin. It was a great oversight. As ever, sincerely yours,

MORRILL WYMAN

of wounded soldiers coming from the front, who drifted in to the hospitals of the North, formed a significant proportion of the cases of surgery of that period.[31] These men, many of whom had become inured both to fighting and to a free use of alcohol, were not favorable subjects for the administration of ether, and I have still a vivid recollection of my efforts as student and as house pupil at the Hospital (1865–66) to etherize these patients. "Going under ether" in those days was no trifling ordeal and often was suggestive of the scrimmage of a football team rather than the quiet decorum which should surround the operating table. No preliminary treatment was thought necessary, except possibly to avoid the use of food for a certain time previous to the administration. Patients came practically as they were to the operating table and had to take their chances. They were usually etherized at the top of the staircase on a little chair outside of the operating theatre, as there was no room existing for this purpose at the time. In the struggle which ensued, I can recall often being forced against the bannisters with nothing but a thin rail to protect me from a fall down an area of three flights. But however powerful the patient might be, the man behind the sponge came out victorious and the panting subject was carried triumphantly into the operating room by the house pupil and the attendant.

But to revert to the period immediately following the introduction of anesthesia, the late Dr. Isaac F. Galloupe of Lynn, who was present at the first operation, and who was one of the comparatively few men in recent years with whom I have had an opportunity to converse upon the events preceding and following anesthesia, told me that in the early days there was considerable skepticism as to the efficacy of ether in general practice. Members of the Massachusetts Medical Society who did not reside in Boston were slow to adopt this method of relieving pain in their practice. Dr. John C. Warren therefore determined to make a convincing demonstration at an annual meeting of the Society. Accordingly, when a large proportion of the Society assembled in the old operating theatre of the MGH, a patient was brought in for the application of actual cautery over the spine. The patient having been etherized, the cautery irons were heated on coals brought in for the purpose and the region of the spinal column from neck to sacrum was seared. The smoke ascended to the ceiling of the amphitheatre, while the patient slumbered quietly on the operating table. All doubts in the minds of

[31] At the MGH the annual totals of surgical patients increased during the Civil War years: 1860, 595; 1861, 802; 1862, 1010; 1863, 989; 1864, 971; 1865, 737; and 1866, 709. Many wounded soldiers were admitted for unhealed wounds and chronic draining sinuses.

those present seemed to float away simultaneously, and the efficacy of anesthesia was never again questioned.[32]

When the Jubilee of Anesthesia took place at the MGH in 1896, it was my duty as one of the senior surgeons to prepare a program suitable for the occasion, and one feature which seemed to me especially important was some account of surgery before the days of anesthesia. I had hoped that surgeons were still living who would be able to give an account of their experiences in that era, but to my surprise there seemed to be no one among those prominent in the surgery of the day upon whom I could call for this purpose. I made an effort, therefore, to secure through my friend Pearce Gould of London a statement from Mr. John Erichsen,[33] but before he could obtain an interview for this purpose Mr. Erichsen died. Mr. James Paget, still living, was in too feeble a state of health to recall the period of which he indeed had formed a part and which he would

[32] J.C.W. refers also to this incident in his presidential address of 1897. Here he describes the patient as "a delicate female, laboring under a disease of the spinal marrow."

The case record of this patient begins on page 462 of Volume 30 of the Surgical Records. She was a dressmaker from Salem, unmarried, and twenty-five years of age. Her hospital treatment extended from Nov. 2, 1846 to her discharge "Not Relieved" on June 24, 1847. One would guess today that her illness was hysteria, although the patient herself attributed her disability to a deep puncture wound in the right thigh inflicted by scissors early in 1845. When admitted, she had a severe contracture deformity of the right leg and had been confined to bed with pain for several months.

The various treatments this patient received at the Hospital included electromagnetism, Hoffman's anodyne, leeches, valerian, assafetida, cantharides plasters, cataplasm of tobacco, cannabis indica, morphine, laudanum, hyoscyamus, and hydrotherapy given by wrapping in a cold wet sheet. Finally it was observed that her integument "resisted the action of caustics and vesicatories," and so she was subjected to two applications of the actual cautery along the spine, the first on April 3d and the second on May 26 before the members of the Medical Society. The record states: "She reports that when the iron was first applied she was conscious but felt no pain. More ether was given and she was brought completely under its effects."

[33] Sir John Eric Erichsen (1818–1896) was professor of clinical surgery at University College, London, and was elected president of University College in 1887. His famous textbook was first published in 1853 and went through ten editions. It is said that a pirated edition was issued by the United States Government to the medical officers of the Federal Army during the Civil War. Erichsen, a Dane by birth, went to London for his medical education. Because of a defect in vision, he was not considered to be a brilliant operator. He taught that surgery was a science to be studied rather than an art to be displayed.

A. Pearce Gould of the Middlesex Hospital Medical School was joint editor with J.C.W. in the publication of *The International Text-book of Surgery* by Saunders in 1900. J.C.W. himself contributed chapters on inflammation, infections, dislocation of the hip, and other topics, and there were many other chapters by American and British authors. In a review of the work in the *Annals of Surgery 33*, 102 (1901), A. T. Bristow of New York was a bit critical of "this multiplication of authors," but hastened to comment that the chapters contributed by J.C.W. were among the best in the book.

have been able to describe with a graphic pen had health remained.

There were, however, a few of the practitioners of the day in Boston and vicinity who had been students of medicine at the time of the introduction of anesthesia. Dr. Galloupe (to whom I have already referred) often had attended operations at that time, and was able to give a graphic account of the system pursued in handling a case for which operation was deemed necessary. In case of amputation, it was the custom to bring the patient into the operating room and place him upon the table. "Your grandfather," he said, "would stand with his hands behind his back and would say to the patient, 'Will you have your leg off, or will you not have it off?'" If the patient lost courage and said "No," he had decided not to have the leg amputated, he was at once carried back to his bed in the ward. If, however, he said "Yes," he was immediately taken firmly in hand by a number of strong assistants and the operation went on regardless of whatever he might say thereafter. If his courage failed him *after* this crucial moment, it was too late and no attention was paid to his cries of protest. It was found to be the only practicable method by which such an operation could be performed under the gruesome conditions which prevailed before the advent of anesthesia.

Operations had to be conducted with great rapidity and but little time could be taken up attending to the details which form so large a part of the technical procedure of the present time. Amputations of the lower extremity were always done with a previous application of the tourniquet, but the only attempt to control the subsequent hemorrhage was the ligature of the femoral artery. A couple of towels were placed crosswise of the end of the stump and firm bandages applied. The wound usually dripped blood for twenty-four hours, by which time the hemorrhage finally ceased. No doubt speed contributed toward reducing contamination of the wound. A free hemorrhage, so far as the wound itself was concerned, was also an advantage in this direction. A few stitches were usually taken to keep the edges of the flaps properly protected. In a case such as a dislocated hip, where it was necessary to effect complete muscular relaxation, an enema of tobacco [34] was freely administered, and

---

[34] The use of tobacco as a cure-all followed the introduction of certain American plants into the pharmacopoeia. Faith in its potency was widespread during the eighteenth century. One of the most popular uses for tobacco was as a resuscitative measure in apparent death from drowning. A pamphlet entitled *The Institution of the Humane Society of the Commonwealth of Massachusetts,* believed to have been printed in 1786, advised that among other measures the following treatment be used "with Persons apparently dead from drowning":

V. The smoke of tobacco thrown up the fundament should be ranked among the earliest applications; if a fumigator should not be at hand, the

while the victim was reduced to the last stages of collapse from nicotine poisoning the dislocated femur was forced back into its place.

No attempt was made by the surgeon to don any special form of costume. Antiquated broad frock coats, which were no longer fit to perform their ordinary duties, were used for this purpose in my time. Operations were performed in the old amphitheatre of Bulfinch and continued there during the whole period of my tutelage, for it was not until 1868 that a new operating theatre was opened and the historic old room was closed to surgery.

As I began to prepare for college and the rigor of schoolboy days was relaxed, opportunities for my father to test my taste for a medical career came more frequently. He made it possible for me to attend operations and occasionally to make ward visits. "Operating day," as noted before, was confined chiefly to Saturday morning and this function was attended not only by medical students but by practitioners as well. As the old amphitheatre was situated at the top of

---

common pipe will answer the purpose of applying this vapour to the bowels. So easy and important an operation should be repeatedly performed, as the good effects of tobacco smoke have been proved in many cases. [As quoted in M. A. DeWolfe Howe, *The Humane Society of the Commonwealth of Massachusetts . . . 1785–1916* (Boston, 1918), p. 17.]

Two sets of fumigators were procured at an early date at the expense of the Society. One set was deposited by order of the trustees in Dr. John Warren's house on School Street.

Belief in the efficacy of tobacco was not limited to the States. The Royal Humane Society of London, in its Annual Report for 1796, set forth in rhymed pentameter all the accepted means for restoring life. The use of tobacco fumes and infusions was thus described:

Tobacco-fumes.

Yet, should not these, with every care succeed,
With vigour still to other means proceed:
Tobacco-smoke has often prov'd, indeed,
Of wond'rous use, in cases of such need.
Try ev'ry means, not even this neglect,
With this herb's fumes the bowels to inject.
Thrice administer the same within the hour;
And, if it proves inadequate in power,
To *clysters* of this pungent herb apply,
Or other juice of equal potence high.

The use of clysters of tobacco smoke so interested J.C.W. that he prepared an article entitled "The 'Pulmotor' of the Eighteenth Century," which was published in the *Annals of Medical History* 2, 14, 210 (1919). In acknowledging receipt of a reprint of this article, Fielding H. Garrison wrote to J.C.W.: "An old Western pioneer once told me that the use of tobacco smoke in reducing hernia was very common in the far West in the gold digging days, and was taken out of Cullen's *Practice of Medicine*." (Letter, December 22, 1919, Warren Papers, vol. 45, Massachusetts Historical Society.)

the building, under the Bulfinch Dome, few operations were performed there on other days, and all emergency cases were dealt with in a room on the ground floor known as the "Bath Room." This name was bestowed upon it because it provided, as far as I can remember, the only bath tub in the entire establishment, if the tub in the house pupils' sleeping room be excepted. The plumbing facilities were of a primitive character, as may be inferred from the legend circulated in my medical student days that the students' bath tub, being not very remote from the autopsy room, was occasionally used to thaw out viscera.

College students who had medical aspirations attended the Saturday clinic, and this gave me the opportunity, after the ice had been broken, to follow up my first experience with occasional attendance at operations even before going to college. It was at about this period, in the latter part of the fifties, that I began to make ward visits with my father during his term of service. My earliest recollections of hospital practice thus disclosed to me were of a most gruesome character. It should be remembered that the period to which I now refer was about the middle of the second decade following the introduction of anesthesia. The members of the surgical staff who had been beginners in 1846 were now in the most active phase of their careers. The field of operative surgery had widened enormously and the surgical wards were now crowded with patients, but the method of treating wounds had undergone practically no change. The conditions were approaching those which prevail during the stress of a military campaign, and patients in the civil practice of surgery were beginning to be exposed to the hazards of infection, secondary hemorrhage, and other dangers which beset surgery in the wars of that period.[35]

The growth of surgery had necessitated a considerable enlargement of the Hospital, and preparations for new buildings were begun by filling in the projection of the Charles River which lay between

[35] During the Crimean War (1853–1856) and the American Civil War, large numbers of the wounded were crowded into improvised hospitals. The principles by which cross-infection can be controlled — cleanliness and the isolation of infectious cases — were then unknown. As a consequence, epidemics of pyemia, erysipelas, and hospital gangrene swept through these military hospitals. It has been suggested by the editor in his Bigelow Lecture of 1955 (unpublished) that similar epidemics, referred to as "hospitalism," which occurred in civilian hospitals during this period may have originated in part from cross-infection introduced into the wards by suppurating wounds that had been cared for initially in overcrowded military hospitals.

The Boston City Hospital, opened in 1864, treated a considerable number of soldiers. There was an immediate and alarming epidemic of "hospitalism," attributed at the time to the fact that this institution had been built on reclaimed land.

the bank on which Bulfinch stood and the new bridge which extended Charles Street northward and which was to form the new water front. As this bit of water was impregnated with sewage and the material used for fill was of the most varied description, the Hospital for the first time in its history faced a crisis in sanitation.[36] It is not surprising, therefore, that my first glimpses of surgical practice revealed some of the most trying experiences which fall to the surgeon's lot.

It was a well-recognized fact that wounds in a hospital ward did not heal as readily as those in the practice of the country surgeon, and this he rarely lost an opportunity to proclaim on his visits to the surgical centers of the day. At a somewhat later period this relative immunity of isolated patients was ably set forth to the medical

[36] The trustees of the MGH recommended in 1854 that the tidal flats on the western border of the hospital grounds be filled in to the low-water mark. Five years later an agreement was negotiated with the city to carry out this project. In the Annual Report for 1860 the resident physician stated that "during the summer months, the atmosphere of the Hospital and neighborhood was rendered offensive and unwholesome by emanations from the flats and newly made land, west of the Hospital grounds, making it necessary to retain many patients as short a time as possible, and to advise others to defer application for admission." Three years later the trustees reported continuing complaints of "an unpleasant miasma from the unfilled flats, under and near the extension [bridge] of Charles street," and the city authorities were requested to complete the filling project.

Although it was customary to attribute septic diseases acquired within the hospital walls to emanations from the materials used in filling the flats, Dr. Henry G. Clark, a visiting surgeon of the Staff, wrote to the trustees in May 1862: "For several consecutive years the disease known as Hospital Gangrene has made its appearance to a greater or less degree in the female surgical wards of the East wing at this season of the year. It is my belief that it may be owing to the drainage, and if so, to a removable cause." He did not attribute the disease "as have most others to the filling and foul odors outside the Hospital, except so far as it had made an extension of the drains necessary." He was referring to the drainage system underneath the Bulfinch Building.

The drains were investigated in 1875 at the request of the trustees by a committee of the Board of Consultation. The largest of the three cesspools beneath Bulfinch was found clogged because the system could drain into the Charles River estuary only at low tide. The committee's report concluded:

> The Board feels it a duty to declare that, in its opinion, no more buildings for hospital wards should be erected upon the land adjacent to the present wards because of this improper filling, and also the imperfect drainage compared with what a hospital should have. Still further, the undersigned believe that, at some future time, it will be for the best interests of the hospital and will contribute to the health of all patients if all the buildings should be given up and a new site selected, one more fitted for the purposes of a hospital than the present one is now or ever can be.

The Boston surgeons of that time seemed unaware that Lister's low rate of sepsis was attained in wards described as "the most unhealthy in the kingdom." The new surgical building opened in 1861 at the Glasgow Royal Infirmary had unwittingly been built on the site of a makeshift cemetery in which thousands of cholera victims had been buried in shallow soil only twelve years previously!

world in the classical paper on "Hospitalism" by Sir James Y. Simpson [37] of Edinburgh, who introduced the form of hospital construction known as the pavilion system, which became so prominent a feature of the army hospital during our Civil War. But at the time to which I refer the old order of things still prevailed. The wards of the MGH were contained within the four walls of the old Bulfinch building with the exception of a small brick building known as the Touro Ward, which contained a few private rooms.[38] As may readily be imagined, conditions invited all the evils generated by crowding together surgical patients, evils that were familiar as the inevitable accompaniment of military surgery. How long such a condition had prevailed the hospital records would probably reveal.[39]

My first experience of hospital practice showed a state of affairs which could hardly have been worse, and of which the medical student of today can have but a faint conception. I had ample opportunity to study all varieties of hospital pestilences in their most typical and flourishing stage of development. Pyemia, septicemia, erysipelas, and hospital gangrene were all features of daily occurrence with which the surgeon had to contend in the after-treatment of his patients. This state of affairs finally culminated in an epidemic of hospital gangrene of the most virulent type. All attempts to control the epidemic

[37] Simpson's paper, serialized in the *Edinburgh Medical Journal* in 1869, presented a compilation of low mortality rates following amputation of the extremities in rural practice and contrasted them with the high mortality rates encountered in the large hospitals of the cities.

[38] This two-story, sixteen-room building, opened in 1855, was known more familiarly as the Brick. It was named in honor of the Touro brothers, who had left generous legacies to the Hospital and also to the Touro Infirmary of New Orleans. Abraham Touro was a merchant of Boston, and Judah resided for more than fifty years in New Orleans.

The Brick stood between the western end of Bulfinch and the water, and was used to isolate noisy and delirious patients. It has been referred to officially as the "Building for Offensive Diseases." In 1876 it became the Nurses' Building, and in 1899 it was torn down to make way for the Domestic Building.

[39] The population of Boston in 1820 was roughly 43,000; by 1840 it had doubled. At the Hospital 115 medical and surgical ward patients were treated in 1822, its first full year of service; in 1840, 362 patients received treatment.

The potato blight first appeared in Europe and North America about 1840. In 1846 the disease wiped out the crop in Ireland, bringing wholesale starvation to what was already a poverty-stricken people. This started the waves of Irish immigration which during the following decades brought such great changes to Boston and steadily increased the need for hospital care. By 1860 the population of Boston had risen almost to 178,000, and the enlarged Hospital was able to care for 1,240 patients in that year, of whom 555 gave their birthplace as Ireland. But private philanthropy was no longer able to keep abreast of the needs of the increasing numbers who required hospital care. The Boston City Hospital was opened in 1864 and transferred a large share of the hospital treatment of the medically indigent citizens of Boston to the taxpayers.

appeared to fail, and the surgical wards were temporarily closed.[40]

It was a generally accepted opinion at the time that the filling in of the Flats and the consequent upheaval of the dock mud of the adjacent waters had much to do with the origin of the epidemic. Looking back from a present point of view, it would seem more probable that the entire absence of surgical cleanliness in a rapidly growing clinic and the great increase in the number of surgical operations which followed hard upon the introduction of painless surgery offer sufficient explanation of such conditions. For many years hospital gangrene continued to be a foe to reckon with, and in the Civil War it was one of the chief contributing causes of the high mortality in military surgery. The treatment of hospital gangrene consisted in the use of powerful escharotics such as the actual cautery, as was the custom of French surgeons in the Crimea, or the use of fuming bromine as recommended by many surgeons in our Northern armies during the Civil War. These were most painful remedies, however, and often necessitated the administration of an anesthetic. In hospital practice a sharp lookout was kept upon granulating wounds, and as soon as the surface of the wound began to assume a grayish tinge, lint saturated with what was known as "acid wash" was immediately applied.

In 1859 I entered Harvard College at the age of seventeen years, having served a schoolboy's apprenticeship first at the Boston Public Latin School and later at Mr. Dixwell's Private Latin School. Part of one year had also been passed at Mr. Sillig's school at Vevey in Switzerland, while my father was abroad for his health.[41] He made

[40] J.C.W. wrote in an article called "A Century of Surgery," which appeared in the *Boston Transcript*, October 15, 1896:

> But with this great increase in surgical activity [after the introduction of anesthesia] came a corresponding increase in the diseases which have been from time immemorial regarded as hospital pests, and the inevitable accompaniments of surgical practice . . . On the breaking out of the Civil War the art of hospital construction received a new impetus. It was thought that, by improving the atmospheric conditions, hospital epidemics could be more effectually controlled. Old buildings, which had served for centuries, were torn down and new and commodious pavilions took their places. During the Civil War, however, notwithstanding the perfection to which this system was carried, epidemics raged with all the freedom which they had in the campaigns of France and Russia and in the naval combats of the last century. The writer can well remember at this period the epidemic of hospital gangrene in the Massachusetts General Hospital, itself a hospital which even at that time had a world-wide reputation for neatness and efficiency and a proper regard for the principles of hygiene. So formidable were its ravages that all surgical operations were for some time abandoned. The only method that existed for controlling such eruptions of diseases was the system of isolation, as carried out in separate or pavilion wards, or by the removal of patients to tents in the open air.

[41] J.C.W. attended Bellerive, the Institution Sillig, in 1855. This famous school was established in Vevey, Switzerland in 1836 and attracted students

two journeys to Europe for this purpose, and on one occasion we passed some months in Edinburgh, where my father had an opportunity to make the acquaintance of Mr. James Y. Simpson, of whom I retain a very distinct recollection.[42]

---

from many parts of the world. Boston's contact with Vevey began in 1837 with the marriage of Ellen Sears to Paul Grand d'Hauteville, whose family estate and château lie near the school. This marriage ended by separation and long-drawn-out litigation concerning custody of the only child, Frederick. The court proceedings in the United States drew wide attention, partly because of issues of international law that were raised. Testimony was offered by Dr. John C. Warren. *Report of the D'Hauteville Case: The Commonwealth of Pennsylvania . . . versus . . . Ellen Sears Grand D'Hauteville* (Philadelphia, 1840).

Mrs. Warren's sister, J.C.W.'s great-aunt, had married into the Sears family, and so it is likely that in 1855 the Warrens thought it suitable to leave young "Coll" in a region where there was a "cousin" about his age. Time had tempered feelings between the Searses and the d'Hautevilles, and in later years J.C.W.'s sons visited their "cousins" at the hospitable château in Vevey.

J.C.W.'s sister Rosamond Warren Gibson (1846–1934) gives this description of travel by carriage:

> In October [1855] we started from Paris in a travelling carriage bound for Rome. It was purchased from Mr. James Davis, and was driven from the hotel to the station, where it was strapped onto a flat car to go as far as Dijon. It swayed a good deal, and the whole proceeding seemed very risky, so that we were all grateful when we reached our destination safely. It was very thrilling to us children, as we traveled by postillion, changing horses constantly. We always had at least four, often six, and once even eight. The carriage was fitted up with a table, swinging pillows, and various devices for comfort. It was very exciting to have luncheon in this way, to get out and run by the carriage up the hills, and to watch the horses being changed. Above all, we loved to see the peasants making wine in the great casks, up to their elbows in juice, crushing the grapes, and sometimes even trampling them with their bare feet! When Nellie [a younger sister] and I amused ourselves jumping rope, they gathered around us with delight, as if we were performing children. At Geneva my mother left us for a day or two and placed Collins in Mr. Sillig's school at Vevey; on her return we started on our trip across the mountains. [*Recollections of My Life for My Children* (Boston: privately printed, 1939.)]

[42] James Young Simpson was a native Scot, born on June 7, 1811. A scholar with a wide range of interests, he found clinical work in the field of obstetrics most congenial to his temperament. He also pioneered in the newer field of gynecology and saw with clarity the intimate relations that bind obstetrics and gynecology together. Simpson was appointed professor of midwifery at the University of Edinburgh at the age of twenty-nine, and shortly thereafter became physician to the Queen.

Simpson was one of the first in Great Britain to appreciate the full significance of Morton's great discovery and immediately began to employ ether in obstetrics after demonstrating its efficacy in a case of version for contracted pelvis. The manner in which ether was administered, however, made it a disagreeable and irritating agent, and Simpson set about a search for another agent of equal potency without these disadvantages. Like Morton, he experimented upon himself, inhaling in sequence whatever volatile fluid he could lay his hands on. On November 4, 1847 he happened to try chloroform. At first he became "very happy, and very loquacious." Then he heard sounds "like those of a cotton-mill, louder and louder; a moment more, then all was quiet, and then a crash!" He woke to find himself on the floor, whence he had fallen from his chair. With his assistants the experiment was repeated many times that night.

Simpson, the discoverer of chloroform anesthesia, was then reaching the height of his reputation. As I remember him, he appeared as a short and stout and genial personage with round full face, chubby cheeks, and dimpled chin smoothly shaven. His bright eyes and cheery countenance, framed by longish locks, gave him a somewhat boyish look. His movements were active and he had a very erect figure.

I had the privilege of meeting him again in later years when, as a medical student, I had completed my education abroad and was about to return home. This was in 1869. On this occasion he asked me to dine, and I recall many interesting incidents of that evening. In discussing the treatment of wounds during our Civil War, he made the somewhat startling statement that Northern surgeons had been in the habit of placing pieces of dead flesh in the amputation stumps of Confederate soldiers. He was of course referring to the use of the ligature of arteries, intending in this way to emphasize the great superiority of his method of acupressure; the pins used for this purpose merely compressed the open end of the vessels without causing any destruction of tissue.[43] He also asked me to inhale a perfume on his handkerchief, which he said would cause me to blush. The violent rush of blood to my head which followed made me realize that the drug, which proved to be nitrite of amyl, was a very potent agent. His was a strong and interesting personality, and the statue in his native city bears testimony to the impression made by him on the progress of medicine of his time.

The only other medical worthy that I recall from my first trips

---

The discovery of the anesthetic properties of chloroform was communicated to the Medico-Chirurgical Society on November 10, 1847, and its use became general throughout Great Britain. Despite its risks, which were soon known to be considerably greater than those of ether, chloroform remained a standard and valuable anesthetic agent for many decades. It is used at the present time only under exceptional circumstances.

Simpson was made a baronet, and he died on May 6, 1870. His name remains one of the greatest among the many distinguished surgeons that Scotland has given to the history of medicine.

[43] Simpson's preface to his book entitled *Acupressure: A New Method of Arresting Surgical Haemorrhage and of Accelerating the Healing of Wounds* was dated at Edinburgh, 21st November 1864. The first paragraph reads:

Acupressure, as a new haemostatic process — founded on the principle of the *temporary metallic compression* of arteries — was first described to the Royal Society of Edinburgh at their meeting on 19th December 1859. An abstract of this communication was published in the "Proceedings" of the Society, vol. iv. (p. 249), and in the *Edinburgh Medical Journal* for January 1860 (p. 645). A few weeks subsequently I sent the histories of the earliest cases of amputation, in which this novel method of arresting surgical haemorrhage had been employed, to the "London Medical Times" of February 11, 1860.

abroad was Jean Civiale, the inventor of the lithotrite, an amiable and venerable gentleman who gave us a courteous and hospitable reception at his villa near Paris. As I was quite a child then, I fail to remember any of the professional discussions which my father doubtless had with him on that occasion.

IV

A Medical Cadet
in Wartime Philadelphia

The Civil War broke out during my sophomore year at Harvard College, a time when I had already decided upon surgery as a life's work. I was then confronted by the decision either to play the immediate role of the patriot by volunteering for the army, or to prepare myself by further studies to serve my country at a later date in the capacity of an army surgeon. The conflict involved in making a decision centered on the fact that by electing the latter course personal benefit would accrue. I was strongly encouraged by my father to keep an open mind about continuing with my studies, and by so doing gradually overcame the youthful patriotic enthusiasm which swept many of my classmates directly into army service. Some went before and others after their graduation. I chose to follow the footsteps of my future colleagues in medicine who were then just entering upon their professional careers and who served in the medical service of the army. A compromise was reached with my parents by which I was permitted during my senior year to take up formally the study of medicine so as to prepare myself for some sort of military medical service. The custom at Harvard College of having a long winter recess made it possible for me to take out a course of tickets for lectures at the medical school on North Grove Street, and although the winter course of lectures overlapped my regular term work in Cambridge I was able to obtain a fairly good share of the first year medical student's instruction. I was also allowed to exchange my one elective study in the academic curriculum for a course of anatomy under Professor Jeffries Wyman, given to a class consisting of C. B. Porter [1] and myself. It was an exceptional privilege to have the opportunity of studying under this distinguished teacher, a man of

[1] Charles Burnham Porter (1840–1909), professor of clinical surgery, was a member of the staff of the Hospital from 1867 to the time of his retirement in 1903. He taught Harvard medical students for thirty-seven years and was famous as a master of style in operative surgery. He was the seventh physician of his family in direct descent from that hard-fisted immigrant surgeon and bone-setter, Daniel Porter of Farmington, who was licensed to practice "physic and chirurgery" by the General Court of Connecticut in 1654. Dr. C. B. Porter's son, Charles Allen Porter (1866–1931), held the John Homans Professorship of Surgery and was chief of the West Surgical Service at the Hospital.

science who, as I now look back upon him and his teachings, was ahead of his time and who, had he been appreciated at his full value by the Medical Faculty, might have taken a more conspicuous part in the great progress of medical science which was then in its inception. Porter and I read Quain and Sharpey's *Anatomy* with the Professor, and a large room in Boylston Hall was probably for the first and last time turned into a dissecting room, a stalwart "subject" having been procured for our special use. I remember many experiments carried on by Wyman with sealed flasks and the exposure of glass plates to the air after it had been thoroughly purified by a fall of snow. These experiments were conducted with a view to elucidate problems connected with the "germ theory of disease," as it was then called, a fact which bore ample testimony to his full appreciation of the great awakening, which was then so near at hand.[2] My class had scarcely finished the college course [3] and was preparing for its final Class Day

[2] Pasteur in 1858 laid the foundations of bacteriology with his observations on "the preservation of watery solutions of decomposable substances." He showed that, if air was excluded, decomposition would not occur. Pasteur referred to "dusts" or particulate matter suspended in the air. "There is now no circumstance known," he said, "in which it can be affirmed that microscopic beings came into the world without germs, without parents similar to themselves." These ideas were expressed publicly at the Sorbonne on April 7, 1864.

Lister for some years held the assumption that microörganisms causing suppuration in surgical wounds were derived solely from the air. As late as 1867 he considered that wounds and abscesses poisoned the atmosphere with putrid exhalations. In 1875 Lister referred to the fermentative and putrefactive changes in organic substances produced by the development of minute organisms such as yeasts, molds, and bacteria. He stated before the Royal Society of Edinburgh:

> The Germ Theory supposes that the organisms are the causes of the changes; that the germs of these minute living things, diffusible in proportion to their minuteness, are omnipresent in the world around us, and are sure to gain access to any exposed organic substance . . . and further, that these organisms, minute though they appear to us . . . originate from similar beings by parentage . . . The philosophical investigations of Pasteur long since made me a convert to the Germ Theory, and it was on the basis of that theory that I founded the antiseptic treatment of wounds in surgery. [*Transactions of the Royal Society of Edinburgh 27* (1875).]

The "germ theory of disease" in its modern form dates from about 1880 and was established largely by the work of Robert Koch. It was based on the growing knowledge about the life history of bacteria and the development of methods for identifying and cultivating them. To establish a causal relation between a certain bacterium and a disease, Koch insisted that: (1) the bacterium must be demonstrated during the course of the disease; (2) it must be isolated and grown in pure culture; (3) it must reproduce the disease in animals (or man); and (4) the same bacterium must again be recovered in pure culture from the reproduced disease. The concept led to the understanding that food and drinking water should be free of disease-producing germs. For the first time in history it thus became possible for people to live together in communities without being exposed to the risks of contagion.

[3] J.C.W. scarcely mentions his Harvard College years, which for a young man must have been heavily overcast by the tensions of the Civil War. He was a

festival when the battle of Gettysburg was fought. We were thus launched upon our future careers at the very "high-water mark of the rebellion," as it was called at the time.

During the ensuing summer months I worked hard at medical studies under my father's guidance, and in the early autumn received an appointment as acting medical cadet to the South Street Army Hospital in Philadelphia. This appointment was dated October 7th, 1863 and signed by John Campbell, Surgeon, U.S.A. Med. Dr. The surgeon in charge of this hospital was Dr. Shippen, assisted by Dr. Meury, a protégé of Dr. Samuel D. Gross, professor of surgery at the Jefferson Medical School. My position corresponded fairly well to that of the hospital interne of 1914. My medical education had of course thus far been a meagre one, but the duties were comparatively simple and consisted chiefly in those of a dresser of wounds in chronic cases of gunshot injury. During the autumn and winter which followed, the army under General Meade was involved in no general engagement and the opportunity for seeing military surgery on a large scale was lacking.

The position of "acting medical cadet" was one which does not seem to have been regarded with much favor in the army, for Dr. Weir Mitchell, whose brother also held a position of this grade, informs me that there were only about forty such appointments made during the war. The technique of surgical dressings was of a simple and primitive character and most of this work was done either by the surgeon or assistant surgeon or by the hospital steward, a grade filled by men with little or no medical training.

After a period of inactivity I began to realize that unless some emergency arose in the period before the spring campaign much valuable time would be wasted and that my leisure moments could be employed to greater advantage by resuming my studies at one of the two schools then flourishing in Philadelphia. These were the Jefferson Medical School and the Medical Department of the University of Pennsylvania. The Jefferson at that time seemed preëminent in surgery because two of the most prominent surgeons of the day held positions on its faculty. They were Professors Gross and Pancoast. Gross occupied the chair of surgery and Pancoast that of anatomy. The combination of two such surgical lights at Jefferson was considered by my father sufficient reason for selecting that school in preference to the Medical Department of the University of Pennsylvania. Dr.

---

member of the six-man freshman crew which rowed the "Thetis" to victory over Yale on Lake Quinsigamond, Worcester on July 24, 1860, and later was president of the Hasty Pudding Club, of which his grandfather, John C. Warren (Class of 1797), had also been a president.

Henry H. Smith was professor of surgery in the latter school and Dr. D. Hayes Agnew occupied a subordinate position, not yet having reached the conspicuous standing in American surgery which he was to hold. Private instruction was very thoroughly systematized in Philadelphia, and from among the great variety of courses offered I selected one on bandaging by Dr. Agnew as the one likely to be of special value to me if called back into the service again.

Armed with letters of introduction from my father to Drs. Gross and Pancoast and under the guidance of the son of the latter, William Pancoast, I enrolled myself as a member of the class at Jefferson. I was cordially received by both these gentlemen. On presenting my credentials to Professor Gross, I met at his house another student on a similar errand, to whom I was introduced by our host. This proved to be J. Ewing Mears from St. Louis, a lifelong friend who, after graduation, cast his lot in Philadelphia, became an assistant to Professor Gross, and rose to a place of eminence in his profession, distinguished as a teacher as well as an operator. He was closely identified with the early history of the American Surgical Association, of which he was a charter member and later president.[4]

Professor Samuel David Gross, then at the zenith of his career, was

[4] J.C.W. published "A Personal Recollection" of Dr. J. Ewing Mears in the November 6, 1919 number of the *Boston Medical and Surgical Journal 181*, 552). He wrote:

> While a student in Philadelphia, during the winter of 1863–64, the present writer had an opportunity of seeing much of the society of his fellow student [Mears], occupying with him a suite of rooms in a well-known hostelry on Broad street . . . Thus, though a certain element of reserve existed between chums, brought together from far distant sections of the country, a common enthusiasm for a chosen calling brought the two young men into a sympathetic understanding of one another and so it came about that this brief association of one college term brought with it a lifelong intimacy.
>
> The all-absorbing activities of the immediately following years did not leave time or opportunity for much mutual intercourse, but summer vacations gave Dr. Mears an opportunity to visit New England and to get an insight into some of its medical institutions . . . Dr. Mears never married and so when his time for retirement from practice came he was free to wander about and to enjoy all the rights and privileges of an American tourist of professional standing. Curiously enough, he began this phase of his career by becoming a student once more and taking part in one of Harvard's summer courses . . . He took great interest in younger men and inasmuch as fate had ordained that he should be childless, he conceived the idea of acquiring an "academic son," and thus it came about that he established a scholarship in Trinity College, Hartford.
>
> The plan to have a "medical son" in the Harvard Medical School was put in operation many years ago and it was his wish to have the recipient enjoy the benefit of the gift from the time of entrance until final graduation . . . But he did not find the task a simple one [and] the numerous problems with which he had to contend on his annual visit to Harvard seemed to take the place of the responsibilities which had been laid aside on his retirement from practice. It proved an admirable means of keeping an old man in close

a man of commanding stature and bearing. Silvery gray hair surrounded strongly chiseled features and eyes set deeply in their sockets. In repose there was a sternness of expression, which gave way to a genial and paternal manner when addressing his pupils. The professor had prepared himself for the duties of a teacher by many years of hard labor on a work on pathological anatomy and later a textbook of surgery in two large volumes, which went through many editions and was the accepted authority of the day. The lecture room was a large, well-shaped amphitheatre into which the class poured tumultuously; it held four or five hundred students and was always well filled. A most painstaking instructor, Gross hammered on the rudiments of surgery with a clearness and force which commanded the attention of the class and left an impression never to be forgotten. Instinctively he selected the small details of rudimentary knowledge for which the student mind was craving and dwelt upon them with patient care, somewhat to the detriment of the brilliant discourse which he was quite capable of delivering. By understanding how to keep on the level of his audience, he kept his lectures both popular and instructive. This was in strong contrast to the many prominent medical lecturers of the day who conversed easily and eloquently with the class but left behind, at least to a beginner like myself, a sense that many difficulties stood in the way of a proper comprehension of their themes.

Pancoast, professor of anatomy, was known as an unusually skilful dissector and operator, and it was to these qualities that he owed his position in the school. Students crowded his clinic in order to see him handle the knife, which he did with a skill and rapidity so characteristic of the school of surgery which existed before the advent of anesthesia and in which he had been trained.

Both Gross and Pancoast gave me every opportunity to see their surgical cases and once in a while to assist them at surgical operations. These occurred principally in their private practice, as neither of the two schools in Philadelphia enjoyed the advantage of having a hospital where their students could obtain systematic clinical instruction. The clinical facilities of both the Jefferson and the University were of the most meagre kind. The entire "plant" of the former consisted of but

___

touch with the progress of science and the changing currents of medical education and student life.

J. Ewing Mears first proposed operating on the Gasserian ganglion for major neuralgia of the face, an operation which became one of the safest and simplest in neurosurgery. His article (Garrison-Morton 4857) appeared in the Philadelphia *Medical News* 45, 58 (1884). In a note of appreciation for J.C.W.'s "Personal Recollection" of Mears, Harvey Cushing referred to this operation as having "relieved a larger amount of suffering than any other operation in all surgery." (Letter, Warren Papers, vol. 45, Massachusetts Historical Society.)

one building, which contained a dissecting room and two principal lecture rooms. There were also a few anterooms which served the purpose of an out-patient department, the patients occasionally being demonstrated to give a clinical flavor to some of the lectures. There were also one or two rooms where patients could remain after surgical operations, which were few and far between.

The Pennsylvania Hospital was not connected with either school, and neither Gross nor Pancoast was a member of its staff. An appointment to the visiting staff of this hospital was the goal of every good Philadelphia doctor, but curiously enough the most prominent surgeons of the day were not to be found there. I recall only two who were associated with this hospital, Dr. Peace and Dr. Hunt. The former had been a classmate of my father in Paris and was a genial gentleman who I think had retired from private practice and enjoyed greatly the society of his colleagues. His Sunday afternoon dinners, where were assembled many colleagues and quite often myself, were models of their kind from both a gastronomical and a social point of view.

Weir Mitchell was then attracting much attention by his experimental work on snake poison and other research which was to lay the foundation for his future great reputation. Even then, half a century ago, his reputation was already a national one.[5]

An account of the medical schools of that day would be incomplete without some reference to the medical students. While inquiring for suitable lodgings I soon found that it was no recommendation to landladies to mention that I intended to study medicine. The Jefferson was an active and hustling institution and was bidding fair to outnumber in students its rival at the University, which had hitherto held undisputed sway in Philadelphia not only by virtue of being the oldest school of its kind in the country but because of its brilliant record. The comparatively recent appointment of Gross, who had been called from Louisville, Kentucky, brought a large following from the southern states. Even under most favorable conditions, the medical students of that day were not of a high educational attainment. Few had the advantages of college training except those in schools such as Harvard and Pennsylvania, which were parts of universities. The material of

[5] Dr. S. Weir Mitchell was a pioneer in the study of snake venoms by nineteenth-century chemical methods. His "Researches upon the Venom of the Rattlesnake" was published in July 1860 (*Smithsonian Contributions to Knowledge*). Later, with E. T. Reichert, he returned to the subject and discovered two components of the venom rather than a single one. This work was the foundation for the studies accomplished years later by Hideyo Noguchi. Of course the 1860 rattlesnake item caught the eye of the Boston Autocrat, who sent Mitchell a copy of his *Elsie Venner*.

the class of which I became a member was of the crudest character. The costume was quite distinctive, the usual street dress consisting of a slouch hat, covering a head which had been thrust through a hole in a kind of blanket, which did duty for an overcoat. Many of them slept five or six in the same bedroom. The custom of tobacco chewing was then apparently at its high-water mark, and few of the southern students were without this article of solace; the lecture room floors between the seats bore ample testimony. The standard of the medical students in the University was of a better grade but, as at Harvard, the class contained a certain admixture of young men who had not enjoyed the advantages of a good preliminary education.

The leaders of the profession here were all men of high standing in the community; many bore names intimately associated with medicine from its early inception in this country and imparted to it as a calling a prestige which was exceptional at that period. In this respect there was a similarity between Boston and Philadelphia. The older men of that generation in both cities had met as students in the clinics of Paris and seemed to have been brought up under similar ideals of professional life, under the inspiration of Louis and other great teachers. This experience had left its impress upon the profession in both cities and is felt up to the present time. It seems to account for the sympathetic attitude held by these two groups toward the progress of medicine and the evolution of effective methods of medical education. An echo of that feeling was given expression at a recent gathering in Boston at which I had the privilege of being present, when around the table presided over by the modern Louis — Osler — sat the sons of the pupils of Louis, bearing the names of Gerhard and Pepper of Philadelphia and of Bowditch, Shattuck, Jackson, and Putnam of Boston.

Two years of Civil War did not seem to have placed much of a damper upon the social life of Philadelphia. This was probably due to a temporary lull in the campaign activities and to the heartening effect of the victory at Gettysburg. Many young officers found opportunity to escape from the dull routine of camp life in winter quarters in Virginia and take part in some of the gaieties of the social season. Philadelphia was the home of General Meade, the commander-in-chief, whose daughter was a debutante of that year. The atmosphere of southern traditions gave a certain aristocratic tinge to society, to which was added the mellowing influence of southern hospitality. The homes of the Ingersolls, the Peterses, and the Cadwaladers, together with those of high rank in the army, gave a cosmopolitan flavor to social life as I saw it.

There was plenty of hard work, however, for the medical student; attendance at systematic lectures (the prevailing method of instruction of that day) occupied the morning and afternoon and sometimes the evening hours. There was no graded system of teaching. Medical students "took out" a full course of lecture tickets each year and tried to attend as many lectures as they could without regard to appropriate sequence. A mass of information was thus forced upon the student mind by learned professors such as Robley Dunglison at the Jefferson, and William Pepper and George B. Wood at the University, but so far as I was concerned much of it left behind only a bewildered recollection. Much detail was unconsciously assimilated, however, and I was encouraged to feel that I was duly preparing myself for any emergency in the course of the war that might present itself.

Fortunately, through the kindness of Professor Gross, who gave me frequent opportunities to attend his private operations and sometimes even to act as an assistant, I was able to acquire a good practical knowledge of the rudiments of surgery. As the winter course was drawing to its close, I recall the final occasion when several classmates and I had the privilege of attending one of his operations. We were gathered around the professor after the operation, while he was replacing the instruments in his bag, to listen dutifully to whatever remarks he had to make. It was a moment of leave-taking and each student received some kindly word of advice or commendation.

Lectures ended in all the medical schools on or about March first. The bulk of the students returned to their homes and the so-called year of study, i.e., time spent at a medical school, came to a close. It was the custom of some enterprising faculties at the more prominent schools to take advantage of the long interval between the regular terms and insert another "course" either in the spring, if the school was situated in a city such as Brooklyn, or in the summer, if the school happened to be a department of some "fresh-water" New England college. Several of my classmates informed me that they intended to take a spring course at the Long Island Medical School, because by taking a "year" at Jefferson and a "year" at Long Island they would thus fulfill the time requirement (two yearly courses at a medical school) and would consequently be eligible for the degree of M. D., if they succeeded in passing their examinations. When successful, these students thus obtained their degree after only nine months of study.

Many students took advantage of these easy-going requirements, which enabled them to enter the army at the desired rank of assistant surgeon because such officers were in great demand. Other students remained in Philadelphia or served an apprenticeship with some physician in their own town until the succeeding autumn and then, after taking a second winter course, came up for the degree a year later. This custom was not peculiar to Philadelphia. All the medical schools in good standing of that day allowed a student to present himself for examination for the degree when he could present a certificate from a practicing physician that he had studied medicine under his tutelage for one year and was able to show tickets to two full courses of lectures. Nominally this implied a three years' course of study, but practically, the bulk of students of that day received a degree after eighteen months of actual study.

Returning to Boston, I entered what was then called the summer course [6] at Harvard's medical school on North Grove Street. This consisted in recitation held at the school by certain members of the Faculty and attendance at Hospital clinics. The number of students taking this course was comparatively small, probably not more than fifty out of the three hundred students who attended the regular winter course. The instruction was of excellent quality and the small size of the class gave each student a much better opportunity for clinical study than was possible during the winter term. Drs. Henry I. Bowditch, Francis Minot, and Calvin Ellis gave courses in medicine and pathology, and Dr. Richard M. Hodges one in surgery. My father had a spring service at the Hospital, and this gave me exceptional advantages in the study of clinical surgery.

Dr. Ellis, afterwards dean of the faculty, gave recitations in Virchow's *Cellular Pathology,* a work then attracting much attention. He also superintended a course in pathological histology, which, although it consisted principally in picking apart with needles small fragments of tissue for microscopical examination, stimulated a taste for the work of a more advanced character which was to come later from European laboratories. The techniques of section cutting and staining of tissue had not yet reached this country. Autopsies were frequently performed by both Dr. John B. S. Jackson,[7] professor of morbid anatomy, and Dr. Ellis. The careful, painstaking work of these excellent teachers was highly appreciated. Dr. Jackson belonged to the older school of pathologists, who were not trained in the contemporary microscopic work, but his vast experience and scientific

[6] The Harvard Corporation authorized the Medical Faculty in 1856 to establish a "summer" course of recitations and clinical observation with the understanding that no additional pecuniary charge be incurred by the University. The Summer School opened in March 1858 and extended through October. Third-year Harvard students were given the novel privilege of electing their own courses. In effect the Summer School replaced and absorbed the Tremont Street Medical School, which had offered a winter evening course and a summer course conducted by individual members of the Harvard Medical Faculty over an apothecary shop at No. 39 Tremont Row.

[7] In a letter to the *Boston Medical and Surgical Journal* concerning Dr. John B. S. Jackson (95, 393, September 28, 1876), Oliver Wendell Holmes wrote, "There was a period of many years during which no good Bostonian could rest quite in peace at Mount Auburn, unless his internal arrangements had passed under the Rhadamanthine inspection of our great pathologist."

bent of mind enabled him to give his students a solid foundation of the broad principles of pathology. Dr. Ellis was a pioneer in the new school of pathology and a clinician whose standard was in advance of his time.

~ V

Wound Surgery
on the Pamunkey River

At the close of this summer term I had spent the better part
of two years in the study of medicine and began to feel sufficient
confidence in myself to respond to any call that might be made upon
me. An opportunity soon came. During General Grant's campaign in
Virginia in the spring of 1864, the wounded accumulated in such
numbers after each engagement as to be quite beyond the resources
of the medical staff. Large hospital camps were established at each
new base of operations. The sick and wounded could not remain long
in these temporary quarters, as the army in its onward march left them
in the rear. Hospital ships were hurried down from Washington and
Alexandria, and the patients were transferred to the many army hospitals established in and around the Capital. At the time of these temporary congestions, the government appealed to the governors of the
states for medical aid. These appeals always met with a prompt
response from Massachusetts.

After the battle of Cold Harbor,[1] there was an enormous accumulation of wounded men in a hospital camp near a place called White
House. Well-made levees on the bank of the Pamunkey River permitted the landing of supplies brought up from Chesapeake Bay and
the transfer of disabled men to the hospital ships. Governor John A.
Andrew of Massachusetts, through his Surgeon General, issued a call
on this occasion for acting assistant surgeons,[2] and among those who

[1] The battle of Cold Harbor (June 1–10, 1864) was a sanguinary action in
which Lee repulsed Grant's Army of the Potomac with a loss of over 13,000 on
the Union side but probably not more than 1,300 on the Confederate side. White
House was a depot of supplies for the Army of the Potomac. From May 5 to
June 10 in the battles of the Wilderness, Spottsylvania, North Anna River, and
Cold Harbor, this army sustained casualties aggregating over 54,000, a number
greater than that of Lee's entire force when these battles began. Of this number,
7,289 were killed, 37,406 were wounded, and 9,856 were listed as missing.
William Swinton, *Campaigns of the Army of the Potomac* (New York, 1866).

[2] The Surgeon General, United States Army, *Medical and Surgical History of
the War of the Rebellion* (Washington, 1883), II, part III, p. 901, states:

> Besides the medical officers of the regular and volunteer staff, and the
> medical officers of regiments, there was a class designated as Acting Assistant
> Surgeons, who were private physicians, uncommissioned, serving under con-
> tract to do duty with the forces in the field or in general hospitals. This

responded were several members of the medical class including Brewster, Langmaid, Wigglesworth, and myself. My appointment as volunteer surgeon was dated June 6, 1864 and signed by William J. Dale, Surgeon General of Massachusetts. I was ordered to report to James K. Barnes, Acting Surgeon General, U.S.A., at Washington. On our way to Washington we found ourselves on board the Sound steamer [3] in company with a large body of physicians who were on their way to New York to attend the annual meeting of the American Medical Association. An incident occurred which not only was characteristic of the time but gave us a foretaste of what we were soon to encounter. A deserter made an attempt to escape from his military guard as the boat pulled out into the Sound, and in the struggle a musket fell to the ground and went off, the discharge lodging in the foot of a physician on board, Dr. Flint of Boston, the brother of Austin Flint. We young men, after administering first aid, left the victim in care of his medical colleagues, of whom there appeared to be a superabundance.

Arriving in Washington, we were assigned to a boat leaving immediately for the landing at White House and found ourselves the next morning steaming up the Pamunkey to a point which I afterwards learned was within twenty miles of Richmond. White House derived its name from a single building situated in a clearing in the woods which was covered with tents and temporary wooden structures, and served as an army base of communications by water with Washington. Here were grouped promiscuously hospital tents and their gruesome neighbors — improvised graveyards — camps of departing and arriving regiments, and masses of military stores of every description. In the distance could be heard the booming of heavy guns "at the front" not many miles away. The levee was crowded with steamers and formed a water front of considerable proportions, considering the situation of the landing so many miles from the sea.

On arrival at our destination we were separated and assigned to various positions and tasks. I was ordered to report to Dr. F. F. Burmeister, Surgeon to the 69th Regiment, Pennsylvania Volunteers, who was in charge of the Second Corps Hospital. I was detailed to take charge of two tents full of patients containing each from fifteen to twenty men. These were all patients from the battle of Cold Harbor

---

class was very large and embraced in its number some of the most eminent surgeons and physicians of the country. The Medical Cadets were generally young men, students of medicine, who were assigned to duty in general hospitals as dressers and assistants.

[3] "Sound steamer" refers to the famous old Fall River Line, whose ships plied Long Island Sound from Fall River and Newport to New York City. Fall River was connected with Boston by the Old Colony Rail Road.

with freshly received gunshot injuries, including penetrating wounds of the chest and abdomen. Little had been done for them beyond "first aid," which was of a very primitive character. I proceeded at once to clean the wounds and apply fresh dressings. No attempt was made to treat penetrating wounds of the cavities (chest and abdominal) other than by external applications. So all that I could do was to make the men as comfortable as possible under the circumstances.

The most effective way of making the wounded comfortable was the use of subcutaneous injections of morphine. Before leaving home I had taken the precaution to purchase a pocket case of instruments and also a subcutaneous syringe. The syringe was a novelty at that time. I had first seen it employed at the Massachusetts General Hospital by my father, who told me that it had been strongly recommended for cases of neuralgia following gunshot injuries of or near the nerves. The first subcutaneous injections which I had seen given were made as near the seat of injury as possible, but it was soon found that these local injections were no more efficacious than those given at a distant point, and eventually the arm was selected as the most convenient site. This little instrument became by far the most valuable part of my equipment, and I have always felt that the lack of modern surgical methods was in a measure compensated for by this device for relieving pain. I have never since seen so much gratitude expressed for relief from suffering as that which came from the poor fellows who had just made the journey from the front and were lying about on the ground awaiting their turn to be assigned to hospital quarters.

There were constant fresh arrivals from the firing line, sometimes of returning regiments and sometimes of prisoners. One regiment's time of service had expired only that morning at 12 o'clock and the men were looking forward with keen anticipation to the return to Washington. They had had all the fighting the most ardent and patriotic soldiers could have desired. With them came a poor fellow shot through the top of the head only a few minutes before he would have been a "free" man. He evidently had but a few hours to live.

An incident which seemed to bring the realities of war home to me even more forcibly was the appearance of a regiment of Confederate prisoners convoyed by a guard of colored troops. The faded gray uniforms of the prisoners were in contrast to those of their well-equipped escort. They swung into camp at a rapid pace although they had evidently been marching a long distance and many of them were not in the best of condition. One unfortunate man of heavy build and haggard countenance was breathing with difficulty. He was obviously quite ill but managed to keep up with the stride of the others by the help of a companion at each shoulder, who almost pushed him along. This was indeed war; humanity for the time was held in abeyance.

My responsibilities did not give me much spare time but I managed to visit the operating tent on one or two occasions with my companions. Trained as we had been in the best schools of surgery in the land, we looked with critical eyes upon the work we saw there. Chloroform was the only anesthetic used in the army on account of its smallness of bulk as compared with that of ether.[4] Operations were performed with great rapidity and often seemed crude and ill planned in our eyes. A total resection of the lower jaw was done for gunshot injury; the hunt for the bullet in each case seemed relentless and often involved very extensive laying open of the tissues. The remedy seemed to us in many cases worse than the disease but, looking back over the accumulated experience of a lifetime, the methods then employed seem worthy of a revised judgment. The large caliber of the bullet then in use produced extensive splintering of the bone and rendered amputation necessary in penetrating wounds of the long bones. Laceration of soft parts by these bullets necessitated free openings for drainage. The projectile often carried fragments of clothing with it, and long-continued suppuration was the result. Pus would burrow in every direction, especially in gunshot fractures; erysipelas and secondary hemorrhages were matters of everyday occurrence. No attempt was made to prevent sepsis by appropriate dressings, and the surgeon could hope for a favorable issue only if foreign bodies were removed at the earliest possible moment. Conservative surgery was already beginning to have its day. In gunshot injuries of the joints resection of the injured ends of the bones quite often enabled the surgeon to save the limb, and this operation was regarded at the time as one of the greatest contributions to the surgery of the day.

One of the striking features of camp life as I saw it was the almost entire absence of women. I say "almost" advisedly, for I recall one exception in the person of a young and apparently well-educated woman, a pioneer, as it were, of the type of hospital nurse with which we are now so familiar. She appeared one evening at our campfire, making herself quite at home among a miscellaneous collection of men. Drifting in apparently from the front like numerous other unclassified persons whose occupations were hard to identify, she seemed to be enacting a role not altogether in keeping with the attributes of

---

[4] Because it is noninflammable, chloroform was found useful for administration in small rooms in the presence of open flames or oil lamps. Before other and safer methods were developed, chloroform with its small bulk had many adherents in the U.S. navy as well as in the army.

her sex. While nothing in her behavior or speech betrayed anything that might reflect upon her moral character, she seemed to exemplify the brutalizing influences of the life to which she had been exposed and of which she formed a component part.[5]

The nurse was not the only one, I recall, who seemed to be out of character. Troops were on the move, regiments were coming and going, and with them went many followers. One evening two mounted men presented themselves to the members of our staff, grouped together at the end of a hard day's work. Their proposal was to trade horses. The animals were shown off by jumping them over newly made graves. Reckless and not entirely nonalchoholic actions seemed to classify the men as an undesirable type of camp follower, and I was not a little startled the next morning, when making my way along the levee behind a regiment drawn up on parade with drums beating and colors flying, to see my two friends of the evening before among the colonel's staff, riding with arms akimbo in military dignity.

Although not actually on the firing line, a hospital in the battle zone is not without great responsibilities and anxieties. An embryo doctor might easily break down under stress such as that which we experienced; indeed, I recall several instances of young men giving way completely under the burden prematurely thrust upon them. One most painful experience of this kind came under my personal observation. We had not been long occupied in hospital work when we were joined by a college classmate from New York State who came as assistant to a volunteer surgeon. The surgeon, who was a full-fledged doctor and, like ourselves, had responded to the emergency call, was soon called away to the front. He left his assistant on my hands. As I have explained, I was then at the close of my second year of medical studies, while my classmate was still a first-year student. He seemed much disturbed at being set adrift by his chief and begged me with much earnestness to take him "under my wing," as he expressed it. He performed his duties under my directions most faithfully until the order came for a change of base, and then he suddenly disappeared. The army had been ordered to move across the James River, and the sick and wounded were dispatched on transports by water to Alexandria and thence to the hospitals in and around Washington. Our party reassembled

[5] Shortly after the outbreak of the Civil War thousands of untrained women volunteered for nursing service. In the North the task of organizing their activities fell to Boston's Dorothea Lynde Dix. An order issued by Secretary of War Cameron and Acting Surgeon General Wood appointed her "Superintendent of Women Nurses, to select and assign women nurses to general or permanent military hospitals."

on the levee on the day of departure and, having received our discharges, began to look about for means of transportation home. We were somewhat disconcerted on seeing the same steamer which had brought us disappear around a bend in the river. While wondering what to do next, I fortunately ran across my former friends of the South Street Army Hospital (Philadelphia), who were now in charge of a steamer of their own. On our offering to do a share of the work, a cordial welcome was extended and we were given comfortable accommodations on board. Each of us was assigned a number of cases, and as I was preparing to do my work who should appear but my lost classmate. He was in a state of great agitation and claimed that he was nothing but a stowaway and in danger of being court-martialed. Although I did my best to comfort him, my efforts were unavailing, and he passed a most distressed night, exposed, as he seemed to think, to many new dangers. This state of mind prevailed after our arrival at Washington, but he appeared to have calmed down when he finally bade us goodbye and left to join his brother, who was, he said, in command of a battery on the outskirts of the Capital. This was the last time I saw the poor fellow, who, though still alive to this day, has been a lifelong inmate of an asylum. I have no doubt that many a mind gave way under the cruel strain to which it was subjected in those trying days.[6] Many of the painful sights which I was compelled to witness in this brief experience of army life have fortunately disappeared from my memory.

It would be an interesting study to contrast some of the clinical details of a field hospital of that day with the more scientific methods of today. The condition of the wounded during transport to the rear under circumstances which knew no protection against infection would be hard to envision.

On my return home after this episode of active service I came to the conclusion that I would be more useful if I completed my medical education before entering regular army service, instead of following the example of those who undertook the responsibilities of the care of the wounded with the slender preparation that was characteristic of so many an army surgeon.

6 This brief description of the behavior of J.C.W.'s classmate portrays also the "shell shock" of World War I, the "N-P" of World War II, and the "battle fatigue" of the Korean campaign. The reaction is not unique to modern warfare. In former times the victim was likely to be court-martialed or summarily shot.

The Old North
Grove Street Medical College

The winter of 1864–65 was passed in Boston attending lectures at the Medical School. The School was still situated at the head of North Grove Street in close proximity to the Massachusetts General Hospital, thus enabling the students to make ward visits and attend operations in the old amphitheatre of historic fame.[1] The School and the Hospital had no official connection with one another, but members of the Medical Faculty were also members of the Hospital Staff and thus had facilities for clinical teaching at their disposal. This union had now existed nearly two decades, but the modern and more systematized method of clinical instruction to small groups of students had not yet been developed. During the winter term the number of students following a teacher in the ward visit was too large to permit much benefit to be derived from a study of the cases. Only those students who obtained clinical appointments or who remained in school during the spring term were able to acquire a good clinical training. "Clinical conferences" were conducted by Professor Henry I. Bowditch to overcome this difficulty. Under his enthusiastic leadership they proved most popular and instructive because they encouraged the student to take an active part in the study of the cases brought before the class.[2]

No description of the Medical School at that period would be complete without reference to the group of able men who composed

[1] The Harvard medical classes also visited Boston City Hospital (just opened), Boston Dispensary, Chelsea Marine Hospital, and the Massachusetts Eye and Ear Infirmary.

[2] A brief history of the Boston Society for Medical Observation published by the organization in 1872 states:

> Among the natural off-shoots from this American [sic] Society for Medical Observation is the "Clinical Conference" of the Harvard Medical School, established by Dr. Bowditch during the first years that he was professor of Clinical Medicine. The exercises carried on at the "Conference" are almost identical with those which took place at the Paris Society for Medical Observation while Louis was President, and the word "Conference" [conférence, the French term for "lecture"] was selected from the fact that Louis, who was as remarkable for his modesty as he was for his other excellent qualities, had selected that term for his own lectures.

its Faculty. Oliver Wendell Holmes was the Parkman Professor of Anatomy and Physiology, and on the occasion of my first attendance at any exercise in the School he gave the introductory lecture of the season. This was a brilliant and witty discourse stimulating and encouraging to those like myself who were entering, perhaps with some misgivings, a course of study which involved many new and strange experiences and great responsibilities. Professor Holmes's work at the School was but a small part of his activities. His role as a scientist was quite subordinate to his career as a writer. There were those who thought that the chair of anatomy should have been occupied by a man of pure science like Jeffries Wyman. Holmes had the ability, however, to invest the dry features of anatomy with an interest and picturesqueness all his own, and his popularity as a teacher, as well as his fame as an author, was a strong drawing card for the School.

Dr. Henry J. Bigelow, professor of surgery, was then approaching the zenith of his career. He had been a visiting surgeon of the Hospital since the year of the discovery of anesthesia, an event in which he played an enthusiastic and prominent part, foreseeing clearly its epochal character. A keen intellect and personal fascination fitted in well with an exceptional mechanical skill to equip him to be a leader in surgery. Although fully appreciative of the admiration of his colleagues and subordinates, he seemed to make no effort to attain popularity. He lectured without apparent effort, although his ability was unequaled in seizing the opportunity to create a dramatic situation in which he could thrust home some great truth of surgery. He had a large collection of colored drawings prepared by a skilled artist whom he held in his employ for several years. These illustrated all phases of surgery and when displayed in great profusion gave added interest to the lectures. But the great artistic product was the man himself, who, whether holding forth in the lecture room or in the amphitheatre, was always the central point of interest.

In striking contrast to these two brilliant personalities, but quite the peer of both as a teacher, was Dr. Edward H. Clarke, the professor of materia medica, a busy and most successful practitioner and much sought after from far and near. His was a subject of practical importance to the future practitioner but it teemed with much dry detail and was handicapped by the many imperfections of the medical science of that era. Undismayed by these inherent difficulties, Dr. Clarke selected eight o'clock in the morning as the only hour he could spare for his lecture. The room was always filled to overflowing and one had to come early in order to secure a good place in the line when the doors were thrown open. Punctually on the stroke of the clock, he entered the room and began to speak at once. The attention of his audience was held riveted until the warning bell announced the approaching close of the hour, when, even if in the middle of a sentence, he instantly ceased and with a bow dismissed the class. The secret of his success lay partly in a perfect diction and clear, well-mouthed delivery and partly in his power to avoid unnecessary detail and to dwell upon important items such as the physiological action of a drug and its characteristic therapeutic properties. These points were brought out with an air of finality which, although it might not always have been justified by the work of the best authorities of the time, gave students well-defined and usable information, good equipment with which to begin practice.[3] It is worth recalling that the two opening lectures of his course were devoted to the influence of the mind on health and disease, and not a word was said about a drug until his views on the psychological relation of doctor to patient had been explained.[4]

Dr. David W. Cheever was then demonstrator of anatomy and a popular teacher. His quiet, reserved demeanor and clean-cut methods of drilling and guiding the student in dissections supplemented well the eloquent lectures of his chief and contributed largely to the success of the department of anatomy.

[The following tribute to Dr. Cheever was written by J. Collins Warren and printed in the *Harvard Graduates' Magazine* for June 1916.]

My earliest recollections of Dr. Cheever date back to a period long before I had ever thought of studying medicine. It was on the occasion of a professional visit to Portsmouth that my father had entrusted me, a boy, to the care of the young man who had just returned from his graduation at

[3] Frederick C. Shattuck recalled in 1900:

> I well remember how, in my student days, we packed the lecture-room of a brilliant lecturer on therapeutics at eight o'clock winter mornings. But today I am not alone in feeling that we were not getting as much as we thought we were getting. We were carried away by the personality of the teacher, a very able and impressive man, who knew how suggestion may be made to enhance the desired effect of a remedial agent as do few practitioners. [*Boston Med. and Surg. J. 142*, 529 (May 24, 1900).]

[4] At this time Dr. John E. Tyler was conducting a weekly recitation in psychological medicine, and in 1866 he was appointed a University lecturer in the subject.

What is heralded today as "psychosomatic medicine" is of course an ancient part of the art. Even that rugged old New England naval surgeon, Usher Parsons, delivered a lecture on "The Connexion and Reciprocal Influence, between the Brain and Stomach" at Providence in 1840. Parsons was surgeon at the Battle of Lake Erie. He studied medicine under Dr. John Warren, and his license as "Practitioner in Medicine," dated Feb. 7, 1812, was signed by John Warren, President, and John C. Warren, Recording Secretary, of the Massachusetts Medical Society.

Harvard. I can still recall the tall and slender youth who, later in the day, for the delectation of his guests, appeared in the costume of a Puritan in which he was to attend some social or civic function. Since the curtain of memory first fell on this little episode, the recollection of the grave and dignified young graduate has frequently come back to me in later years as a sort of prologue to the future relations — an *entente cordiale* — which were happily preserved in after life between teacher and pupil, and to the role which this representative of fine old New England stock was to play in the interesting medical drama soon to be placed upon the stage.

Ten years and more had elapsed before I again came in contact with Dr. Cheever. As Demonstrator of Anatomy he had charge of the personal instruction of the students under the supervision of Oliver Wendell Holmes. Of Holmes, Cheever says: "Wit, gentleness, keenness of intellect made Dr. Holmes a delightful master." Contrasted with the breezy ways of his senior were the quiet and businesslike methods of the taciturn young man.

Cheever was a popular teacher, for though his manner often seemed cold and reserved, the class always felt perfect confidence in the justness of his decisions. To the close of his career as a teacher he retained a tender interest in the welfare of his pupils, as is shown in the foundation of the Cheever Scholarship for young men entering the Medical School.

There was no one of the surgical staff at the School who could compare with him as a lecturer. Dr. Bigelow's personality had always contributed largely to the prestige of the surgical department and his course of lectures were characteristically punctuated by one or two interesting or brilliant episodes with which he knew only too well how to garnish them. But Cheever's lectures were marked by a clockwork-like precision: the ground laid out beforehand was covered systematically from beginning to end. A cool and clear head, a reposeful manner showing the speaker to be perfectly at his ease, a well-modulated voice and simplicity of diction enabled him to hold the attention of his class from start to finish. Lasting proof of the accuracy of this statement is given in that admirable book containing his course of lectures, which were taken down *verbatim* by a stenographer and printed subsequently almost without change. This quality as a teacher enabled him to shine conspicuously at the bedside in clinical instruction. I well recall certain Sunday morning visits at the City Hospital. They were models of what such visits should be. No extraneous matter was injected into these talks. There was no wandering from the point which each particular case illustrated.

Our relations on the teaching staff were always regarded by me as leaving nothing to be desired. The elder man always took a sympathetic interest in his junior's welfare. No occasion calling for a word of encouragement or congratulation was ever passed unnoticed; and if criticism was necessary, it was always skilfully concealed under the guise of a fatherly suggestion. I have often wondered whether the current of academic waters flowed as smoothly in other departments of the University as they did in ours while he was chief. Perhaps it was because his depth of character brought a serenity which permeated the whole staff, one and all of whom were glad to acknowledge him as their leader.

Through all the period which I have attempted to cover in the course of this personal sketch, the estimate of the man which had impressed itself so forcibly on the child still seemed to hold true. In whatever role he might appear in after life, either as the bold surgeon or the unflinching leader in a good cause, or the quiet gentleman in sombre clothing in his daily rounds, I seemed still to see the Puritan garb which was so typical of his ancestry and his character. And when, at the recent Convocation of the American College of Surgeons, the honorary degree of the college was conferred upon him, and I saw him for the last time, in the robe of the order, he seemed to me to have come into his own again. The sombre folds of the academic gown served as an appropriate setting to the grave and intellectual features of the man, and while, during a pause in the proceedings arranged to allow him to retire, he passed slowly down the aisle, leaning upon a proferred arm, his assembled colleagues rose as one man to do him honor as a recognized leader in their chosen profession.[5]

The study of anatomy had a very different scope from what it has today. Instruction was limited to descriptive and gross anatomy. The microscope [6] was a luxury into which the students were allowed to peep one by one after some simple demonstration at Dr. Holmes's lecture. Aside from the dissecting room [7] and a chemical

[5] The late Dr. David Cheever read a paper on "The Warren Stock and Some of its Scions" on October 22, 1928 before the Boston Medical History Club. One paragraph, in which he identified himself as "the son of David W. Cheever," outlines the interlacing pattern of the Warren-Cheever relationship in Boston surgery:

In 1779 a young man, Abijah Cheever by name, began the study of medicine under Dr. John Warren. His son, Charles A. Cheever, pursued the same study under John C. Warren the son of John. Subsequently when this Cheever was stricken with a mortal disease it was J. Mason Warren, the son of John C. Warren, who operated on him at the Massachusetts General Hospital and cared for him tenderly afterward. His son, David W. Cheever, studied medicine at Harvard during the only period when no Warren was a member of the teaching staff, but he himself became a teacher of J. Collins Warren, the son of J. Mason Warren. Still another generation and J. Collins Warren became the teacher in surgery of the son of David W. Cheever and finally that son for many years was closely associated with John Warren, the son of J. Collins Warren, in teaching anatomy and surgery at the Harvard Medical School and he now makes acknowledgement with gratitude of the help and sympathetic assistance received from him. [*New England J. Med. 200*, 857 April 25, 1929).]

[6] The Medical Faculty requested Dr. Holmes to commence a course of lectures on the microscope in 1863. In 1865–66 Calvin Ellis fitted up a small room in the basement of the North Grove Street school for microscopic study in normal and pathological histology.

[7] J.C.W. gives a glimpse of an old-time dissecting class in his contribution to "Memorials to Dr. Thomas Dwight" in the Jan. 4, 1912 issue of the *Boston Medical and Surgical Journal* (*166*, 7). Dwight, a cousin of J.C.W., was a fellow member of the dissecting class.

Dr. Cheever was at that time demonstrator of anatomy; the class in dissecting was often held in the evening in the little one-story dissecting room at the foot of the western wall of the building on North Grove Street. In the daytime it was lighted by a skylight. The character of this wing was well known to the hoodlum element of the neighborhood, and at night, when work was going on there, the light always shone brightly through the roof. One evening while we were absorbed in class work, a brickbat crashed through the glass. Dr. Cheever's equanimity did not forsake him, but calmly looking upwards and then down at us he said, "Up, guards, and at them!"

laboratory, there were no laboratories in the modern sense of the term. Histology was taught from a book. Only a few brief moments were assigned to embryology, and the course also embraced several lectures in physiology. The anatomical department of the School was nevertheless popular with the students, and deservedly so, for under Holmes's and Cheever's guidance the class obtained a good working knowledge of the elements of anatomy. This knowledge was of a character which they could retain easily in memory and formed a fairly sound foundation for further studies in the medical course and for later practice.

Dr. Richard M. Hodges had been the predecessor of Dr. Cheever in the position of demonstrator of anatomy. He became adjunct professor of surgery, and had recently been appointed a visiting surgeon at the Massachusetts General Hospital. He shared with Dr. Bigelow the instruction in surgery. I was present at the first operation performed by Dr. Hodges in the amphitheatre of the Hospital. Had it not been for the overshadowing prestige of his chief he would have made a more lasting name for himself in surgery. To me he appeared to possess ideal qualities as a surgeon: self-reliance and skill in the use of the knife by virtue of his anatomical training. He was a fearless operator because he possessed a thorough knowledge of the ground. But in his great loyalty to his chief Dr. Hodges was always reluctant to place himself in any position which might be considered that of a rival.

The early experiences of these teachers of surgery had been in the period which preceded the dawn of the antiseptic era. Operative surgery continued rapidly to increase in volume and attempts were made to bring new methods and new regions of the body into its field. These efforts met with many discouragements. The time seemed to have arrived when the limit of the surgeon's skill was about to be reached. Reckless attempts were made by some bold spirits to accomplish what seemed the impossible to more conscientious minds. These conditions bred in a strong nature such as that of Dr. Hodges a certain cynical outlook toward the progressive surgery of the day and a scepticism toward many of the new operations which were being advocated. This critical attitude toward the surgery of that

---

We needed no further urging and sallied forth *en masse* to drive off the intruders. Dashing through one or two unoccupied lots of land surrounded by a high board fence, I suddenly found myself face to face with a pugnacious opponent. And while we were squaring off to settle matters, then and there I suddenly discovered my opponent was none other than Dwight himself, who, in the darkness, had mistaken me for a foe, and although I was much the larger, he had not hesitated to rush upon me with all the force of his outraged dignity.

period is noteworthy, coming as it did from a man approaching his prime and endowed with qualities which entitled his opinion to respect. His subsequent career as a medical practitioner was so successful that one could not help feeling that a truly brilliant future might have been in store for him had he flourished during the era that was soon to come.

It is hard to realize at the present time how limited was the number of subjects in the medical curriculum. This was because of the almost entire absence of the specialties. Obstetrics had long been recognized as a department, and was presided over by David Humphreys Storer, a most picturesque personality and representative of the physician of the old school. His tall and slender figure was surmounted by a well-shaped head, sharply defined features, and a full brow backed by a fanlike frame of wavy hair. He was one of those who still adhered to a full-dress suit of black broadcloth and a large expanse of white shirt bosom. His manner was genial and vivacious, and the lecture hour passed rapidly while with much earnestness and gesture he endeavored to impress upon his hearers the great principles which should guide the obstetrician in his practice. There was no hospital clinic in Boston [8] covering this branch, and most students were obliged to content themselves with an academic knowledge of the subject.

It was not until the late 1860's that instruction in diseases of the eye was started by Dr. Henry W. Williams, who was eventually appointed professor of ophthalmology. The Eye and Ear Infirmary was already a long-established institution, but operations on the eye such as those for cataract and strabismus were still considered a part of the province of the surgeon at the General Hospital. So far as I

---

[8] Although Harvard had established a professorship of obstetrics and medical jurisprudence as early as 1815, clinical instruction in obstetrics remained undeveloped largely because of prejudice against student participation in midwifery. Later the Tremont Street Medical School made it a point to give some clinical instruction in this field.

The Boston Lying-in Hospital, founded in the South End in 1832, was closed for financial reasons from 1856 to 1873. During the 1860's the trustees of this institution were able, through sale of its property, to support about fifteen free beds for lying-in patients at the New England Hospital for Women and Children. About this time negotiations were conducted privately for a union of the Lying-in Hospital with the MGH, but without result. When reopened in January 1873 it moved into a building at No. 24 McLean Street close to the MGH but maintained separate identity.

The hazards of puerperal fever previously encountered in attempts to practice obstetrics in hospitals admitting all types of disease were well documented. Largely for this reason the MGH did not develop an obstetrical service when the community first experienced need of such a service supported by philanthropy. After Lister had shown how to control cross-infection, however, newly founded hospitals did not hesitate to include an obstetrical department.

remember, little or no instruction in diseases of the ear was given at Harvard during my student years.

The first graduate students to return fresh from the schools of the German-speaking countries made their appearance while I was still an undergraduate. Among them were Drs. James C. White, B. Joy Jeffries, and Hasket Derby. They returned full of enthusiasm for the great schools in Vienna and Berlin and clinics such as those of Hebra for diseases of the skin and of Arlt and Graefe for diseases of the eye. Dr. White brought home new knowledge of the subject of urology as well as dermatology, and gave instruction in both specialties. He had already prepared a course of lectures on diseases of the skin and was ready to assume the professorship of dermatology when that department was created a few years later — the first in this country. He was a pioneer in his specialty and justly regarded as a leader in this field. His efforts to establish a special ward in the Massachusetts General Hospital solely for patients with skin diseases met with much opposition, and although he succeeded in having such a ward opened in the early seventies, it was afterwards closed. From time to time single cases were admitted to the general wards. Dr. White was able to establish a dermatological clinic in the out-patient department, where subsequent followers of this specialty obtained their education.

Great credit should be given to Dr. White for his early efforts in behalf of reform in medical education.[9] Harvard was a pioneer

[9] Dr. James C. White completed his medical course at Harvard in the spring of 1856 and, on the advice of Dr. Calvin Ellis, made Vienna his chief place of study abroad. "At that time," wrote White in his *Sketches from My Life* (Cambridge, 1914), "few American or English medical students visited Vienna. I was the first of the former, I believe, to spend a full year there . . . for the fame of its incomparable teachers . . . had scarcely spread to America or England."

The sources of the foreign influences which played so large a part in the course taken by American medicine were, broadly considered, British from 1750 to 1820, French from 1820 to 1860, and German from 1860 to 1895 (Shryock). White was thus one of the first of what was to be a long procession of young American doctors enthusiastic over the spirit of the scientific medicine which was gathering headway among the German-speaking people of Europe. Mention of only two of the many leaders with whom these Americans were to come in contact will illustrate the reason for the turn of the pilgrimage to Germany and Austria. Carl Ludwig in Vienna and later in Leipzig was to introduce entirely new ideas of bodily function and stimulate scores of young men to enter upon careers in medical research; Rudolf Virchow in Berlin was to launch his concept of cellular pathology in 1858.

Although France, the nation which had exerted the predominant influence on American medicine in the preceding decades, was to yield her position to Germany in the second half of the nineteenth century, such men as Claude Bernard carried forward the great tradition of the Paris school, and Louis Pasteur in the 1860's opened the vast field of research into infectious disease. Only the single example of Charles Darwin need be cited as a reminder that creative science in Britain was by no means languishing, for his book *On the Origin of Species,* published in

in the movement to rearrange and grade the course of study, which began about 1870 after President Charles W. Eliot had begun his term of office. Dr. White strongly advocated the graded three-years' course and was one of the leaders of the Medical Faculty in bringing about this change. In later years, through the various steps taken during the period of reform, his influence was always felt in the Faculty debates. He has a just claim to be regarded as one of the founders of the new system.[10]

1859, brought forward a concept which fertilized biological thought and investigation in all fields. So a separation of national schools of intellectual activity in the development of scientific medicine is far from precise; the sources of organizational patterns of medical institutions imported to America are more easily identified.

The scholars who traveled to Europe during the formative decades of American medicine often returned, as did White, to influential positions in medical schools. The particular situations to which they returned determined the nature and extent of the reforms they were able to introduce quite as much as the intrinsic merits of the changes involved. Some of the steps in the evolution of medical education at Harvard brought about by J. C. White, J. Collins Warren, Henry P. Bowditch and many others, including President Eliot, are described in these Reminiscences. While these men were inspired by their experience in the universities of Europe, the Harvard Medical School was not reconstructed by a direct transfer of European educational patterns to Boston. The realities of a university, a medical school, and a group of hospitals already formed and staffed in the American tradition confronted the pilgrims on their return. These institutions had been built by predecessors strongly steeped in British or French traditions. Even if J.C.W.'s generation had desired it, the opportunity to make a fresh start and thereby abridge the evolutionary process was denied them in Boston.

In contrast was the situation in Baltimore. On September 20, 1884 Dr. William Henry Welch began a voyage to study in Germany. On return, Dr. Welch and his associates Mall, Halsted, and others were given opportunity to found a new medical school and hospital. These they shaped largely by a direct transference of Continental patterns. At the new Johns Hopkins, professional training was from the start placed in a research-centered environment, a momentous achievement. Even such detail as the graduate training of surgeons in the hospital duplicated in so far as possible the pattern Dr. Halsted had observed in the German clinics. "It was our intention," he stated, "originally to adopt as closely as feasible the German plan, which, in the main, is the same for all the principal clinics of the German universities." (Annual address in medicine delivered at Yale University, June 27, 1904.)

President Eliot was well aware of the difficulties which may arise from the introduction of educational patterns observed elsewhere into long-established American institutions. In 1864 he had remarked that a German university would suit Harvard freshmen about as well as a "barn-yard would suit a whale." During the early decades of the present century "abridgment of the evolutionary process" became the leitmotiv of Abraham Flexner in his efforts to transplant detailed organizational patterns developed by German scientific medicine to America. It is not surprising to find Mr. Flexner a vigorous critic of Mr. Eliot and usually quite cool toward the Medical School with its faculty conducting themselves in accord with what has become generally identified as the "Harvard Plan."

[10] Dr. Calvin Ellis, who became dean of the Medical Faculty in 1869 and resigned only a few months before his death in 1883, played a part in educational reforms which must not be overlooked. President Eliot wrote of Dr. Ellis in his

Beyond the departments mentioned, little was done in the way of teaching the specialties of medicine. Many of them indeed had not yet begun to exist, at least on this side of the ocean. One in which Americans may claim to have pioneered was gynecology. Thomas A. Emmet of New York was one of the recognized leaders of what is now called plastic surgery in gynecology. The names of J. Marion Sims, Edmund R. Peaslee, the Atlee brothers, Horatio R. Storer of Boston, and Walter Burnham and Gilman Kimball of Lowell were associated with the new operation of ovariotomy. No facilities in a special clinic at the School were offered students at that time for studying the diseases of women. During my term as an undergraduate there was no instruction in laryngology, although Dr. Henry K. Oliver took up the specialty in Boston about this time. Orthopedic surgery was coming into notice as a recognized special branch of surgery through the work of Dr. Buckminster Brown,[11] and previously had been developed to a certain extent by his father, Dr. John B. Brown, but there was no special clinic and patients with club foot or other long-term orthopedic disorders had to take their chances in the shifting services of the surgical wards in the General Hospital.

Report for 1882–83: "He actively furthered all the many improvements made by the Faculty during his long term of service, and the changes made in 1870–71 could not have been effected without his support — a support which was as sturdy and strong as it was indispensable."

[11] Dr. Buckminster Brown's mother was Dr. John Warren's daughter Rebecca. Buckminster Brown's personal resemblance in features and expression to his distinguished grandfather was said to have been remarkable. His legacy to Harvard in 1895 was applied to the foundation of the John B. and Buckminster Brown professorship of orthopedic surgery.

~ VII

House Pupil at the
Massachusetts General Hospital

The course of lectures in the winter term of 1864–65 was completed on March first, and the Civil War was so near its close that my plan of serving in the army in a medical capacity had to be abandoned. I accordingly applied for and received the appointment of house pupil at the Massachusetts General Hospital for a service of one year beginning in the month of May. The term "house pupil" was one which had probably originated in England and dated back to before the time the first staff of the Hospital was organized; several members of the first staff had received their education in London hospitals where this term was in official use.[1] I doubt not that many of the early customs of the Hospital had their origin in the traditions of the English school, and many were still surviving during my student life. There were four surgical and two medical house pupils, a staff sufficiently large to do all the work required at the time. There was no organized out-patient service. Two rooms near the rear entrance were reserved for the reception of out-patients;[2] they were examined by the visiting surgeon or physician at the close of his morning visit, and subsequent treatment was carried out by one of the house pupils.

Our staff of house pupils consisted of Francis B. Greenough and Jeremiah Whipple on the Medical Service, J. Orne Green and Calvin Pratt on the East Surgical Service, and Arthur H. Nichols and myself on the West Surgical. Although rejoicing in the courtesy title of

[1] The term "house pupil" was used in 1811 at the Boston Almshouse to designate Harvard Medical School students who accompanied their instructors on ward visits. At MGH the house officers, appointed after formal medical studies were completed, were called apothecaries until 1828, house physicians and house surgeons until 1849, house pupils until 1922, and house officers (interns) and residents thereafter.

[2] Out-patients came through the Blossom Street gate opposite McLean Street and through a door on the north side of the Bulfinch. They sat on settees in a waiting room until interviewed initially in the office of the admitting physician at the northeast corner of the building. The Blossom Street gate was operated by a wheel inside a small wooden "lodge," which stood until 1881 when it was replaced by a brick lodge, which in turn stood until ground was broken for the Research Building in 1949.

Doctor, we had not as yet received our degrees, a rule of the Hospital being that no graduate in medicine would be allowed to serve in the capacity of house pupil. The policy of the Hospital Trustees and the Staff, as my father explained to me at the time, frowned upon allowing these subordinate officers to assume too much responsibility. Experience in the past had shown that a graduate officer was too strongly disposed to take advantage of his position to do work which belonged only in the province of the visiting staff. The title "pupil" was also, for the same reason, jealously maintained.

The duties of a visiting physician or surgeon in the early days of the Hospital were not of an onerous nature. The prescribing of a pill was considered an affair of much more importance than it would be today and one involving an amount of responsibility which it seemed best to leave entirely in the hands of the chief of the service, and not delegate to house pupils. This policy evidently grew out of the conditions under which apprentices first were allowed to take part in the hospital service. A concession to public opinion seemed unavoidable at the time of this innovation, and the Trustees felt that these young men were in the Hospital on sufferance and should be allowed the privilege of performing hospital service only under carefully defined restrictions.[3] A single sleeping room was set apart for the use of our house pupil staff of six, and we were not allowed to take any meals in the hospital. This latter regulation was the result of a quarrel between our predecessors in office and the Matron, but it unfortunately remained in effect during my whole term of service. I remember quite distinctly being told by one of the Trustees, with whom I happened to be personally acquainted, that we ought to be thankful that we were allowed to sleep within the hospital walls, for this had not been part of the original plan of hospital organization.[4] In his opinion this seemed to be a doubtful

---

[3] The report of a committee of both houses of the Massachusetts Legislature which recommended in 1810 "An Act to incorporate certain persons by the name of the *Massachusetts General Hospital*" described the educational function of the proposed institution as follows:

The immense benefits to be derived from a General Hospital, as a school for improvement in surgery and physic, are too obvious to require illustration. It is well understood that for want of such an institution, many students belonging to Massachusetts, resort annually to New-York or Philadelphia, for the completion of their medical education. The location of the proposed Hospital, is intended to be such as will accommodate students in the metropolis, and at the University in Cambridge, and the skill thus acquired, by the increased means of instruction, will be gradually, and constantly diffused, through every section of the Commonwealth.

[4] The house pupils' sleeping room was on the first floor at the southwest corner of the Bulfinch Building. The house pupils' office was the room within the right angle formed by the west corridor as it turns south into the central portion of the

concession. Dr. Benjamin S. Shaw was the Superintendent,[5] and on a stormy morning would occasionally invite to breakfast those of us who had to go far for meals. Conditions of our hospital life stand in striking contrast to those of a metropolitan hospital of today.

The Surgical Staff of the Hospital consisted of six visiting surgeons. They were as follows, placed in order of seniority: Drs. J. Mason Warren, Henry J. Bigelow, Henry G. Clark, Samuel Cabot, George H. Gay, and Richard M. Hodges. The old Bulfinch building contained large open wards [6] and its central portion was given up to the Superintendent's family and to private rooms. The east and west wings were devoted to the medical and surgical services, and hence arose the terms East and West Services.[7] Drs. Warren, Gay, and Hodges presided over the West Surgical, each serving a term of four months. My father had the spring service from March first to July first, Dr. Gay had the summer service, and Dr. Hodges served in the winter term as the opposite or colleague of Dr. Bigelow — the latter two thus having an opportunity to use their wards and their patients for the purposes of surgical instruction from November through February. These months covered the greater part of the period assigned to the winter course of lectures at the School.

My appointment as house pupil was a source of great gratification to my father, as it gave him an opportunity to instill into my mind the principles of surgery as he saw them and enabled me to acquire

---

building on the first floor. The corresponding room at the turning of the east corridor became the house pupils' dining room in 1860. The cancellation of the meal privilege mentioned by J.C.W. continued in effect until 1873.

[5] The official titles of the chief administrative officer of the Hospital have been: Superintendent (1821–1858), Resident Physician (1858–1921), Director (1921–1949), and General Director (from 1949).

[6] Before 1846 the Hospital maintained 93 beds in 14 wards, each room containing from one to twelve beds. There were nine male wards with 53 beds, and five female wards with 40 beds. The new wings of 1846–47 added four 57-by-50-foot wards, bringing the total number of beds to 141. The Touro Ward of 1855 had sixteen isolation rooms.

[7] During the first quarter century of the Hospital the surgical patients were cared for as a single group or service. When the two new wings were added in 1846–47 these patients were divided into two groups for professional supervision, designated as the East and West Surgical Services in accord with the location of the wards in the east and west wings. These two services remain to this day as the residuum of "general" surgery and form the backbone of the teaching of surgery at the Hospital. The increases in bed capacity during the past half century have been accompanied by the creation of specialty services, namely, orthopedic surgery, urology, neurosurgery, and gynecology. On two occasions a third service in nonspecialized surgery was split off for a time: the South Surgical Service in the 1890's and the Third Surgical Service in the 1920's. Each was subsequently returned to the parent service. In this and other respects the "two-service" organization at the MGH provides interesting analogies with the "two-party" system of national politics.

an amount of detailed knowledge that under less intimate relations could not fall to one in my position. One of the advantages thus obtained was understanding the attitude of my father toward the old traditions which enveloped the Hospital and its staff. These traditions were treasured by all members of the staff, who took much pride in thus setting the standard of behavior of physicians toward patients in this great charitable institution of Boston. The training which I had at my father's hand at that time left a lasting impression and proved a valuable guide to professional conduct in later life.[8]

The routine work of the house pupil differed materially from that of the present-day [1914] house officer.[9] Surgical dressings were of a primitive type. Lint was one of the staple articles used for dressing wounds and was made from old cotton or linen which had been picked to pieces for this purpose, oftentimes by the convalescent patients. No subsequent cleansing of the material thus prepared was thought necessary. The lint was heaped up in neat-looking little piles on a rolling table with shelves, on which was placed the bean-shaped pus basin, an ordinary wash bowl, and a Davidson syringe or some form of douche apparatus, the whole surrounded by rows of roller bandages and towels.

Each student was supplied with an instrument case of leather containing scissors, dressing forceps, probe and director, a porte caustique, a pair of artery forceps with toothed edges and blade held firmly together by a ratchet. A two-bladed knife with a tortoise-

---

[8] In his presidential address before the American Surgical Association in 1897, J.C.W. recalled: "As a house officer at the Massachusetts General Hospital, I can well remember the tone of despair with which my father remarked, on learning from me of a fatal result following one of his operations: 'I am often nearly disgusted with surgery.'"

[9] The work of the 1957 surgical resident differs from that of the 1914 house officer in even more striking respects. The period of intramural practice under supervision has been extended to a minimum of five years. The post of chief resident on either of the two services adds another year for its incumbent. If compulsory military service is deferred until a man qualifies as a doctor, two more years intervene between the M.D. degree and a possible start in practice. This prolongation of the period of hospital practice by the young surgeon not only develops a competent and experienced surgeon for the community but provides a quality of professional care to the patients of a hospital service never previously equaled. In the full flush of enthusiastic and vigorous teamwork, armed with the latest advances of scientific medicine, and guided and inspired by the consultative advice and wisdom of the senior staff, the surgical residents of today give their patients surgical care of unprecedented excellence.

With the lengthening of hospital practice, conscious efforts have been made to convert what was formerly an apprenticeship into a true educational experience. The problem that remains is to pay these young men an adequate stipend for their service to the community during the years of intramural practice. Financially, they are still exploited as apprentices by institution, profession, and community.

shell handle completed the outfit, which, it should be observed, was specially adapted to the conditions existing at that time. The dressing forceps resembled the artery forceps now in use but had no clamp. The end of the blade was somewhat larger and more oval in shape, the serrated edges surrounding a slightly concave center. They were intended to grasp easily a foreign body in the wound and extract it; they were also employed to introduce drainage tubes. It was an instrument much used as it was often necessary to grasp and remove sloughing tissues, fragments of bone, or pieces of silk ligature, one end of which was supposed to hang out of the wound so that it could be easily extracted after the ligature was ready "to come away." The curved end probe (pointed) was also much in use, for in those days of suppurating wounds the burrowing of pus was of frequent occurrence and sinuses had to be relentlessly opened up along the groove of the director.

No anesthetic was thought necessary for these little operations, which were daily incidents of the morning visit. The visiting surgeon on inspection of a wound would laconically say "Knife!" and a fluctuating spot would be lanced or a few sinuses sliced open without further ceremony. I remember on one such occasion handing a knife from my pocket case to Dr. Hodges, who after one glance flung it on the bed and demanded contemptuously a "clean" instrument. The lessons thus inculcated were seldom forgotten and were often gratefully remembered in later life. The porte caustique held a stick of nitrate of silver or lunar caustic, which seemed to be indispensable to the healing process. Granulating wounds were numerous and generally of large size; as the healing from the edges progressed slowly, the exuberant granulations or "proud flesh" had to be cut down by the application of the caustic. This remedy maintained its reputation as a favorite in spite of the disfiguring stains it produced on the hands of the surgeon and the contents of the pocket case.

Ward work in those days presented problems of grave responsibility. Surgical wards did not show the rows of smiling convalescent faces now so characteristic a feature. Wounds were always "doing badly" and although the sanitary conditions were improved after the epidemic of hospital gangrene which I have already mentioned [chap. III], we were always on the alert for some complication. When the granulations began to lose their healthy reddish color and assume a grayish tinge, hospital gangrene was to be feared. Although this disease rarely assumed an epidemic form, it was regarded as one of the complications to be expected, as were also erysipelas and pyemia. All of these hospital pestilences were accepted as necessary evils.

If a wound became foul and offensive to the other patients, the sufferer would be transferred to the "Brick," where there were rooms for isolating such cases. Erysipelas was supposed to be noncontagious, the result of catching cold, and patients thus afflicted, as well as pyemia cases, were allowed to remain in the open ward. Secondary hemorrhage was of not infrequent occurrence, of course, and these and many other emergencies incidental to septic surgery called for an exercise of quick decision and an exhibition of skill which put the qualities of the house pupil often to the severest test.

So far as the field of operation was concerned, no preparation of a patient for operation was thought necessary. An examination would be made of the patient's general condition and attention paid to the digestive apparatus. The importance of an "ether breakfast" was recognized. The instruments were kept in plush-covered cases and it was the province of the house pupil to wash them himself after the operation and replace them. It was his duty also to attend to the "layout" for an operation. This consisted, in addition to the requisite instruments, in towels fresh from the laundry, compresses of cotton cloth, and bandages. There was also a wooden tray which contained a number of small round sea sponges which had been washed after previous use by one of the ward tenders and were supposed to be as clean as soap and water could make them. No attempt was made on the part of the operator or his assistants to attain any special personal cleanliness. The surgeon's toilet was regarded as a postoperative ceremony. An old broadcloth frock coat, as I have said, which had seen too much service to be useful for any other purpose was dedicated in future to surgery.

The method of operating in a case involving a large wound, such as an amputation or an excision of the breast, can be set down briefly at this point. Although no special precautions were used for surgical cleanliness, there was always an abundant supply of clean linen. In the case of an amputation, care was taken to have the operation as nearly bloodless as possible. The limb was carefully bandaged with an ordinary roller bandage before the tourniquet was applied. Later, when rubber bandages were used for this purpose, this preliminary emptying of blood from the limb was known as the Esmarch method, but the method had been utilized for many years at the Massachusetts General Hospital. Where no tourniquet could be applied no special attempt was made to control hemorrhage during the operation other than by the use of small sea sponges which were crowded into the wound by the assistant. After the operation had been completed, these were cautiously removed one by one and the bleeding vessels were seized by long-handled, toothed dissecting forceps, which were firmly closed by the hand of the surgeon while the assistant applied the ligature. These artery forceps, as they were then called, were made after a pattern which formed part of a set of gilt instruments enclosed in a mahogany case and given to the Hospital by my father.

The ligatures were of large size, silk, and heavily waxed, a cake of wax being kept in the operating theatre for this purpose. After the ward tender had cut the threads into six table lengths and waxed them, they were placed in perforated brass plates which were hung on the wooden post at each end of the first row of seats in the amphitheatre. From these plates a ligature could readily be extracted without disturbing those that remained. Sutures were kept in pincushions, the needles inserted horizontally around the edges so that they could be removed readily. Pins to secure dressings occupied the centre of the cushion.

A ligature having been tied, one end was cut off close to the vessel; the other was left long enough to escape from the wound. These long ends were then collected together to form a single strand and were allowed to protrude from the wound at some convenient point. Interrupted sutures were then applied, as now, and the edges of the wound were closely approximated. A folded towel usually served as a dressing and was held firmly in place by an appropriate bandage. Healing by first intention was the dream of the surgeon but one that rarely came true. At the end of the second or third day the patient would be found to be suffering from "constitutional disturbances," as they were then called, and about which many learned dissertations were written. The dressings would become foul and on their removal the lips of the wound would be found tense and reddened. Stitches would be removed, much to the reluctance of the surgeon, and a large flaxseed poultice applied. The poultice was in those days so important a feature of the routine work of those employed in dressing wounds that much attention was given to the proper methods of its preparation. The knowledge of how to make a flaxseed poultice was considered a most essential feature of the elementary teaching of the surgical student.[10] Pus would now flow freely from the wound, which would be considered as doing fairly well if no complication such as erysipelas intervened. A free discharge of "creamy" pus would be followed by the appearance of healthy granulations and the wound would gradually "heal from the bottom" in about six weeks.

[10] The practical art of making a flaxseed poultice hot, but not quite hot enough to raise a blister, was relegated to nursing technics many decades ago. It was still being demonstrated to medical students in the early twenties, but it is doubtful whether doctors of a more recent vintage could qualify as poultice makers.

Adhesive straps of diachylon plaster [11] were used freely after the removal of the stitches. Collodion was coming into use for this purpose, having been recently discovered by Dr. John Parker Maynard of Dedham. Dr. Maynard hoped that this agent would enable the surgeon to dispense with the suture, but the preparation employed by him was contractile, the flexible collodion not yet having come into use, and so its inventor did not acquire the amount of credit for his discovery which he justly deserved.

It is hard to realize at the present time that the surgeon had so few of the guides that exist today to help him in the management of wound healing. The clinical thermometer had not yet come into use. During the following three years that I spent in Europe I saw and heard nothing about body temperature until my visit to London in 1869, where I first saw a clinical temperature chart. I do not think I was familiar with the normal temperature of the body and the changes ordinarily observed in the course of disease until I had entered upon the practice of medicine. The pulse was practically the only guide to the condition of the patient, but the heat of the skin, the patient's facial expression, and his general bearing were taken into account perhaps more accurately than they are today. Having no fever chart to look at, one looked at the patient himself.[12]

Ointments were used freely in the later stages of the healing process, and a jar of simple cerate with a spatula was an essential item on the house pupil's dressing table. Fractures of the thigh were healed by either a long Desault or Buck's extension apparatus. The former was a most complicated affair but when skilfully applied displayed the dresser's skill in bandaging in all its glory. Buck's extension was then coming into fashion and also afforded an opportunity for the exhibition of the art of bandaging, in which the house pupils took much pride and for which the Hospital enjoyed a well-deserved reputation. To maintain a high standard, the house pupils whose dressings were likely to be shown to the class on its visit with the professor of surgery were sometimes tempted to renew the bandages more often than was consistent with sufficient repose of the broken bone. Plaster bandages were not much in use at this hospital, although already employed in the army.[13] Fractures of the leg were healed

[11] A diachylon plaster is an adhesive made of litharge and olive oil.

[12] At the MGH, paste-in "thermographs" began to appear in the patients' records about the middle 1870's.

[13] The credit for introducing plaster of Paris bandages or "casts" into military surgery is usually given to the Russian surgeon Nikolai Ivanovich Pirogoff, a pupil of Langenbeck (Chapter XI). Pirogoff served in and around Sevastopol in the Crimean War (1854) and was the first military surgeon to grapple on a rational basis with the problems of sepsis encountered in mass casualties. This experience

in fracture boxes, a sort of wooden trough the sides of which were hinged to enable the surgeon to apply pads so adjusted as to press fragments into position. These fracture boxes were constantly getting out of order and were a source of much trouble and anxiety. These methods of treating fractures enabled the surgeon to apply dressings to the wounds and obtain drainage in compound fractures, which were accompanied by much septic infection. Pus formed and burrowed in many directions, entailing a most tedious and protracted convalescence and great suffering.

Bed sores among hospital patients were regarded as a necessary evil. Nothing illustrates better the wonderful changes in the care of the sick brought about by trained nursing than the elimination of this painful and very serious complication. Ulcers the size of a dinner plate were not uncommon, and portions of the sacral bone and even the trochanter were sometimes exposed. This complication might be a more serious affair than the original illness.

It is not surprising that surgeons and dressers themselves, coming into contact as they did so freely with suppurating wounds, were frequently the victims of an infection. The loss of a nail or the development of a palmar abscess was not an unusual occurrence, and many a surgeon bore some scar to his grave.

Operations on the cavities of the body were very limited in number. Trephining was performed principally in cases of compound fracture of the skull. The operation was also done for cases of epilepsy where marked depression of the bone indicated the presence of a previously existing fracture. Trephining was regarded as a very serious surgical risk and was resorted to only in the most severe types of the disease. Operations on the thoracic cavity were limited to the treatment of empyema. The attempt was usually made to heal the abscess cavity by drainage without resorting to resection of a rib. Dr. Henry I. Bowditch's method of tapping the chest with aspiration of the exudate from the pleural cavity was an epoch-making advance in the surgery of this region. The profession took much pride in this innovation.[14]

---

led him to refer to war as an "epidemic of trauma." Pirogoff used ether anesthesia early in 1847.

[14] While Dr. Henry I. Bowditch was active in the introduction of thoracentesis into clinical practice, he invariably gave full credit to Dr. Morrill Wyman for devising the method and first demonstrating its use. Morrill Wyman (1812–1903), brother of Dr. Jeffries Wyman under whom J.C.W. first studied anatomy (Chapter IV), was the second son of Dr. Rufus Wyman (1778–1842). Rufus Wyman in 1818 was appointed physician and superintendent of the Asylum for the Insane in Charlestown, the first department of the newly founded Massachusetts General Hospital to be opened for patients and now known as the McLean Hospital in

The abdominal cavity was practically a terra incognita to the surgeon. The operation for the relief of strangulated hernia was about the only one which he felt justified in attempting.[15] The treatment of penetrating wounds of the abdominal cavity was chiefly medical. Surgical attempts were often made to cure fecal fistula, or artificial anus, but these operations did not involve deep dissection within the interior of the abdomen. Gallstones were accessible to the surgeon only when they became isolated from surrounding organs by the walls of an abscess cavity. Suprapubic cystotomy was a recognized operation although seldom performed. Cutting for stone was done almost exclusively by the perineal route.

Ovariotomy was an operation already advocated by a few adventurous spirits. A tumor of the ovary was one of the few abdominal lesions the nature of which was understood at the time, and the cry for relief by the patient was strong and persistent. But, as I have already shown, orthodox surgery did not yet regard the risk of operative interference as justifiable. Temporary relief was afforded by tapping, and this minor operation was freely resorted to when the accumulation of fluid became sufficiently large to interfere seriously with vital functions.

Waverley. Dr. Morrill Wyman was a house physician at the MGH in 1836 under Drs. James Jackson and Jacob Bigelow. He then established himself in the regular practice of medicine and surgery in Cambridge.

In 1850 Morrill Wyman devised a fine trocar and cannula fitted to an exhausting syringe and in February of that year used it to aspirate twenty ounces of an effusion from the chest of a patient. Six weeks later he was invited by Dr. Bowditch to puncture the thorax of a house painter in Woburn and on doing so evacuated nine ounces of pure pus. The patient recovered and a case report was published by Dr. Bowditch in the *American Journal of the Medical Sciences* for April 1852.

Henry Ingersoll Bowditch (1808–1892) was the third son of Nathaniel Bowditch, the famed mathematician, navigator, and actuary of the Massachusetts Hospital Life Insurance Company. Henry's brother Nathaniel Ingersoll Bowditch was a trustee of the Hospital and author of the first *History of the Massachusetts General Hospital* (1851). Dr. Bowditch, together with James Jackson, Jr., Oliver Wendell Holmes, and J. Mason Warren, had walked the wards at La Pitié with Louis. Although he had a keen interest in surgical pursuits, operative surgery was not undertaken partly because of an ankylosed finger. He focused attention professionally on diseases of the lungs and heart. The surgical instincts of Dr. Bowditch, however, crop out repeatedly in his contributions and writings, somewhat in contrast to the conservative and pedantic approach of so many of the physicians of the period. Thoracentesis has been referred to; another example is his intense interest in diaphragmatic hernia, a subject on which he published a treatise in 1853. "Finally, as a last resource," he wrote, "might not a cutting operation be attempted?"

Henry Pickering Bowditch (1840–1911), whom J.C.W. joined in Paris in the autumn of 1868 and who figures so prominently in the final chapters of these Reminiscences, was a nephew of Henry I. Bowditch.

[15] The first American surgeon to perform an operation for strangulated hernia (1807) was John C. Warren, who had been a pupil of Astley Cooper.

It should be remembered that my story is now approaching the end of that era of surgery which began with the advent of anesthesia and lasted until the dawn of antiseptic surgery. The number of operations performed was constantly on the increase during this period. Surgeons were becoming more skilful technicians, and many new operations had been devised and introduced because patients were more ready to accept operative interference than they were before the days of anesthesia. So far as the actual technique of a surgical operation was concerned, there had been a notable improvement, and attempts were made to introduce more conservative methods, for example, the substitution of resection of a joint in cases where amputation would previously have been the only recourse. Operative interference became much more prompt in cancer, and operations upon the bone both for osteomyelitis and for tuberculosis were designed to save the joint or even portions of the bone itself. But further progress by those who had a strong conviction of the advantages of conservative surgery was still thwarted by the dangers of sepsis and by the apparent impossibility of obtaining healing by first intention. Surgery as an art was trying to forge ahead but surgery as a science was lagging behind.[16] The "germ theory of disease" was indeed a phrase which was finding its way into the literature, but the revolution which its application to surgery was to bring about had not been dreamed of.

Surgery during these years was in a phase which had certainly not been paralleled at any other time in its history. A good means of

[16] Surgery as a useful or practical art is not unlike building, agriculture, warfare, and other primitive activities of man. As such, it recognizes only the lessons of experience and has little ability to distinguish in advance between a proposal which may prove to be a step backward and a discovery which will lead forward to greater effectiveness. When the risk of doing harm is calculated as minimal, surgery may move ahead by the "try-and-see" method, but this same method can also lead to a retrograde movement under plausible but false beliefs. As a practical art, surgery places little value on concepts or theory, for, as in warfare, "the battle is the pay-off" and every matter must be put to the test before judgment is made. The score for a new surgical opus brings little renown to its composer; the credit passes to the performer who renders it with technical proficiency. The laurels for priority do not decorate the blueprint or design for an operation which has never been carried out, but are reserved for the performer of the first "successful case." This is all as it must be in a practical art.

Anesthesia came as a happenstance of this old try-and-see method of the art. The most casual bystander was instantly convinced that it was "no humbug," and so it won quick and ready acceptance. In a similar manner, other fortuitous happenings have attracted the attention of some clearheaded observer and new skills and devices have been added to the art. When surgery finally accepted the germ theory of disease, the art raised itself from medieval impotence and became in part an applied science. Midway in the twentieth century, surgery as a science is still lagging behind. The doctrines of the practical art are likely to dominate the long apprenticeship to which the young surgeon must subject himself.

understanding its status can be provided by reference to two publications of my father, the senior surgeon of the Hospital. His surgical experience had coincided closely with the period following the introduction of anesthesia. In 1864 he delivered the Annual Address before the Massachusetts Medical Society, the title of which was *Recent Progress in Surgery*. Referring to the healing of wounds, he made this statement:

I remember the time, when after an amputation, or the excision of a breast or a large tumor, it was the universal rule to bring the edges of the cut integuments together nicely with straps, compresses, and a bandage, with the full assurance of finding the wound nearly healed on the removal of the dressings. At the present day, however, such a result is seldom attained in city practice; union by first intention being, for the past twenty years, the rare exception. Occasionally, the margins of the skin seem at first to unite, and promise a speedy cure; but suppuration almost always ensues in the deeper parts, and it soon becomes necessary to give vent to the secretions, either by breaking up the newly formed adhesions, or by making a new opening.

The causes of the change which has taken place here in the processes of repair are found in the impaired hygienic condition of our city, arising out of the great increase, and consequent crowding, of its population; for it is only necessary to travel a few miles into the country to find again the same favorable influences which we formerly enjoyed.

Attention was called to the fact that in Paris at this time no attempt was made to secure healing by first intention, but wounds were packed with dressings so as to keep them open for the escape of the sloughs and debris from the granulating surfaces beneath. In referring to cranial surgery he said: "The great mortality of operations on the skull, performed to elevate depressed bone after accidents, has led, perhaps, to the extreme of conservative practice, which may possibly be modified by future experience." In referring to amputations he gave a list of major amputations performed at the Massachusetts General Hospital from 1822 to 1860, divided into separate periods. Of those performed between 1822 and 1850, there were 173 cases of which 141 recovered and 32 died, giving a percentage of deaths of 18.5. Between 1850 and 1860 there were 207 cases, of which 160 recovered and 47 died, the percentage of deaths being 22.7. The mortality per cent of all 380 amputations performed between 1822 and 1860 was 20.8. These statistics show both the rapid increase of surgery during that period and also the rising of the death rate which seemed inevitable.[17]

Considerable space was given in this address to the excision of

[17] The statistics cited do not include amputations at the hip and shoulder joints. In the decade 1850–1860 at the MGH, there were two hip amputations with one fatality, and 16 shoulder amputations with six fatalities.

joints. My father mentioned that he had performed excision of the knee joint three times with gratifying success. It was a new operation just coming into fashion. He said: "The advantages of excising the head of the humerus and the articular surfaces entering into the elbow-joint are undoubted. The decision in the case of the knee-joint can be hardly yet considered as finally made."

Much interest was taken in plastic surgery at that time, and the address teems with allusions to this field of surgery, including the operations for cleft palate in which my father took especial interest.[18] Of radical cure of hernia, he said: "Within the last twenty years, operations for the radical cure of hernia have attracted considerable attention; and for a disease so extremely common, and so very inconvenient, and in some cases even dangerous, it is remarkable that no safe and effectual operation has yet been discovered for its relief." Injections of stimulating liquids in the neighborhood of the neck of the sac have been practiced, he said, with some success. Mr. John Wood of King's College Hospital, London, had advocated an operation by means of a subcutaneous suture, which was practically the sole operation attempted until the introduction of the modern operation for the radical cure of hernia. Reference to abdominal surgery, as we understand it today, is conspicuous by its absence in this address. Ovariotomy was mentioned and reference was made to a single case in which cure followed tapping, drainage, and the use of iodine injections.

Three years later [1867] the second publication of my father to which reference has been made appeared. This was a book entitled *Surgical Observations, with Cases and Operations.* From an historical point of view its table of contents provides a list of the operations which were being performed at that period. The chapter entitled "The Abdomen" contains, in addition to a reference to hernia, a subheading on "Iliac Tumor" under which a number of cases are described which we would regard now as cases of chronic appendicitis. In the chapter on "Miscellaneous Cases" I find reference to a case of gangrene of the appendix vermiformis, but there is no suggestion of operative interference. A number of cases of penetrating wounds of the chest and abdomen are recorded but in none of these cases did there appear to be any serious internal complications calling for a deep exploration. Under "Anaesthetics" there is reference to "Local Anaesthesia." This was employed by my father at the Hospital in 1852, the anesthetic agent being a freezing mixture of pounded

[18] Dr. J. Mason Warren performed what appears to have been the first successful free transplantation of human skin. His account of this operation may be found in *Boston Med. and Surg. J.* 22, 261 (June 3, 1840).

ice and salt. "Lately," he wrote, "a much more convenient method of effecting complete local insensibility has been demonstrated by Dr. Richardson, of London, by the invention of an apparatus for the rapid evaporation of ether, applied to the diseased part. This has been improved on by Dr. H. J. Bigelow, by substituting an agent which he has named rhigolene, which produces a much more rapid reduction of temperature than any other substance hitherto employed." Local anesthesia was limited, however, to brief operations such as the incision of a felon, the evulsion of a nail, or the puncture of an abscess.

Thus surgery went on. Pioneers were held back by what seemed insurmountable obstacles at the time, and in an appraisal of the work they accomplished one should not fail to keep in mind the responsibility they assumed and the limitations with which they had to contend. I sometimes feel that the surgeons of those days were made of sterner stuff than the skilful mechanic of our time, whose work has all been cut out for him.[19] Surely those who did not have nerves of steel must have suffered to a degree that those who practice surgery at the present time would find hard to comprehend.

[19] Perhaps it would be more precise to say that the old-time surgeons had a *conviction* that what they were doing was essential and important. See note 1, Chapter XIII.

ᘒ VIII

Surgical Observations
in London

The winter term of 1865–66 closed my course of studies at the Medical School. Regular examinations were held on the first days of March and July, but my hospital term of service did not end until the first of May, and, because I was anxious not to delay my departure for Europe until July, I was given a private examination. The method of examining for the degree of M.D. was of a very primitive character in 1866. The graduating class assembled in a room adjacent to the anatomical museum, where the members of the Faculty awaited them. Each professor occupied a small alcove by himself. There were six subjects in which examinations were held, and therefore six students were admitted at one time to go the rounds of the professors, each interview lasting but five minutes. There were no written examinations, and this half-hour test covered the entire medical course. If the student was successful in passing the majority of these examinations, he was given his degree. In my special examination I was examined on surgery by Dr. Hodges, and as he was a very busy man the only time he could give me was during a trip in his buggy.

I also took precaution to present myself as a candidate for membership in the Massachusetts Medical Society, because a long stay in the medical schools of Europe would otherwise prevent my joining it perhaps for several years, and my standing from the point of view of seniority in the profession would thus be altered materially.[1] The ordeal of the examination, which was conducted by some of the younger members of the Society, was more severe than anticipated, and I came away with the feeling that I had not made an especially good impression upon the members of the Board. However, both of my examinations were passed successfully, and I sailed for Europe on May 9th, 1866 for a long sojourn.

[1] The statement that the date of admission to membership in the state medical society established seniority and thus possessed prestige value is interesting evidence of the dignity of professional societies of a century ago.

J.C.W. also joined the Boston Medical Association in 1866. This had been organized sixty years earlier for the purpose of promoting a "code of Medical Police," that is, a system of rules of conduct for medical practitioners. Drs. John and John C. Warren were numbered among the original members. J.C.W. served this association first as secretary and later as president.

Medical students in this country, particularly those who had received a college education, were beginning to appreciate the fact that our system of medical education was far below the standard that ought to be maintained by educational institutions. Emerging as I had from four years of undergraduate instruction in the academic department of the University, I found the contrast in the curriculum of the Medical School a most startling one. It was also quite evident that medical education here was distinctly inferior to that offered by institutions in Great Britain and continental Europe. Reports brought home by immediate predecessors showed that the tide of science was turning towards the great centers of the German-speaking countries. Berlin and Vienna had become the two great objective points, and all the members of our set who were able to afford a European education were unanimous in their opinion that these should be given preference over the older centers of London and Paris, to which American medical students had been accustomed to migrate.[2]

My father had given me letters of introduction to many prominent members of the profession in London and on my arrival there in the latter part of May, I had a good opportunity to see them in the full tide of their season's work. Mr. John Erichsen was at the University College Hospital, Mr. Paget (afterwards Sir James Paget) was the leading light at St. Bartholomew's, and Sir William Fergusson was the senior surgeon at King's College Hospital, occupying perhaps as conspicuous a position at that particular period as any of the London surgeons. Mr. Paget had already published his lectures on surgical pathology, his reputation was fully made, and he was in the height of that professional practice which was to turn his attention away from the scientific part of surgery which had been a consuming interest during his early years.[3]

[2] In the German-speaking countries patients flocked to the large governmental hospitals staffed by university faculties. In a department the professor reigned supreme, surrounded by a corps of assistants. The young surgeons advanced more rapidly in operative experience than was the case in London, Paris, and the United States, where opportunities to operate were withheld until late in one's surgical career. As a result, in Germany promising young assistants were called to professorial chairs at an early age. For example, Czerny became professor of surgery in Freiburg at the age of twenty-nine; Kocher and Billroth in Bern and Zürich, respectively, at thirty-one; and Thiersch in Erlangen at thirty-two.

[3] At the time of Henry J. Bigelow's studies in Europe (1841–1844) the practical relations of the new science of microscopic patholgy to surgery were just beginning to attract attention. Mr. James Paget, the rising surgical star in London, was assembling what was to be the Pathological Catalogue of the Royal College of Surgeons. On May 30, 1843 Paget was appointed to the lectureship in physiology at St. Bartholomew's and in August accepted the post of warden of the new Hospital College. From 1843 to 1851 Paget lectured on general anatomy and physiology, turning to the subject of morbid anatomy on Saturdays. Presumably it was to attend the Saturday lecture that Bigelow made

Calling upon Mr. Paget one day about noon, and waiting until he had finished his morning consultations, I was invited to drive in his coupé to St. Bartholomew's, which was in a part of London quite distant from the residential quarter. I find it recorded in my diary that during this hospital visit I saw many resections of the knee joint which were turning out very satisfactorily; the healing of the soft parts was going on rapidly and union of the bones was taking place. The results seemed distinctly better than those I had seen at home. I also find that I recorded the fact that hospital gangrene was said to be very rare in St. Bartholomew's.

At the University College Hospital I saw Mr. Erichsen perform Pirogoff's amputation for a diseased ankle. I also watched Mr. Thompson (afterwards Sir Henry Thompson), who shortly before had operated by lithotomy on Leopold the King of the Belgians, perform a similar operation and also a crushing for stone.[4] When I returned to London two years later I had an opportunity to see more of Sir Henry, and I vividly recall a morning's round with him in his private carriage. His only instrument was a lithotrite which he kept up the sleeve of his coat. His patients were scattered about in certain regions of London, usually occupying ground floor rooms in small boarding houses. The carriage would arrive at the door, a ring at the bell would be promptly answered, and we would be ushered into a back room where a patient would be lying in the middle of a four-posted bedstead. I would be introduced hurriedly as a visiting foreigner, and while the introduction was going on the lithotrite would flash from

---

his weekly journey from Paris to London, and it is said that Bigelow derived some of his skill and effectiveness as a lecturer from the example of Paget. In 1847 Paget was appointed professor of anatomy and surgery to the College of Surgeons and held this position until 1852. His famous Lectures on Surgical Pathology, prepared and delivered during this period, were published in 1853.

[4] J.C.W.'s memory seems to have failed him with respect to the nature of the operation performed on the King of the Belgians. Leopold had been the patient of Civiale (note 2, Chapter I) and of Langenbeck (Chapter XI), neither of whom had been successful. On June 6, 1862 at 9 o'clock in the morning Thompson crushed a bladder stone, using a brand new lithotrite. The story is told in a colorful style in chapter V of *The Versatile Victorian*, a biography of Sir Henry Thompson, Bt. by Zachary Cope (London: Harvey and Blythe, 1951).

In 1872 Thompson carried out a stone-crushing operation on the exiled Emperor Napoleon III at Chislehurst, England. The calculus was the size of a date and had caused exquisite suffering for several years. The Emperor was in poor health, however, and died not long after the procedure. Autopsy showed advanced pyelonephritis (*ibid.*, chap. VII).

Sir Henry's life span (1820–1904) coincided closely with that of Queen Victoria. He was a capable artist and exhibited at the Royal Academy and the Paris Salon. He also wrote novels. Despite the fact that the public expects nothing but surgery from a surgeon, he escaped being stamped as a dilettante, and carried on a large practice at the top of the clinical ladder.

beneath his coat sleeve and be inserted rapidly into the bladder. The stone would be seized and crushed two or three times, the instrument withdrawn, and the whole performance occupy hardly more than five minutes' time. I saw several of these operations during the morning.

It was Sir Henry's principle at that time to do so little at each sitting as to inflict as slight trauma as possible upon the bladder walls. Clover's syringe, I think, had already come into use but I do not recall that Sir Henry employed it in any of these cases. His method was to perform if need be as many as thirty or forty crushings in each case, doing the least possible amount at any one sitting. He was working along these lines when Dr. Henry J. Bigelow first planned his operation of litholapaxy. Sir Henry reminded me of Dr. Bigelow in many ways. He was a picturesque and interesting character, entertained in a most scientific and agreeable way, and had ideas about special diet not only for his patients but for his guests. He was always a conspicuous figure in the lecture room or operating theatre, and his clinics were largely attended, he being regarded as the leading exponent of diseases of the urinary organs.

Another surgical worthy whom I find mentioned in my diary at this time was Mr. Timothy Holmes of St. George's Hospital, the editor of *Holmes' System of Surgery* in six volumes.[5] This work was a standard surgical authority of that day and remained so for a much longer period than works of a similar character survive at the present time. It was a period of much less rapid change, and the work became widely known in both England and the United States and sustained a high reputation for several decades. I saw Mr. Holmes operate for cleft palate but was not so favorably impressed with his skill as an operator as I had been with his reputation as an author.

I had a letter to Mr. Francis Sibson, a prominent medical practitioner who had made a name for himself on the heart and medical anatomy, but my stay in London at this time had to be a very brief one. I shall have more to say of my sojourn there following my return two years later.

[5] The first edition of the famous and long-lived treatise edited by Timothy Holmes appeared in four volumes between 1860 and 1864; the American edition published by Wood between 1869 and 1871 had six volumes. The *System* brought together the experience of many men, most of them hospital surgeons of London. The excellence of the writing as well as the orthodoxy of the opinions put forth justified the reputation the work attained. As an example of its merit, Sir Geoffrey Jefferson recently said that the chapter on injuries of the head, written by Prescott Hewett, "scarcely has been bettered to the present day."

❧ IX

Dresden and
the Six Weeks' War

The unsettled state of political affairs on the Continent at this time necessitated my early departure from London because the war between Prussia and Austria was on the eve of breaking out. As I had decided to spend the summer in Dresden in order to obtain a knowledge of the German language, I felt it wise to lose no time in reaching this destination. Leaving London on June 5th [1866] and passing through Cologne and Frankfurt, I arrived in Dresden, the capital of Saxony, on the 12th. This was none too soon, for in a few days I found myself isolated from the rest of the world, my travelling companions having deserted me and the bridges over which they had retired having been blown up. The Saxon army was on the move and troops were daily passing through the city on their way to join the Austrians. On this occasion the smaller German kingdoms, such as Hanover, Saxony, and Bavaria, were arrayed against Prussia. Dresden was soon caught between the two contending armies. Taking the advice of the American consul, I remained in the city, although all American and English residents and tourists had disappeared. This seemed in one respect a desirable feature of the situation, for it relieved me of all temptation to indulge in my native tongue. Comfortably established in lodgings and having secured the services of a German teacher, I awaited events. These were not long in coming to pass.

On crossing the Schloss Platz one morning I heard the sound of a bugle. A squadron of Black Hussars appeared and quickly occupied the bridge over the Elbe which had been built by Napoleon. They cleared the way for masses of Prussian troops to come pouring into the square, where they formed a sea of spiked helmets. With the Old World setting, the illusion of *coup de théâtre* was complete. The city soon was occupied by the entire right wing of the Prussian army, moving southward, but the occupation was of a peaceful character and during the next few days Dresden assumed the appearance of a center of active mobilization rather than a captured capital. The tide of war swept on, however, and the city was once more apparently deserted.

The King of Saxony on leaving Dresden had left orders that everything should go on as usual and that even the performances at the
court theatre were to continue. This promised me a much desired opportunity to pursue my study of the German language, and as the
repertoire was both varied and of the highest quality I looked forward
to a nightly attendance. On the first night, to my astonishment, I
found myself almost the sole occupant of the spacious auditorium.
Two light pieces were given and the royal company did its best to
entertain the single occupant of the parquet. But my knowledge of
the language was slight and my ear untuned to the Teutonic rhythm,
and so the efforts of the actors did not appear to meet with a sufficiently sympathetic response. After three nights of valiant endeavor
the effort to keep the theatre open was abandoned.

Although it was only a six weeks' war, the summer which followed
seemed a long and dreary one and it was not until the victorious
Prussian army returned that Dresden seemed to come to life again.[1]
Although the good city was still in the possession of the conquerors,
the situation was accepted philosophically. The superb Dresden gallery was reopened, after having been closed and placed under the
protection of the British Embassy. The court theatre resumed work
and gave of its best. The operatic performances furnished a brilliant
spectacle, the house being always packed with officers in uniforms of
every hue.

An amusing episode seems worth mentioning as an illustration of
the social etiquette of the time and place. A classmate, availing himself of the opportunity to make a week-end visit from Leipzig to
Dresden, invited me to dine with him at one of the fashionable hotels
on a Sunday. On entering the spacious dining hall we found only one
table at the far end, already partially occupied by a group of officers
(evidently of high rank) and their wives. We took our places at the
lower end of this table after a polite salutation from mine host, who
in German fashion presided at his own table d'hôte, and conducted
ourselves with the modest reserve appropriate to youthful strangers.
Dinner over, we decided to beat a quiet retreat. As we walked with
caution over the parquet floor and had nearly reached the distant
doors, a loud scraping of chairs warned that we might not be playing

[1] Mr. Alexander Bruce, F.R.C.S., writing in *Lancet*, Aug. 25, 1866, saw Dresden
from a different point of view. He reached this city on July 16, thirteen days after
the battle of Königgrätz or Sadowa. He worked as a volunteer in the overcrowded
military hospitals of Dresden and did many autopsies on fatal cases of pyemia,
which he called "the scourge of the hospital." Wounds were irrigated from a tin
vessel with an attached india-rubber tube ending in a bone nozzle. Sponges "were
frequently carried from patient to patient, necessarily often loaded with the very
poison of pyaemia."

our part in a manner suitable to the occasion. I murmured to my friend, and we both turned briskly around to find every officer standing at attention by his chair and all eyes turned on us. Fortunately, a long course of instruction from a prince of dancing masters [2] had prepared us to then make good our departure in a manner worthy of the occasion.

[2] The "prince of dancing masters" was Count Lorenzo Papanti, formerly an officer in the royal guard of the Duke of Tuscany. A political quarrel forced him to flee Italy, and the sympathetic crew of "Old Ironsides" is said to have brought him to Boston. After playing for some time as a violinist in theater orchestras, he ventured to start a dancing academy in 1827. At first he encountered difficulties, for dancing was not considered proper in Boston, but when the widow Mrs. Harrison Gray Otis became his first pupil of rank, the academy became a focal point for proper Bostonians. The ballroom subsequently opened at No. 23 Tremont Street was resplendent with French mirrors fitted in between high windows, a prismatic chandelier of crystals imported from Paris, and the first "spring floor" built in America. Lucius Beebe in *Boston and the Boston Legend* (New York, © 1936, Appleton-Century-Crofts) says: "All good Boston children went to Papanti's, where his lean figure, glossy wig and elegant patent leather dancing pumps, and above all his pointed fiddle-bow, used both as an instrument of correction and harmony, struck terror to all juvenile hearts."

Vienna in
Its Medical Heyday

The war was now over and the way open to Vienna, and so I took advantage of the company of some travelling companions passing through Dresden to make my escape from that city. I shall never forget the intense relief of being able to converse again in my native language. Having been obliged to speak German or keep silence during the past two months, I seemed almost to have lost the use of my tongue. After a trip through the Austrian Tyrol, I arrived in Vienna toward the end of September [1866] and established myself in an apartment near that great hospital, the Allgemeines Krankenhaus.

Vienna was changing from an old walled town into a modern capital. The *Stadt,* or the city, formed the center around which was the *Glacis,* the open space, which had existed in front of the walls. Beyond this was the *Vorstadt,* or the suburbs. The open space which thus encircled the center of the city at the time was being converted into boulevards lined with ornate public and residential buildings. Vienna owes much of its reputation as a beautiful city to the well-directed efforts of that day.

The renowned Allgemeines Krankenhaus, dating from 1784, consisted architecturally of a group of low, two-story buildings which covered a space of some twenty acres and formed a series of courtyards. The wards were barracklike in their simplicity. A plain wooden bed occupied each space between windows. The mattresses were large bags of ticking filled with straw and, uninviting as this may seem, it had the merit of permitting frequent change of the filling, and thus was more conducive to cleanliness than it appeared. The hospital contained accommodations for between two and three thousand patients, who represented the lower social strata and came from all quarters of Austria. This mass of suffering humanity constituted "material," to use the expression of the teachers of that day, and offered unexampled opportunities for study. In a letter written just a decade earlier by Dr. Henry K. Oliver,[1] a detailed account is given

[1] Dr. Henry K. Oliver, one of the visiting physicians of the Hospital, introduced laryngology as a special subject into the Harvard Medical School in 1866. The first mirrors for viewing the larynx were made of highly polished steel, and these Dr.

of the clinical opportunities in Vienna, and judging from his description there seems to have been little change in the conditions as I observed them. The popularity of Vienna as a center for medical education seems to have been due both to this vast material which was at the disposal of the student and to the development of the special branches of medicine by groups of men who may be regarded as the pioneers of specialization.

I found upon my arrival that the school term would not begin for several weeks. This was a year in which cholera visited many cities in Europe, and it was at that time in Vienna in active epidemic form. Cholera was no great novelty to me, however, and indeed created but little excitement in general. An occasional epidemic of cholera or smallpox was still looked upon as a more or less necessary evil. I had passed through quite a severe epidemic of cholera in London about ten years before. During the Vienna epidemic there were said to be about one hundred new cases daily. A large section of the hospital containing several wards was set apart for patients with cholera, and at the suggestion of my classmate Dr. Francis B. Greenough that here was an opportunity which might never present itself again (I am thankful to say he was entirely right), we obtained an introduction to the surgeon in charge, Dr. Rose. We were invited to make the daily morning visits with him. This gave us an interesting occupation for several weeks until the coming of cold weather caused the epidemic to disappear. Although little could be done in the way of treatment, much was accomplished for the care and comfort of the patients. The impression left upon my mind was quite different from what one would suppose a cholera ward would make. Nothing could have been quieter and neater, and the casual visitor might have passed down the aisles between the beds without an intimation that the occupants were suffering from so fatal a disease. That cholera was in some way due to a germ was, I think, already the accepted opinion here, for I recall Dr. Rose's frequent reference to *Pilze*.[2] I find in my notes that

---

Oliver had brought from Paris. A large collection of instruments illustrating the development of techniques in laryngology was assembled by Dr. Oliver and presented to the Hooper Memorial Room, where they are still exhibited. It is said that Dr. Oliver had such enthusiasm for the developing specialty that he had all of his students in turn examine his larynx with a large lozenge-shaped mirror. [Harris Peyton Mosher, "The Teaching of Laryngology in the Harvard Medical School," *Laryngoscope 16*, 883 (1906).]

[2] An informative contemporary appraisal of the relation of microscopic fungi (*Pilze*) to cholera was provided by an editorial in the *Lancet* of August 31, 1867. Nearly twenty years earlier it had been suggested that vegetations found in cholera evacuations were the cause of the disease, and the term "cholera-fungus" had been in circulation. At the time J.C.W. was in Vienna, excitement was stirred up by the observations of Ernst Hallier of Jena. Working at Berlin and Eberfeld,

camphor and sulphuric ether were used in the form of injections when asphyxia occurred. Not only was I in close contact with the disease during the days, but my nights were passed in lodgings where the main stairway communicated directly with the sewer. After the janitor had closed the door, the odor of sewage was overpowering; and yet the principles of modern sanitation show that one can easily experience such conditions without contracting contagion. The epidemic began to wane soon after the first of October, and I found plenty of other work to do.

The list of special courses offered to graduate students was a novel and attractive feature, and was the magnet which was beginning to draw so many students from Paris to Vienna. My education thus far having been very largely surgical, it seemed important that I should take advantage of the unusual facilities to pursue internal medicine. At the head of this department of the school were the two distinguished exponents of clinical medicine, Skoda and Oppolzer. Vienna was also famous at that time for another medical light of the first order, Hebra, the head of the department of dermatology.

The opportunities for the study of midwifery were probably unequalled elsewhere in the world. The large amount of space given to the obstetrical wards furnished accommodations for patients who flocked to the hospital from all parts of Austria. Social conditions were such that the peasants who availed themselves of this opportunity had no provision for proper care in their own homes. Furthermore, marriage license laws were strict, with the result that illegitimacy was common. From these and other causes the clinic was always crowded with expectant mothers who sought the protection of the government in their hour of need. The clinic was divided into two distinct portions, one for the education of nurses and the other to furnish clinical opportunities to medical students. An entire ward was set apart for patients in the active stage of labor and contained, as I remember it, about fifty beds. There were on an average throughout the year about twenty-five deliveries daily, a number which afforded an opportunity for one to become familiar with all the complications of labor as a

---

Hallier claimed to have isolated and cultivated filaments and cystlike bodies which he believed represented the "cholera-contagium," the active agent in the evolution of the disease.

At that time the word "germ" was used in the broad and original sense of a bud or seed, rather than with reference to a disease-producing bacterium or microbe. While the association of minute organisms with certain diseases had already been recognized, it was still held by some that a disease might begin from nothing, and that any associated organisms would arise by spontaneous generation. Pasteur early described particulate matter carried by the air as "dusts"; these included "flakes of mouldiness," or the *Pilze* of Dr. Rose.

Praktikant. I was permitted to go on duty at stated periods for twenty-four hours and personally care for my share of the patients who came into the ward. This work I continued during the autumn semester and thus was able to acquire a practical knowledge of a subject which could be obtained at but few places in the world. During the time that a student was on service, which usually covered a period of one or two months, almost every complication that one would meet with in a lifetime would have presented itself. In all my experience I can look back upon no other clinic which afforded such unparalleled opportunity as was furnished by these wards. At the head of this department was Professor Carl Braun, whom I saw perform the Caesarian section with great skill. This was an operation almost unheard of elsewhere.

Professor Ferdinand von Hebra's course in dermatology was a feature of the curriculum. Here was an opportunity for the American student to see for the first time a large variety of diseases of the skin. The clinic was held in a small amphitheatre in which the audience literally surrounded the professor and his patient, so that the class, which was not a large one, could have the opportunity of seeing distinctly the peculiarities of the skin lesion which each patient presented.[3] Hebra was a short and heavily built man, with large head and genial, humorous countenance. A beautiful series of plates had given him an international reputation and his course brought fame to the Vienna School. Hebra was in fact the pioneer in modern dermatology. As a lecturer his style was quite informal and was flavored with much wit and humor, which made the clinic hour pass rapidly. He also had the gift of conveying sound instruction and inculcating many truths which remained permanently fixed in the memory of his hearers.

Of the courses on clinical medicine, I selected that of Oppolzer rather than that of Skoda. As I look back upon him, Johannes von Oppolzer presents himself to my memory as a type seen in the engravings of the teachers of medicine during the early part of the

---

[3] In a letter to the dean of the Medical School dated 24 February, 1916, Dr. Charles J. White referred to the Upper Out-Patient Amphitheatre of the MGH as one "which my father [Dr. James C. White] designed so perfectly for the needs of teaching dermatology . . . If this room is destroyed [to make room for another project] my ability to demonstrate patients properly to a large class of students is gone."

In 1856 James C. White was introduced to dermatology as a special field of medicine in Vienna and later brought back this concept to the United States. In 1900 he served on the MGH staff committee which planned the new building for out-patients and so had opportunity to design this pleasant and commodious amphitheater, in which patients may walk in front of each tier of benches so that their skin can be closely examined by the students.

century. His figure was tall and slender; his head and features were of the Jewish cast; his black hair was long and smoothly plastered down, hanging in a smooth straight fold on each side and covering the ears. His complexion was pale and his hands were lean. His dress was of the conventional broadcloth of the period; he wore no collar but his neck was encased in what was probably one of the last examples of the black silk stock. The striking feature of the man was a pair of dark and piercing eyes. These made one forget the quaint and antique costume. Combined with the genial expression of his face, the eyes held the student in a sympathetic frame of mind while the teacher himself wandered through the intricacies of a complicated case problem. Oppolzer's lectures were all at the bedside, and although the size of the class was large enough to make it difficult to get near him, I remember no medical visits which I look back upon with more pleasure and profit than those of this very able and celebrated clinician.[4]

In planning to devote the academic year 1866–67 to medical rather than surgical instruction, I had scanned with much interest the program of the medical department of the university for the winter semester. This contained a list of something like eighty different courses in all the specialties of medicine, and I felt that here indeed was an opportunity to acquire information on subjects in which but few opportunities for study were offered in the United States. One of the new specialties of that day was laryngology, given by Schroetter, a teacher who endeared himself to many generations of pupils by his enthusiastic and painstaking instruction.[5] Courses were given on the eye by Carl Ferdinand von Arlt and by Jaeger, on the urine by Johann

[4] Dr. James C. White saw Oppolzer in the winter of 1856–57. He wrote in his *Sketches from My Life* (Cambridge, 1914):

> I cannot give my first impression of him. It was, perhaps, that his pictures belie him, that he had made a very hasty toilette, had forgotten his collar, and had not made the same use of the Danube as we do of the Cochituate . . . We may pardon the want of neatness, when we consider the low rank in social life to which the scientific men of Austria are condemned.

[5] Dr. John Brooks Wheeler, a graduate of the Harvard Medical School, and a house pupil at the MGH in 1878–79, was for many years professor of surgery in the College of Medicine, University of Vermont. He reached Vienna in 1879 for postgraduate studies and gives this account of Schroetter's clinic:

> The most remarkable feature of this clinic was an old woman, Frau Gely, between seventy and eighty years of age, with only one eye. What became of the other, I never knew, but she always wore a big black patch over the socket. Schroetter hired her to come to his clinic and let students examine her throat. She knew the anatomy of the throat perfectly and could tell you exactly the locality that you touched with your probe and give the correct anatomical name for it, left arytenoid cartilage, epiglottis, posterior pharyngeal pillar, uvula, etc. She had on the tip of her tongue the names of all the

F. Heller, and on venereal diseases by Sigmund and by Hermann von Zeissl. Sigmund was an ambitious and popular teacher and a man of striking personality. He was somewhat of the same old-fashioned type as Oppolzer and, as I remember him, bore some faint resemblance to Disraeli. A large number of beds in the hospital were placed at his disposal for the treatment of syphilis, and his clinic gave ample illustrations for the study of its protean manifestations. Abundant opportunities were offered to the students for the daily study of the patients. It might here be remarked that either from temperament or lack of education, or from the survival of an old tradition, the patients accepted as a matter of course their role as part of the great mass of "material."

In a great hospital like the Allgemeines Krankenhaus there were not only the varied classes of cases which I have already referred to but also many forms of contagious diseases in which there was naturally a high rate of mortality. Cases of smallpox were interlarded with cases of pneumonia and typhoid fever for the better instruction of the class. No difficulty surrounded the obtaining of postmortem examinations, such as prevailed in our own country at that time. The amount of pathological "material" was therefore enormous and fresh specimens of every sort of disease from every region of the body were served up daily for inspection by the class. Carl Rokitansky, the great teacher of pathology in his day, was then an old man about to retire from active work. The morning pathological demonstrations were conducted by Scheithauer, who, although of no great scientific attainments, was able to impress important truths upon the memory by a facile flow of language. These were the main courses to which I gave my attention during the first year in Vienna, because they seemed to supplement and round out those subjects in which I had received little or no instruction at home.

These activities gave me but little chance to indulge in the social life of the capital, although an unusually favorable opportunity existed in the presence of the American Minister to Austria, Mr. John Lothrop Motley, and his family.[6] My father was a contemporary of Motley

---

structures that were at the root of it, and years of practice had given her such perfect control of her reflexes that I never saw her gag or wince even under the manipulations of the clumsiest bungler. Much could be learned from her of the superficial anatomy of the pharynx and larynx and of the way of handling the throat mirror. As in the case of a professional singer, her throat was her fortune . . . many of the students paid her for coming to their rooms and letting them practice on her. I think she supported herself entirely in this way. [*Memoirs of a Small-Town Surgeon* (New York: Lippincott, 1935), p. 134.]

6 John Lothrop Motley, historian, statesman, and patriot, was appointed minister to Austria by President Lincoln in 1861. He remained at this post during the Civil War, only to become the victim of an incident which is not without parallel

and the two families were on more or less intimate terms of acquaintance. Society in Vienna was rigidly stratified. The top class comprised the old nobility, which formed a more exclusive set than was to be found in any other capital in Europe. At the same time there was a greater simplicity and social freedom among the young people of that set than existed in similar circles of London and Paris. This could be attributed of course to the intimacy engendered by a small and somewhat isolated court. I was on terms of intimacy with the younger members of the Motley family who had taken part in social life in Boston, and was well trained in the terpsichorean art, then in a state of high cultivation in that city, and consequently it would have been natural to assume that I was available as a single young man for the social functions in which the diplomatic families took part. Under existing rules of etiquette this could only have been accomplished by appointing me a member of the legation staff. Such an opportunity was courteously offered to me by Mr. Motley but, while expressing my thanks, I replied that this was not what I had come to Vienna for and that my time was too much taken up to afford opportunity for the enjoyment of much social relaxation. Despite my reply, I think Mr. and Mrs. Motley appreciated greatly the presence of their young fellow townsman, and the hospitalities of the legation were freely extended. The Vienna court had the reputation of being the most aristocratic in Europe and its society was correspondingly inaccessible. The result was that Viennese nobility came into little

---

in present-day public life. A letter bearing a false signature was addressed to President Andrew Johnson in 1866. This letter was filled with accusations directed against various public agents, ministers, and consuls, and in particular singled out Mr. Motley for abuse. At the President's request, Mr. Seward, the Secretary of State, addressed questions suggested in the letter to Mr. Motley who, considering that his loyalty and honor were being questioned, promptly resigned. Motley did not hesitate to say that he held opinions with reference to Reconstruction and other domestic issues. "These opinions," he wrote, "in the privacy of my own household, and to occasional American visitors, I have not concealed . . . A minister of the United States does not cease to be a citizen of the United States, as deeply interested as others in all that relates to the welfare of his country." The resignation was accepted in a curt letter dated April 18, 1867. In June 1868 Mr. Motley returned with his family to Boston and became established at No. 2 Park Street in the absence of the Warrens. The incident provoked great indignation among his Boston contemporaries. Dr. Oliver Wendell Holmes gave vent to his feelings in words that ring true in all times of national tensions:

> Among the "occasional American visitors" spoken of above must have been some of those self-appointed or hired agents called "interviewers," who do for the American public what the Venetian spies did for the Council of of Ten, what the familiars of the Inquisition did for the priesthood, who invade every public man's privacy, who listen at every key-hole, who tamper with every guardian of secrets; purveyors to the insatiable appetite of a public which must have a slain reputation to devour with its breakfast, as the monster of antiquity called regularly for his tribute of a spotless virgin. [*John Lothrop Motley* (Autocrat edition; Boston, 1906), p. 426.]

contact with the outer world, and Motley once remarked that during his residence there no intimation was ever made which implied knowledge of his being an author.

Mrs. Motley was a charming hostess.[7] She had a keen interest in the politics of the day, and because her husband had enjoyed a lifelong intimacy with Otto von Bismarck, they having been fellow students at Göttingen,[8] her arguments were often strengthened by quotations from a source which quite naturally I never dared to challenge.

Mr. Motley's relations with my father were such that I was treated with a certain paternal feeling, and his attitude toward me was quite different from that which he presented to the world at large. I found him a most interesting person and one who has remained clearly defined in my memory; his tall and refined figure, easy graceful bearing, and manly beauty were characteristics which have lost none of their vividness with the lapse of time. His was an amiable disposition, full of life and animation and interest for every one about him. He seemed to take a personal interest in our doings and was keenly anxious to do all he could for young men in spite of being greatly hampered by local conditions. It is a pleasure to recall this picture of as distinguished and attractive a representative of the United States as ever graced a European court. He was an example of the type of manhood of which patriotic Americans may justly be proud.

Two of his children, Miss Mary and Miss Susan Motley, were members of the family circle at that time; another daughter, Mrs. Ives (afterwards Lady Harcourt), was then living in this country with relatives of her first husband.[9] Mary (afterwards Mrs. Sheridan) had been my partner in many a dance at home and was then a member of the social set in Vienna. She and her younger sister Susan (afterwards Mrs. Mildmay) were both very bright, and intellectually of the calibre expected in daughters of such parents. The conversation at the family table was always lively and interesting, and it required the full use of my mental capabilities to feel satisfied with the part I had played. The embassy was an old palatial residence situated pleasantly in one of the municipal suburbs. In the rear was a charming garden, easily accessible through the long French windows of Mr.

[7] Mrs. Motley was the former Miss Mary Benjamin of No. 14 Temple Place, Boston.

[8] Oliver Wendell Holmes, when preparing a biographical sketch of Motley in 1878, addressed a letter to Prince Bismarck hoping to learn more of this association. Bismarck's reply described their intimacy both at Göttingen in 1832 and at Berlin in 1833, where they were fellow lodgers. (*John Lothrop Motley*, p. 342.)

[9] When Mr. Ives was twelve years old, he was the first child to undergo surgery under ether. The operation was performed on December 15, 1846 by Dr. J. Mason Warren.

Motley's library, the entire setting being appropriate to this author, diplomat, and patriotic American.

The winter semester ended the last of February, and I took advantage of a recess of two months before the spring term to take a trip to Italy. On February 25th [1867], in company with my Medical School classmate Dr. Arthur H. Nichols and my Harvard College classmate Capt. Nathan Appleton, I started out for Venice. Our visit was well timed, for this was the first opportunity of the Venetians to celebrate their freedom from the Austrian yoke and it so happened that we arrived in Venice during the carnival period. In spite of cold and somewhat disagreeable weather we attended a masked ball in the Piazza san Marco and a carnival procession the next day on the Grand Canal led by Prince Amodeo and his suite. This was followed by an illumination in the evening. The "Carnival of Venice" was a well-known piece of music in those days. We were delighted for this chance to see and take part in the celebration.

Unfortunately we missed a reception for Garibaldi by Americans on the day before our arrival in Venice, and so were very much pleased to learn at Padua that he was in this town. With Capt. Appleton as a guide we obtained an interview without difficulty. On receipt of our cards, all those who were waiting in the anterooms were thrust aside and we were immediately introduced. I find the following memorandum in my diary: "A very striking picturesque figure with his smoking cap and a long cloak over his red jacket, his hair and beard lighter than I had supposed. A man of very simple manners and conversing quite fluently with us in English." On Appleton's mention of General W. Francis Bartlett, who had been with us in college, Garibaldi informed us that while he was in Boston in 1854 he had been under great obligation to Bartlett's father, who had given him much financial assistance in establishing himself in the tallow chandler business. He seemed genuinely interested to meet two young representatives of the land of his temporary adoption.

Parting company with Capt. Appleton, Nichols and I continued our trip through Florence, Rome, and Naples, thence to Genoa and Milan. At Rome the season was at its height. The French army was still in occupation of the city, and Pius IX had not yet become the prisoner of the Vatican. There was a large American contingent in Rome, including many Bostonians. The sculptor William W. Story was then at the height of his popularity and fame, and his daughter Miss Story figured in many of the pleasant gatherings and exercises.[10] Mr. Hiram

[10] J.C.W.'s sisters also visited the Storys the following winter (1868), but Rosamond was not impressed. "Nellie and I," she wrote in her *Recollections of My Life for My Children* (Boston: privately printed, 1939), "went one evening to one of the Sunday evening receptions at the William Storys . . . but as Mrs. Story introduced us to no one, we had a horrid time, refusing ever to go again."

Powers, perhaps best known for his statue of the "Greek Slave," had a studio in Florence, and at the time of our visit gave us an account of receiving an order for a statue of America to be placed on top of the Capitol dome in Washington, President Pierce in the meantime giving a second commission to Thomas Crawford, whose statue is now there. Powers' statue was finished but burned in a bonded warehouse in New York.

In Milan we visited an old hospital [11] capable of containing three thousand patients, but at that time there were only sixteen hundred. The wards were high-ceilinged and well ventilated. My notes state that pellagra was a frequent diagnosis. Passing through Verona and the Brenner Pass to Innsbruck, we made our way back to Vienna, arriving on April 21st, Easter Sunday. By this time the spring term was already in full operation at the hospital, but as the day after Easter was a holiday Vienna was given up to festivities. There was a steeple-chase with gentlemen riders in the Prater, the great Viennese park. My notes state that Prince Esterhazy won. It was here that I had the only view of the Empress that I remember during my two winters' stay in Vienna, for although the Emperor was often seen at the opera, on gala occasions, and at parades, the Emperess was never at his side.

The spring semester extended through June and part of July, and in my notes I find recorded courses on diseases of the skin, on laryngology, and also on auscultation and percussion, in accord with my plan to devote myself chiefly to medical rather than surgical studies during this year. Hyrtl's course on topographical anatomy is also mentioned. Josef Hyrtl was a man of commanding presence, of large frame and head, with heavily molded features and deep-set eyes. He occupied a most conspicuous position among the anatomists of his day. His lectures at half past seven on Saturday and Sunday mornings were attended by a large number of students and lasted until nine. One had to come early to get seating space. There were no prepared illustrations of any kind, but his large and mobile hands seemed able to represent almost every part of the body. With a piece of chalk

[11] This was almost certainly the Maggiori Hospital, founded by Duke Francesco Sforza and opened in 1464. This famous hospital is of great interest as a prototype of the philanthropically supported voluntary hospitals founded by wealthy and pious men. The beginning of the voluntary hospital movement is usually traced back to the opening of Guy's Hospital in London, 1728. Sforza, however, founded the Maggiori Hospital 'as an act of acknowledgment to Almighty God for innumerable benefits received by him during the whole of his life, to be devoted to the relief of the poor and sick forever." The hospital was managed by twenty-four citizens of Milan, known as the Chapter. With the concentration of wealth in the hands of the few and the overcrowding of Italian cities, the Maggiori was not able to cope with the problems that confronted it. Some help was given by the Holy See, but this proved inadequate. In 1811 the government began to take a hand and ultimately the institution passed into its control.

and the blackboard, and occasionally the assistance of the cadaver, he was able to give a most effective exposition of the subject. His lectures, like his book on topographical anatomy, were interspersed with many humorous anecdotes which served in the case of some striking anatomical peculiarity to impress one with the point he wished to make. Hyrtl was a good deal of a Bohemian and mixed little with the outer world. He was absorbed in the work of his Museum, as attested by the many beautiful anatomical and corrosion specimens which his collection contained.[12] He may be considered as one of the particularly bright stars in the galaxy which made the Vienna of that period famous.

The winter climate of Vienna, although not severe, was trying to those susceptible to bronchial affection. Conditions were so favorable for pulmonary affection that consumption enjoyed the distinction of being known as the "morbus Viennensis." But now spring was well advanced and Vienna was beginning to justify its reputation as the "Paris of Germany." With the month of June at hand, the characteristic open-air life of a continental city began to assert itself. There were many attractive parks in the city and many pleasure resorts in the surrounding country, and on Sundays and holidays these were freely patronized by the Viennese, who swarmed into them in large numbers. The cafés and restaurants threw open their doors and gave opportunities for overflow into every available space facing on the streets and boulevards.

One of the most distinctive features of the city life at this time of the year was the Volksgarten, situated at a central point on what was formerly the glacis of the old walled town. Here both high and low collected of a summer afternoon to listen to the open-air concerts conducted by the famous Strauss brothers. Johann, the eldest of the three, had recently composed the "Blue Danube," and he and his brother Joseph alternated as conductor. The orchestra performed in an ornamental pavilion around which, seated at small tables, all classes of Viennese society enjoyed themselves in democratic fashion. Strauss music enjoyed a world-wide reputation and no public ball given in Vienna was considered a success unless a new Strauss waltz had been written for the occasion. Edouard, or *der schöne Eddie* as he was called, was the youngest and long survived his elder brothers but never equalled them as composer.

[12] The anatomic preparations of Hyrtl were famous throughout Europe. The corrosion specimens were made by injecting the blood vessels of a part or organ with a colored wax and applying acid to remove the surrounding tissues by maceration. The fine ramifications of the vascular tree stand out as an intricate network. The Warren Anatomical Museum at the Harvard Medical School contains similar specimens prepared by Oliver Wendell Holmes and other anatomists of the period.

The work and activities of the spring semester were continued well into the month of July, and I find recorded that we were busy with special courses on the ear by Gruber, on the skin by Isidor Neumann, on electro-therapeutics by Benedikt, and on pathological anatomy by Scheithauer. On looking back over the year's work I felt that to have selected courses on medical and special subjects rather than on surgery had been a wise choice. The work had been almost exclusively clinical; with the exception of a course on the urine by Johann Heller and a course on practical histology by Carl Wedl, no laboratory work had been attempted. I was looking forward to a second winter in Vienna and more advanced (and perhaps to me more congenial) work covering surgery and pathology, when an event occurred which not only gave a sad ending to a delightful and profitable season's work but came near cutting short this most important portion of my medical education.

On July 25th I left Vienna in company with Dr. Hayden, intending to meet some classmates for a short trip through Switzerland and then to work my way slowly towards Paris and perhaps London. The condition of my father's health had caused me a great deal of uneasiness and I felt that I should be prepared at any moment to respond quickly to a call from home. This came on the very first night after my departure from Vienna and on arrival in Munich. I returned to my hotel about midnight to find a telegram from Vienna repeating a cable message to "return home immediately." Although I had left no directions other than to forward letters to Paris, my friend Dr. Arthur Nichols happened to know that I was to pass the night in Munich. It spoke well for the police system of a German city that a stranger could be almost instantaneously located, for the telegram reached me without delay.

By four o'clock in the morning I was aboard the Vienna-Paris express on my way home. Catching the Inman Line steamer *City of London,* I sailed from Liverpool on July 31st. Atlantic liners were not yet built on a modern scale; their tonnage was small and a passage of ten or eleven days was considered good time. Unfortunately this was a particularly slow boat and was two weeks upon the water. Nevertheless I arrived home in time to see my father several days before his death, which occurred on August 19th, 1867.[13]

---

[13] The death of Dr. J. Mason Warren was due to internal cancer, complicated with intussusception. At a special meeting of the Suffolk District Medical Society reported in the *Boston Medical and Surgical Journal* on August 22, 1867 (see also the August 29 issue), Dr. Charles G. Putnam, the attending physician, gave an account of the last illness of his distinguished patient, and Dr. Oliver Wendell Holmes presented an obituary address. Dr. Warren had been president of the Suffolk District Medical Society from 1864 to 1866.

It is not within the purpose of the present narrative to go into family details of a distressing character. At the very outset of my career I was suddenly deprived of aid and counsel such as only a father can afford. This, at the time, seemed quite beyond my power of estimation. The problem of whether to remain at home and at once take up the work that my father had left, or to return to Europe and carry out my plans for a well-rounded medical education was one which I had to consider carefully and decide promptly. The advice of Dr. Oliver Wendell Holmes that "A Dr. Warren does not depend for his future success upon the patronage of the corner grocery" remains in my memory.[14] This was the keynote which persuaded me to abandon the opportunity to obtain a lucrative practice by remaining at home. I decided to return to Europe and complete the plan of education which had been formulated for me by my father a year previously, and left Boston on the Cunard steamer *China* on October 25th.

I was fortunate enough to have as a fellow passenger Mr. T. Spencer Wells of London, to whom I was introduced by Dr. Horatio R. Storer, who had come to see him off. Dr. Storer was a pioneer in ovariotomy, and the visit to this country of so distinguished an exponent of that operation as Mr. Wells was to him an event of much

---

J. Mason Warren left a small bequest to the Hospital, the income of which was to be awarded from time to time for the best dissertation considered worthy of a premium, on some subject in physiology, surgery, or pathological anatomy. It was requested that the award be called the Warren Prize in memory of Dr. John C. Warren. In carrying out this bequest over many decades the Hospital has received periodically, in response to each advertisement of the prize, a score or so of competing manuscripts from all parts of the world. The award was based on the recommendation of a committee. The wide range of scientific subjects submitted made it increasingly difficult to compare the relative merits of the contributions. Recently it was decided that the Warren Prize should be awarded to a scientific investigator selected because of some outstanding contribution to medical science, and he is invited to present the Warren Prize Lecture (or Lectures) as a public event. The first Warren Prize Lectures were delivered by Dr. René J. Dubos in the fall of 1953 on the "Biochemical Aspects of Infection" and published as the *Biochemical Determinants of Microbial Diseases* by the Harvard University Press (1954).

[14] As it stands, the meaning of this quotation is not altogether clear, though the effect of what Holmes said makes obvious his intention. A less ambiguous statement might have been, "A Warren does not measure his professional success by patronage, as does a corner grocer."

The same thought was expressed more gracefully by James G. Mumford when writing of Dr. C. B. Porter's devotion to teaching and hospital duties at the sacrifice of his practice: "Mere success in private practice . . . gives a man no great claim to professional distinction, though we admit that such success is sweet." [*Boston Med. and Surg. J. 162*, 776 (1910).]

What is true for the individual physician is equally true when applied to the Hospital as a whole. It took many years for the MGH to realize that its claim to professional distinction must be based on educational and research activities in addition to the care of the patient.

significance. He accepted this as a vindication of his own position relative to these early steps in what was destined to develop into abdominal surgery. These early operators, however, were still known as ovariotomists, for little was known about other surgical affections of the abdominal cavity.

Spencer Wells had visited several of our cities and made his last stop in Boston, where he expounded his views on ovarian disease to the members of a local medical society.[15] Feeling about the propriety of this operation ran high, and a leading exponent of the orthodox views of that day ventured to criticise the position which the London specialist had taken. This criticism was expressed in terms which the friends of Spencer Wells (especially Dr. Storer) regarded as unnecessarily severe. It is fair to say that although I saw much of Mr. Wells and his family during the voyage, and later during my course of study abroad had an opportunity of meeting him in London, I never heard him comment on this episode. I refer to it here as a sidelight on the surgery of an era which was drawing to its close.

After passing through London I paused in Paris for a few days to visit the Exposition of 1867. The Palais de l'Industrie had been erected for the purpose on the Champs Elysées and was a creation of such a substantial and decorative character that it was preserved to become the home of the annual "Salon" exhibit. As such it was a familiar landmark for nearly a generation until finally removed to make place for the approaches to the new bridge named for Czar Alexander and a group of new buildings which were to be a prominent feature of the Exhibition of 1897. I had already as a boy visited the Crystal Palace in London, which was built in 1851, and looked upon the French effort of 1867 as an enormous advance, but both seem trivial in comparison with achievements of a later date.

Early in November I was again in Vienna and found a much larger attendance of English and American students than the year before. During the second winter I intended to give more attention to surgery. This department of the university was under Professor Theodor Bill-

[15] The following item appears in the October 3, 1867 issue of the *Boston Medical and Surgical Journal* (77, 199):

> Mr. Spencer Wells, the distinguished ovariotomist, has just made a flying visit to this country, returning home by the steamer of the 25th ult. While in New York, he delivered a lecture on Ovariotomy at Bellevue Hospital Medical College . . . In Boston, he addressed the Boston Society for Medical Improvement on the same subject. There can be no doubt that the practical good sense of his remarks will have a powerful influence on the minds of medical men here, who have been heretofore far from unanimous in regarding this capital operation with approval . . . In Boston Prof. D. H. Storer [father of Horatio R. Storer] gave a number of his professional friends opportunity of becoming personally acquainted with him.

roth, who had just been chosen to fill the chair of surgery.[16] During the previous year Johann Dumreicher had been the only representative of surgery in the faculty and he was nearing the end of his career; futhermore, the university was beginning to feel the importance of taking steps to strengthen the surgical department. Billroth had been the assistant of Langenbeck in Berlin prior to 1860 and had already shown qualities which marked him as a pioneer in the new school of scientific surgery. The selection was a most happy one and enabled the Vienna school not only to maintain its prestige but to take a place in the front rank in the new era of surgery which was now so near at hand. Billroth was both a bold, brilliant operator and a leading exponent of thorough training in the pathology of those affections which belong in the domain of surgery. His early professional life had been spent in Berlin, a school which was at the time beginning to feel the dominance of the great pathologist Virchow. Billroth's book on surgical pathology and therapeutics appeared at a time when Paget's lectures on surgical pathology, which had enjoyed a long and successful career, began to need a successor more in accord with modern laboratory methods of research. It immediately gained its place in the surgical literature of the day, was later translated into English, and maintained a position as a standard work through many editions — this despite the fact that because of the great variety of subjects treated, both scientific and practical, it was not possible for the author to dip deeply into scientific problems. The text was most readable and the book did much to bring students of surgery to realize that education in the laboratory and familiarity with the use of the microscope were fully as important as the drill of the amphitheatre.

I was a frequent attendant at Billroth's clinic and saw many operations which were new and interesting. I recall particularly his operation upon the thyroid gland. Goiter was a far more common affection all over continental Europe than in this country, and especially prevalent in southern Germany and Switzerland. The "material" was abundant and Billroth made free use of it. This operation was performed with great fearlessness and rapidity, but I fear the mortality was high. This did not discourage him, however, and the impression left upon my mind was that of a masterful spirit waging war against disease under the almost insuperable obstacles which still encumbered all efforts to enlarge the domain of surgery. Although I had but little opportunity to follow the after-treatment of his patients, it was well

[16] At the age of thirty-one Theodor Billroth became professor of surgery and assumed the responsibilities of the surgical clinic in Zürich (1860). He was called to the chair of surgery in Vienna on August 21, 1867.

known that his wards contained their quota of pyemia and erysipelas in undiminished frequency. This was quite evident in the number of cases which found their way to the autopsy table. I was witnessing one of the last battles being waged by a valiant surgeon under the handicap of sepsis, a handicap which happily was destined soon to be removed.[17]

Despite the surgical activity of which I write, it should be remembered that at this time the operations performed at this clinic or indeed at any clinic in Europe did not include operations in any of the main cavities of the body. Cranial surgery had not advanced beyond the old-time operation of trephining for depressed fractures, and the abdominal cavity was still, surgically speaking, a terra incognita.

I had not expected to profit greatly by attendance at the surgical clinics in any of the great centers of medical education in Europe, and there was little in the way of operative surgery which I had thus far seen which could remove this impression. The German schools were attracting students from all over the world on account of their well-organized medical clinics, particularly those of the specialties. Students were also attracted by the advances made by their leaders of medicine in the knowledge of pathological anatomy. Laboratory research was conducted on a scale more extensive and more system-

[17] In his scholarly paper, "The Operative Story of Goitre," Halsted noted that during Billroth's first ten years in Vienna, 1867–1877, he rarely operated upon the thyroid gland, fearing to repeat his disastrous experiences in Zürich, where 8 of his 20 patients operated upon for goiter had died. J.C.W. was in Vienna in the fall of 1867; in Billroth's entire preantiseptic period (1860–1876) he operated upon a total of only 36 goiters (Zürich, 20; Vienna, 16) with 13 deaths. This high mortality (36.1 per cent) led him to abandon the operation until antiseptic methods became available. [*Surgical Papers by William Stewart Halsted* (Baltimore, 1924), II, 257–423.]

In the same paper Halsted goes on to quote Anton Wölfler's report from Billroth's Vienna clinic covering the years 1877–1881: "Five years have now elapsed since Professor Billroth as result of his experiences with the antiseptic treatment of wounds took up again the operative treatment of goitre and developed it in typical manner" (*ibid.*, p. 335). By the early eighties Billroth had operated upon more cases of goiter than anyone else.

It was not until 1872 that Theodor Kocher, at the age of thirty-one, became director of the surgical clinic in Bern. In the following two years Kocher performed 13 extirpative operations upon the thyroid gland, and in 1883 he published his famous paper standardizing the operation of thyroid lobectomy. By this time he had performed 101 operations upon the thyroid.

Halsted first visited Europe in 1879. He wrote later:

> I recall vividly an operation in Vienna performed by Mikulicz in 1879 in Billroth's clinic. Americans, newly arrived in Austria, we were greatly amused at seeing perhaps a dozen clamps (*Scheiber*) left hanging in a wound of the neck while the operator proceeded with his dissection, and were inclined to ridicule the method as being untidy or uncouth. Slowly it dawned upon us that we in America were novices in the art as well as the science of surgery (*ibid.*, p. 364).

atically organized than in any other country. England was far be-
hindhand in the science of pathology. In France, with a few brilliant
exceptions, the whole fabric of medical education and research had
been forced to adapt itself to an inelastic and antiquated bureaucratic
system. In the United States the value of the microscope in medicine
was regarded as a matter still to be proved, and by many this apparatus was looked upon good-humoredly as a fad for the idealist
rather than a useful tool of the teacher or the practitioner. It was not
for operative surgery but largely because I envisioned the importance
of a laboratory training that I had decided to return to Europe.

Vienna was endeavoring to hold her place in laboratory medicine,
and although Rokitansky had not definitely retired from the faculty,
Biesiadecki had been called from Warsaw to place pathological histology on a thoroughly up-to-date basis. Here was a new field for the
American student because the techniques of section cutting and the
staining and mounting of histological preparations were practically
unknown in our medical curriculum. I was fortunate in being able
to arrange for a private course with Biesiadecki in his laboratory. He
was a most conscientious and sympathetic teacher and a young man
who already ranked high among the pathologists of that period. My
desire was to devote myself largely to surgical pathology, a subject
which then concerned itself principally with the study of tumors.
Virchow's work on morbid growths had recently appeared and placed
the classification of tumors on a new basis. It also had cleared up
much of the confusion which had existed between genuine neoplasms
and those growths of an inflammatory nature which are caused by
some form of infective process (granulomata). The laboratory technique of that day was of the simplest character. Sections were cut by
the free-hand method with an ordinary razor, and carmine was the
only staining fluid in use. There was as yet no trained *Diener* to do
this part of the investigator's work for him. The situation was an
enormous advance on what had existed before, however, and great
strides were being made in the knowledge of pathological anatomy.
There was also an increasing appreciation of its bearing on the practice of medicine and surgery.

After I had acquired a sufficient training in this new technique, I
was able not only to obtain a practical knowledge of tumor classification but to carry on an *Arbeit*. Before leaving Vienna it was possible
for me to prepare a paper on the development of keloid, which through
the good offices of my teacher was published in the *Proceedings of
the Imperial Academy of Science* for 1868. A course of lectures on
pathology by Scheithauer supplemented this work. I also found time
for a course on operations on the eye by Arlt and a course on opera-

tive surgery on the cadaver [18] by Mosetig, whose name, if I am not mistaken, later became associated with the introduction of iodoform. Owing to the abundance of material which Mosetig had at his disposal and the small size of the class, which was composed of a few of my fellow countrymen, this course proved to be of the greatest service in enabling me to perfect many details of operative technique. Thus ended my second winter course of study at Vienna. As I felt I had acquired all that could be expected from the opportunities afforded in the various specialties there, I decided to devote at least one term to work in Berlin.

I cannot take leave of Vienna without referring to a memorandum in my diary of the date of January 15th, 1868: "The skating season is over." Thus far in my stay in Europe I had seen little evidence of an appreciation of the importance of physical culture. In Vienna one heard or saw little of the student corps such as those which made Heidelberg famous. Even among those organizations the predominating motive seemed to be semimilitary training. The riding school also seemed to be reserved for those who were preparing themselves for service in the army. For the medical student, and indeed for the people at large, no popular form of exercise or national game seemed to exist. Therefore when wintry weather brought ice in its wake, I was not surprised to find that little or no knowledge of the art of exhibition skating existed. In the United States, just before the outbreak of the Civil War, there had been a great awakening to the healthful advantages of open-air exercises. In a winter climate like Boston's, this took the form of an enthusiastic devotion to the art of skating. The sport had been growing in popularity and its development reaching the point where the country might claim world preëminence, when the Civil War brought it to a halt. Fortunately, I have managed throughout life to preserve the taste thus acquired and have often congratulated myself that, although of a generation which in its youth did not enjoy a varied athletic training, I could count myself among the pioneers in a more rational mode of life than that led by my predecessors. Among them, all work and little play seems to have been the prevailing custom. In selecting an outfit for my sojourn in Europe, a pair of American club skates had been included as an essential item. In Vienna the lake in the Stadt Park was crowded daily with skaters, but there was no evidence that any effort had been made to build up a "school" which might place this pastime on a scientific basis.

---

[18] Exercises in operative surgery on the cadaver were very popular in Continental surgical centers. They attracted the American students, who did not have such opportunities at home.

It was in the midst of my second winter's skating in Vienna that an American professional made his appearance. Jackson Haines, "the great American Skater" as he styled himself, came fresh from the Imperial Ballet at St. Petersburg, where he had appeared in a winter scene in "Le Prophet." A small man, well knit together and trained as a professional ballet dancer, he possessed all the necessary attributes for an ideal exhibition skater. An open-air performance was arranged on specially prepared ice with the regimental band of a duke for accompaniment. His exhibition before the assembled members of the family of Kaiser Francis Joseph produced a lasting impression, and this occasion was without doubt the beginning of the development of a new style of skating known today as the "Continental system." Haines never returned to his native country and is said to have died in an obscure village in Norway many years later. But the new cult under the auspices of a professional school of skaters, of which he was the pioneer, continued to flourish. A system based on scientific principles of balance and motion was elaborated, and has become the accepted school at St. Moritz and many other health resorts in Europe. The artificial ice rinks now in existence in all European capitals are products of this movement, and within recent years the system has been reimported into this country to displace the cruder methods of our antebellum days. Now, nearly a half century later, the Jackson Haines pattern of skate is one of the accepted models adopted by many of the American Skaters Associations. This episode is an example of the rise and progress of the athletic habit which has been so important a feature in the physical development of the present generation.

One important political event occurred during my stay in Vienna — the formal ceremonies attending the union of Austria and Hungary. On June 8, 1867, Francis Joseph was crowned King of Hungary in Pest (Pesth, as it was then called). Unfortunately I was unable to be present at this most interesting festival, although many of my classmates found time to make the journey. The occasion was interesting not only because of its political significance but on account of its being a function typical of bygone days. The Emperor mounted on his horse rode to the top of a mound in the public square and the iron crown of Hungary was placed upon his head. He was surrounded by his nobles, gorgeously attired in jewelled raiment, and accompanied by their followers in true feudal style. Whole oxen were roasted in the city streets and the populace feasted as in olden time.

~ XI

The Three Masters
of Berlin

The winter semester of 1867–68 closed about the first of March and soon thereafter I found myself established in Berlin. Here was the true center of scientific medicine, and at the Pathological Institute of Virchow and the Charité Hospital one could study all that was newest in the world of medical research. I recall Friedrich Theodor von Frerichs as the leading clinician; he occupied a position in Berlin corresponding to that of Oppolzer in Vienna. But my chief interest lay in surgery and pathological anatomy. As an exponent of surgery Langenbeck was the most prominent teacher of his time in the German world. He held a position equivalent to that of surgeon general in our army and was the trusted advisor of King William, soon to become Emperor. Associating as he did with those high in rank both at court and in army circles, Bernhard von Langenbeck gave the impression of a man of distinctly superior breeding. He was a courteous and refined gentleman with a great amiability of temperament. Nowhere during my stay abroad do I remember enjoying so greatly my relations with a teacher as I did in Berlin with this great surgeon.

Here, as in Vienna, there was a recess during the months of March and April, with the spring term continuing into July. Special courses, however, were to be obtained during the interval between the winter and spring terms, and I found I was just in time to enter a private course with Langenbeck on operative surgery on the cadaver. This was given from six to eight o'clock in the morning so as not to interfere with his daily routine, and as the place where this exercise was held was at a considerable distance from my residence, it was necessary for me to become a very early riser.

Langenbeck was greatly interested in osteoplastic surgery. The recent war between Prussia and Austria had furnished abundant opportunity for excision of joints for gunshot wounds, and Langenbeck prided himself upon his methods and the success with which they were attended. He laid much stress upon saving the periosteum in excision of the elbow, knee, and ankle joint. Subsequent experience with this form of excision of the elbow joint convinced me that the method was likely to be followed by ankylosis. In the ankle joint, however, the reproduction of new bone under these conditions made it possible to remove considerable portions of the tibia and fibula with excellent results. Langenbeck used to mention with pride the case of a soldier thus treated who later obtained a position as footman at court and was obliged to wear knee breeches and white stockings. This he was able to do without disclosing any deformity of the ankle upon which the operation had been performed. Langenbeck had performed fourteen cases of resection of this joint with but one fatality. An operation which he regarded as one of his own devising was an osteoplastic resection of the upper jaw for nasopharyngeal polypi. I practiced this operation many times [on cadavers] under his careful supervision, and later in life resorted to it frequently with much success.

Langenbeck performed many of these operations in his clinic, which I attended regularly. They included several resections of the hip joint and also operations for cleft palate. His method of operating for the latter deformity enjoyed a great reputation. The original feature of his procedure lay in carefully peeling off the periosteum from the hard palate with a view to obtain a regeneration of bone in closing the fissure. He also claimed to have performed a subperiosteal resection of the mandible with complete regeneration of the bone. Of course I heard and saw nothing of any abdominal surgery.

I recall a visit of my former teacher, Professor Pancoast of Philadelphia, and an interesting evening passed at Langenbeck's house, where these two masters in surgery discussed many of the surgical problems of the day. This interchange of views was made possible by Langenbeck's perfect command of the English language, for Pancoast was no German scholar.

The dominating personality in Berlin, and for that matter in all medical Europe, was Rudolf Virchow. He was still a comparatively young man [47], although in appearance he seemed old to me, perhaps not so old in years as in experience, so much of which had been crowded into his early life. A vein of quiet, somewhat sarcastic, humor showed itself in the lecture room and laboratory. It was currently said that Virchow could have attained distinction in the political world as easily as he had in that of science, and his admirers, with much pride, claimed that he had once had the honor of receiving a challenge from Bismarck but had scornfully waved it aside. His *Cellular-Pathologie* was an epoch-making work which placed a great department of medical science on a new and modern basis. In addition Virchow contributed a new classification of tumors and solved the puzzle of embolism, the means by which disease is conveyed from one region of the body to another.[1] A man who had made these contributions to science and also had found time to make a name as the leader of a political party [2] seemed to be one whose life history might be regarded as complete. In reality his career was only at its beginning. His productive life was to round out the century, and at the meeting of the International Congress in Paris in 1900 he appeared as the grand old man of the great German school to receive the homage of many generations of pupils from every land. Here he finally achieved the recognition which I had known he merited a third of a century before. Virchow's "railroad course" was a very popular exercise and its fame had already reached the United States before I left home. The tables in his laboratory were arranged to form a continuous roadway on which was laid a set of miniature rails. A small truck on wheels supported the microscope on which was placed a section of a preparation to illustrate the subject of the lecture. In this way a demonstration of many different specimens could be made for the personal inspection of classes of fifty or more students. The members of the class also were expected to study and explain preparations of their own making, which the Professor in his rounds would have an opportunity to criticize. Woe betide the luckless individual who failed to pass through this ordeal in a manner satisfactory to his teacher! Many a broad truth or detail of technique was thus firmly stamped upon the memory. Virchow gave systematic lectures at which there was a much larger attendance, the class being composed chiefly of undergraduates. These lectures gave opportunity to hear him expound his views of some of the great problems of the day. But it was at the demonstration of pathological specimens, or at the autopsy table, that one saw the great teacher at his best. His method of conducting a postmortem examination was in itself an object lesson. This exercise gave the student an opportunity to see certain morbid conditions and also was an occasion for a homily on training the mind to observe. It was here that many students who later gained renown as teachers or investigators received inspiration and also developed their skill in the interpretation of the manifold changes in the tissues that are wrought by disease. The true ring of the great teacher never failed to leave an impress upon those who counted themselves fortunate to be his pupils.[3]

Although I deeply appreciate the advantages of having been a

[1] The concept of embolism is thought by many to have been Virchow's greatest single achievement in pathology.

[2] In 1862 Virchow became a member of the Prussian Lower House and in 1880, a member of the Reichstag. He served in the latter until 1893.

[3] The following private letter signed with the initials J.C.W. was published in the *Boston Medical and Surgical Journal* for June 25, 1868:

member of the classes of such distinguished men as Langenbeck and Virchow, I now look back upon my student days in the laboratory of Cohnheim with more interest than is evoked by any other medical experience which came to me in Europe. Julius Cohnheim was a man of middle age, of Jewish extraction, of high intellectual attainment, and of amiable disposition. He was not only a keen observer teeming with original ideas, but endowed with an unusual facility for communicating his knowledge to others. Shortly before my visit he had made himself famous for his contribution to the knowledge of the action of the cells in living tissue. Cellular pathology was the keynote of medical research, and Cohnheim had supplemented Virchow's great work in this field by experiments which demonstrated the ability of the white cells of the blood to pass through the walls of the capillary

---

It may, perhaps, be not uninteresting to you to hear something of the course of study in Berlin. Its advantages are not as great as those of Vienna certainly, as the latter city is universally acknowledged to be the best place for a general course of study for a *stranger,* and especially for one who wishes to accomplish a great deal in a short space of time. The Berlin men, however, call the Vienna school "superficial," and for certain specialties Berlin is far ahead of the Kaiserstadt. Graefe, Langenbeck and Virchow are not only looked upon here as the first men in Germany in their special branches, but, what is more important to the student, are the *best practical teachers.*

Virchow is most indefatigable in his work. He gives, every morning, a practical course on pathology, lasting from two to three hours, beginning at 7 o'clock, and also a daily theoretical lecture from 11 to 12. Monday morning it is an autopsy, and, Monday last, attending for the first time, I stood three hours, by my watch, by the table, lost in astonishment at the number of interesting pathological points which he was able to discover in one unfortunate subject for our edification. Tuesday morning, it is a microscopic course; Wednesday, demonstration of specimens, of which he has several tablesful, and so on. In addition to all this, he frequently hurries from the lecture room to deliver a two-hour speech in Parliament. I may mention, as one of his chief peculiarities, his great power of sarcasm, which he uses most unmercifully against any young gentleman who happens to have a dirty object-glass, or on any of those enthusiastic beginners who see so much of pathological interest in an oil-globule or air-bubble. It is a very great treat to hear him snub a man — i.e., when you don't happen to be the unfortunate party yourself.

Langenbeck's clinic is every afternoon. His material is quite large, and as he is a bold as well as original operator, one may see, during the week, many exceedingly interesting operations. Only this afternoon, I have seen him split the soft palate in order to remove a large tumor from the posterior wall of the pharynx. After removal of the tumor, he applied actual cautery to the wound — all without chloroform.

His favorite operations seem to be the subperiosteal resections of joints, in which he seems to have made great advances over the old method. Some of his plastic operations are really quite wonderful. All of these one has an opportunity of seeing at his private operating course. I doubt if there is any one clinic on the Continent where there is so much of interest for the surgical student. The only disadvantage is, and that indeed not a small one, he never allows any "visits" in his wards.

J. C. W.

vessels. His discovery of the "emigration of the white corpuscles" produced a profound sensation among the pathologists of the day and was received with great enthusiasm by them as the harbinger of still better things to come. Pathological histology had to be studied again from the new point of view. Many and long were the discussions by such men as Stricker of Vienna and Cohnheim of Berlin on the mutual relations of the fixed and the wandering cells of connective tissue. Cohnheim was a prolific writer as well as a fluent lecturer, and his work on pathological histology was the first classical exposition of the behavior of the tissues under conditions which bring about inflammation.

In working with Cohnheim it was natural to feel that one was imbibing knowledge at the very source, and the enthusiasm thus engendered was augmented by the unusually favorable circumstances under which study was carried on. Cohnheim took a personal interest in the members of his class and I recall many pleasant excursions under his leadership on Sundays and holidays to the suburbs of Berlin. If my memory serves me correctly, medicine was about the only profession in the Germany of that day in which the Jews had an opportunity to make a career for themselves. At least they were not allowed to take rank as officers in the army nor did they have an opportunity to shine in the world of politics. I recall being much amused at the enthusiasm with which Cohnheim received the announcement that Disraeli had been appointed Prime Minister of Great Britain.

I have never visited Berlin again but doubt not that it ranks higher as a great metropolis than it did in 1868. The Franco-German War was yet to come and although Prussia had shown what she was capable of accomplishing in the campaign against a united southern Germany, I could not believe that she was yet a match for the Napoleonic armies, nor was I alone in such an estimate. Although Vienna was still looked upon as the "Paris of Germany," Berlin gave the impression of the capital of a modern and progressive community, despite lingering traces of a provincial character. There was to be sure the great central thoroughfare, Unter den Linden, running from the triumphal Brandenburger Tor to the Royal Palace. But royalty itself was content to reside in democratic simplicity on one or two of the adjacent street corners. King William could often be seen by the passer-by, standing at his parlor window. Here was his residence while Prince of Prussia and here he chose to stay although the Palace itself was near at hand. A block or two below was the home of the Crown Prince, brushed against daily by the passing throng.

It has been said that the civilization of a people can be accurately gauged by the standard set in the care of its thoroughfares. Here Berlin was lamentably deficient. The streets of the entire city were paved with the old-fashioned boulderlike cobblestones; this type of pavement was not confined to the roadway but covered also the chief portion of the sidewalk, along the center of which there was a narrow footway, grudgingly conceded to the needs of suffering humanity. There appeared to be no systematic provision for the sewage of the city, and in many of the principal thoroughfares the gutters still ful-filled the duties of the common sewer, as in medieval times. All this was in strong contrast to the modern improvements in the French capital, which had been expanding for nearly two decades under the influence of Baron Haussmann. So far in advance of its time was this movement for a city beautiful that Parisians might have been pardoned in a measure for their somewhat benighted attitude towards the "barbarians" across the Rhine.

At the close of the spring semester I parted company with Cohn-heim with much regret and with the understanding that I should return the following autumn and establish myself as a special student in his laboratory. It was much to my regret that I learned, shortly before the time arrived for my return, that Cohnheim had been called to Kiel. Although I received an invitation to follow him to that school, I thought it best not to make the attempt, as under the new conditions I felt it doubtful whether it would be possible to enjoy the advantages of a "privatissimus" as had been planned for in Berlin.

I had been obliged to make a flying trip to London in the middle of the spring term to meet members of my family and escort them to Paris. In July I left Berlin to join them again, this time at Heidelberg for a trip through Switzerland.[4] Here I had an opportunity of visiting once more my old school at Vevey, the Pension Sillig. The interval of thirteen years seemed a long one, but I did not have an opportunity of repeating this visit for nearly forty years, when accompanied by one of my sons I was able to identify the desk at which I had sat as a boy half a century before. So far as I could see and remember, nothing had been changed. Travelling facilities, however, had greatly im-proved over those of 1868. The old diligence had departed, and with

[4] J.C.W.'s mother and sisters Nellie, Annie, and Rosamond sailed for Europe in April 1868 on the *Scotia*, the last of the side paddle-wheelers. They stayed in London during May and in June took an apartment on the Rue Jean Gougon in Paris. Their stay in Europe was prolonged for another year, and visits were made to Germany, Switzerland, Rome, Florence, and Interlaken. They returned home on the *Scotia* in October 1869. J.C.W. had sailed for home on July 30 and was already established at No. 2 Park Street when the ladies reached Boston. Although their paths must have crossed several times in Europe, J.C.W. makes but brief reference to his family, and Rosamond writes of only one meeting in her *Recol-lections of My Life for My Children* (Boston: privately printed, 1939).

it the postillion; but it was not until my final visit that the chauffeur had come to take his place.

During this trip I acquired a taste for mountain climbing. I recall an excursion over the Ober-Aar-Joch, a mountain pass about ten thousand feet above the level of the sea. After wandering among the clouds tied to a skillful guide, we coasted with his coat for a sled over a vast field of snow and suddenly shot out into the sunlight of the valley of the Glacier du Rhône. Another climb of interest was the Cima di Iazi, a peak of Monte Rosa, and also the Grands Mulets on the slopes of Mont Blanc. When taken in moderation, as these examples show, one enjoys all the sensations of more ambitious mountain climbs without the attendant dangers. Here above the snow line we became conscious of an Arctic stillness and an exhilarating sense of isolation from the world among inspiring surroundings.

Rumors of Carbolic Acid
Heard in Paris

With this physical preparation for another year of hard work I found myself in Paris early in the autumn of 1868 with the intention of returning soon to Berlin. There was little in the way of medicine to see in Paris so early in the season, but I was fortunate to find my friend Thomas B. Curtis, who was an interne at the Lourcine Hospital. As his parents resided permanently in Paris he had, after graduating at Harvard in the Class of 1862, enrolled himself in the École de Médecine. Here he greatly distinguished himself as a scholar. The course of study extended through four years and opportunities for hospital service were awarded to upper classmen who successfully passed the rigid examinations for which the French system was famous.

I recall attending one of the competitions for an "internat" to which the public was admitted. The faculty was seated behind a table raised on a platform above the floor of a large amphitheatre. Facing the professors was a small desk on which was placed a stop clock the hand of which was set in motion by pressure on a button. The competing student was admitted to an adjacent room and on entrance was handed a question in writing. He was allowed ten minutes to prepare notes for his answer. At the expiration of that time the door was thrown open and he was ushered by an attendant to the amphitheatre. As he took his seat at the table opposite the clock, the button was pressed and the hands began to move. During the fifteen minutes in which one hand described a complete revolution, the student was required to deliver an improvised lecture on the subject which had been assigned to him. He was expected not only to occupy the time with a correct statement but to systematize his discourse so as to give each detail the proportionate amount of time which its importance demanded. Etiology, pathology, and treatment were each to receive due attention. The topic on this occasion was "tumors of the popliteal space" and on this subject the young man dilated with Gallic eloquence entirely unconscious of what to an Anglo-Saxon would have been very embarrassing surroundings.

The *concours* seemed to be the dominating feature of the French system, and the ranking students, of whom Curtis was one, devoted their energies principally to memorizing blocks of textbook knowledge and to perfecting themselves in a highly specialized style of examination-book authorship. The competitions culminated in the struggle for a medal which was awarded to a member of the graduating class each year. Success brought a national reputation to the medalist, who would receive an invitation from the Emperor to visit the court at Compiègne. Dieulafoy, who subsequently became famous as the inventor of the aspirator,[1] was the medal scholar of that year, and Curtis would probably have occupied the same enviable position the following year had not the breaking out of the Franco-German War put an end to this academic function.

Dr. Curtis, after graduating with high honors, returned to this country and secured an appointment on the surgical staff of the Massachusetts General Hospital, serving as surgeon to out-patients. He was a man of learning and intellectual acumen, and was destined for high rank in the medical profession had not his early death cut short what was already a brilliant career.[2] Although but a junior member of the

---

[1] Dieulafoy's publication on this subject, *De l'aspiration pneumatique sous-cutanée* (Paris, 1870), failed to mention thoracentesis as introduced by Morrill Wyman and Henry I. Bowditch in 1850. See note 14, Chapter VII, and also V. Y. Bowditch, *Life and Correspondence of Henry Ingersoll Bowditch* (Boston, 1902), I, 233.

[2] Dr. Thomas B. Curtis died on December 11, 1881. An unsigned obituary notice published in the *Boston Medical and Surgical Journal* on December 22 (*105,* 599) was almost certainly prepared by J.C.W. It contains these additional biographical notes:

> Among other hospitals he was on duty at the Hotel Dieu, the Lourcine, the La Riboisière under Verneuil, the Charité, the Enfants Malades where he passed two years under M. Roget, and the Necker under M. Guyon. It was during this period that he gained his very extensive and varied experience in medicine and surgery, and laid the foundation of that wide, accurate, and available acquaintance with the literature of our profession for which he was so remarkable.
>
> At the outbreak of the Franco-Prussian war, Curtis inscribed his name upon the staff of the first ambulance to be sent to the front, but withdrew it on account of the uncertain state of his father's health, though greatly to his own disappointment. During the siege of Paris, when still at the Hôpital des Enfants Malades, he was attached to the service of M. le docteur Lannelongue, at the Palaise de l'Industrie, and subsequently assisted M. le Professor Daremberg on an ambulance especially devoted to fever patients. At the close of the first siege, repairing to Versailles he offered his services to M. Delaroche, President of the Society for Aid to the Wounded at Versailles, and was under fire at the skirmish at Châtillon, and later was stationed for six weeks at Puteaux, attached, as surgeon, to an ambulance. After the suppression of the Commune, he returned to his duties as *interne.*
>
> In his last year but one he competed with his colleagues for the silver medal, sharing with another, if we remember rightly, the first place on the list. During his last term of service as *interne* he carried off the Prix Civiale, a money prize established by the celebrated Civiale, open to competition

Hospital staff, his seniors had a high appreciation of his erudition. Curtis had given special attention to diseases of the genito-urinary system and while in London had been a pupil of Sir Henry Thompson. Many were the discussions on interesting topics of the day, especially

---

among the *internes* of the hospitals, and awarded, we believe, every four years. Curtis's thesis, "Du Traitement des rétrécissements de l'urèthre par la dilatation progressive," was based upon seventy cases observed at the Hôpital Necker in the service of M. Guyon, and upon these he formulated ratios of mortality and drew certain general rules as guides for operating upon urethral strictures, given various local and general conditions. This thesis, after being "crowned" by the judges, served Curtis, according to our memory, for his graduation thesis, and was published by Baillière in 1873. It was praised by the journals at the time of its publication. We were in Paris and saw much of Curtis at this period, when we may say he was at his very best, and recall with admiration the vigor, keenness, and activity of his mind.

A little later he went to England, and there made the acquaintance of Sir Henry Thompson, profiting still further by his skill and teaching in the particular branch of surgery to which so much of his recent attention had been devoted. Returning to Paris, Curtis translated two of Sir Henry Thompson's lectures for the *Gazette Hebdomadaire,* and also contributed to the same journal an account of the death from the administration of a mixture of ether and chloroform which occurred here in Boston at that time.

This issue of the *Boston Medical and Surgical Journal* also contains an account of a special meeting of the Boston Society for Medical Improvement held on December 14, commemorative of its president, Dr. Curtis. J.C.W. spoke of Curtis as a medical student in Paris and gave a further description of the *concours* for the medal:

At the time I have mentioned Curtis was about to compete with a few other well-known stars for the silver medal which is, if my memory serves me right, awarded to *internes* in their last year but one of service. A preliminary examination, to weed out the weak ones, consisted of a written essay on some subject, three hours to be given in which to prepare it. It was not a question with these men of filling up the time, but to so drill themselves by rapidity of writing and special mental training as to deliver themselves of the maximum amount of work within the given period.

The subject selected on this occasion was the Iris! a task which Curtis, however, seems to have had no difficulty in mastering, for he distanced all his competitors and came out at the end of the series even with another man at the head of the list. In one of these examinations, that intended for competition for the internat in a list of one hundred and fifty names, his was second. Dieulafoy, whose name is well known to us all in connection with the aspirator, was one of his colleagues, but his name was no more familiar to the thousand medical students of Paris at that time than that of Curtis. Coming suddenly upon him, as I did at this period of his career, I remember well the powerful impression produced upon my mind. His highly polished manner, the modesty with which he bore his honors, his genial intercourse with friends, combined to form an ideal type. It was a privilege to the medical profession of this city to receive such a man into its ranks. Although he has been with us but a few years, his peculiar gifts have not been without their influence upon all of us, both young and old. I shall not attempt to point out what his future might have been had he lived; we all know what benefits would arise from contact with a man who seemed to give a new meaning to that old phrase, "The scholar and the gentleman."

with Dr. Henry J. Bigelow, the senior surgeon on the staff. In these Curtis always took a prominent part. Dr. Bigelow's subsequent work on the treatment of stone in the bladder and his development of the operation of litholapaxy seemed to me to have been one of the outcomes of these hospital debates.

Through Curtis' help I was able to gain a good deal of valuable information about the opportunities for postgraduate work which existed in Paris. When I learned later that Cohnheim had left Berlin, I concluded that it would be wiser for me to remain in Paris than to follow him to his untried field of work at Kiel. I never had occasion to regret this decision because, quite apart from the relative merits of the two cities and the opportunities for continuing my laboratory studies, remaining in Paris brought me into contact with Dr. Henry Pickering Bowditch, with whom I established the foundation of a friendship which lasted through life.[3]

Dr. Bowditch was the elder brother of my Harvard College classmate Charles Pickering Bowditch, and had graduated from the College in 1861. After honorable service as an officer in the Civil War he had taken up the study of medicine. Obtaining his degree in 1868, he came to Paris to begin his studies in physiology under Claude Bernard at the Collège de France. It thus came about that Bowditch, although belonging to an older class at Harvard, had fallen into line as my contemporary in medicine. The Collège de France was an institution whose organization was quite independent of the École de Médecine. To hold one's position as a student in the Collège it was necessary to submit to the ordeal of the *concours* at stated intervals. This was also the case with those members of the medical faculty who aspired to promotion. Genius was given an opportunity to follow its own bent and expand quite unimpeded by the restrictions which hampered medical scientific investigation elsewhere in France.

Claude Bernard was pursuing his investigations on the function of the sympathetic system of nerves. His findings had given a great impetus to all physiological research. Bernard had achieved a world-

---

[3] The Harvard Medical School as planned and built in 1906 might be regarded as a product of this friendship. The editor, in an Alumni Day address commemorating the fiftieth anniversary of the buildings [*New England J. Med. 255,* 1035 (November 29, 1956)] suggested that the School was conceived during the winter which J.C.W. spent in Paris with Bowditch. Early in 1869 Bowditch wrote to his mother:

> I have been building all sorts of laboratories and medical schools in the air. In this labor I have been materially assisted by Coll. Warren who is quite convinced that something ought to be done to raise the standard of scientific education in our community. I mean, of course, particularly medical science. [As quoted in *Bull. Harvard Med. School Alumni Assoc.* (March 1927), p. 12.]

wide reputation and was already well advanced in years [4] but still absorbed in research work. To me he appeared as an elderly man with a great simplicity of character and an agreeably natural and unassuming manner, always ready to listen sympathetically to the enthusiasms of his younger colleagues. There was also a delightful trace of that Gallic temperament which enabled him occasionally to pull aside the curtain of science and peer for a moment into the world of wit and humor, so often an unknown land to men engrossed in scientific research. It was in Claude Bernard's laboratory that I found Bowditch, and it was largely through his suggestion that I decided to become a student in the Collège de France and pursue laboratory studies under Ranvier.

Victor Cornil and Louis Antoine Ranvier had recently written a textbook on pathological histology. Although the work was of an elementary character, it had given the authors a well-earned reputation. Ranvier was looked upon as a free lance in his new position at the Collège de France and as a man destined to "make good" in his role of an independent investigator. His work on the finer anatomy of the nerve fibre gave him permanent recognition. He was still a young man, with a powerful physique which seemed hardly in keeping with work requiring a light and almost feminine touch. His massive head with bright and cheerful countenance was protected by a heavy growth of hair and beard and set firmly upon a sturdy frame. Bernard and Ranvier, although pursuing entirely different lines of work, were close neighbors in the laboratory, so that although I was working primarily on pathology I heard much about new problems in physiology. Thus I came gradually to appreciate the fact that pathological physiology was a subject of quite as much moment to the surgeon as pathological anatomy. This feeling was engendered largely by the broad views of Bowditch on the significance of his chosen specialty to the practical problems of clinical medicine and surgery. Although I do not now recall any special line of work under Ranvier that materially added to my stock of pathological knowledge, it has seemed to me that these congenial surroundings had a ripening effect upon my enthusiasms for the science of surgery which later on enabled them to remain alive through a period when the scientific doctor was regarded with some suspicion by his colleagues. I was not surprised to learn from Ranvier that he had been unable to satisfy himself in regard to Cohnheim's observations on the emigration of the white corpuscles, and it was with no little satisfaction that I succeeded in convincing him of this migration by repeating Cohnheim's experiment on the loop of the frog's intestine.

[4] Claude Bernard was then fifty-five years of age.

There were few opportunities in Paris for postgraduate work in the hospitals. I was surprised to find that it was contrary to the policy of the government to offer facilities to graduates of other schools to visit the hospitals and follow the clinical services of the prominent men of the day. Strangers were referred to the Bureau de l'Assistance Publique, where a ticket might be obtained which permitted the bearer to make a single visit to a given institution. Possession of such a pass usually enabled the bearer to make the visit with the attending physician or surgeon for an indefinite period, but this privilege was likely to be cut short at any moment by the hospital janitor or other administrative subordinate. This power seemed to be exercised quite independently of the wishes of the medical staff. As a result of this system some of my best-laid plans came to an untimely end. This was my fate in the case of efforts to attend the clinic of Aristide Auguste Verneuil, one of the leading French surgeons of his time. Verneuil was a good teacher and took much interest in his pupils, and I found his service most instructive. But one fine day, after a long journey across the city to attend his early morning visit, I was denied admission by the guardian of the gate, who pointed out that I must make renewed application at the Bureau. An appeal to the professor himself disclosed the fact that much to his regret he was quite powerless to intervene.

I recall frequent visits with Jacques Gilles Maisonneuve at the Hôtel Dieu. Maisonneuve was a typical specimen of the old school. He was the inventor of an urethral divulsor in which he took great pride. Paul Broca was surgeon to La Pitié and Gosselin was on the staff of La Charité, but I recall nothing of their work. I followed for a time the service of Roget at the Hôpital des Enfants Malades and became myself the victim of an epidemic of whooping cough. As I had already suffered from this malady, the attack was fortunately of a mild order and was easily dispelled by a visit to Pau in the south of France, where the Christmas holidays were passed in company with many Boston friends.

Pau was then, as now, a great hunting center and a large American contingent was on hand to join with the members of an English colony in the patronage of this sport. Mr. Bennet Forbes and his son Murray, Charles H. Gibson, later to become my brother-in-law,[5] and Dr. Jeremiah Whipple, my classmate at Harvard Medical School, were all prominent members of the hunt, and thus it came about that not long after my arrival I found myself mounted and following the hounds. The climate of Pau was well suited to this form of exercise

[5] Rosamond Warren (1846–1934) married Charles H. Gibson on December 12, 1871 at No. 2 Park Street. They resided at No. 137 Beacon Street, Boston and also at Nahant.

and the fine open country, backed by the Pyrenees with the snow-capped Dent du Midi, supplied an environment which has always made this a resort of great popularity. Great as were the social attractions here, the necessity of completing my winter's work in a satisfactory manner brought me back to Paris by the middle of January 1869.

There was a short session of skating in Paris during the latter part of January. The Cercle des Patineurs was an organization which found excellent opportunity to make this pastime popular on the lakes of the Bois de Bologne. Judging from the patronage of both sexes, I found the art had greatly advanced since my earlier visit in 1861, when the appearance of a woman on skates was a matter of much comment.

My thoughts were now beginning to take a homeward turn. I had been nearly three years in Europe and was completing my sixth year as a student of medicine. Beyond the courses already mentioned, I found few opportunities to study any of the specialties in Paris, for in this respect the city afforded a strong contrast to Vienna. A course on ophthalmoscopy given by LaCouer is mentioned in my diary and stands out prominently in its solitude.

Actually, I found comparatively little in the various clinics to draw me away from my work with Ranvier. My impression of the surgery in Paris had not been one to arouse much enthusiasm. The facilities afforded to students who were not regular undergraduates were limited, and there was little in the work of the leading surgeons which stood out conspicuously. There was some attempt to improve upon the old-time surgical dressing, and I began to hear about a substance known as *acide phénique*.[6] A distinct effort was being made to develop

[6] Jules Lemaire described the properties of coal tar and its derivatives, the phenols, *"acide phénique"* or *"carbolique,"* and others, in 1860, 1861, and 1865 in several communications to the French Academy of Sciences. These studies made particular reference to the prevention of fermentation or decomposition and also of the formation of pus (*"empêcher la formation du pus"*). The preservative and disinfective properties of carbolic acid thus were known as a result of Lemaire's demonstrations, and carbolic acid was used to preserve anatomic and natural-history specimens. In the American Civil War this agent was in supply as a disinfectant.

With regard to the use of carbolic acid in some of the military hospitals during the Civil War, Dr. John J. Caldwell of Brooklyn, New York stated in an article published in the *Boston Medical and Surgical Journal* [1 N.S., 342 (July 1868)]: "Hence, in weak solution we used it to dress wounds, with the very best results; in stronger solutions, we used it in scrubbing our wards and privies, in washing and disinfecting clothing, and for many other purposes." Credit for this development was given at first to E. R. Squibb, the pharmaceutical chemist of Brooklyn, but in 1868 Squibb wrote a letter (*ibid.*, page 416) disclaiming any share in the introduction of carbolic acid. He had merely acted on directive to procure the agent from domestic coal-tar distillers and put it up for army use.

a more permanent type of dressing and thus allow the healing process to go on without the incessant interruptions which were an inevitable accompaniment of the old technique. Cotton batting was used for this

---

It had been taught by surgeons since Hippocrates that dead flesh turns into matter or pus whether within or without the living body. This decomposition or putrefaction was envisioned as a chemical action in some way connected with miasms, or with poisonous substances developed in animal matter in the course of putrefaction. Agents which arrested decomposition were termed antiseptics or disinfectants.

The state of knowledge in 1863 was precisely expressed by Acting Assistant Surgeon Jenkins, who was referred to as an "expert chemist" attached to the Departments of the Ohio and the Cumberland during the Civil War. Jenkins was charged with the investigation of hospital gangrene, erysipelas, and pyemia. His statement, in the form of a letter addressed to Dr. M. Goldsmith, U.S.V., was inserted in the latter's report on these diseases to the Surgeon General of the Army submitted under date of September 1, 1863. Although carbolic acid is not specifically mentioned, it was, as stated, known and used as a disinfectant or antiseptic in the hospitals of the U. S. Army.

Louisville, Ky., April 2d, 1863.

Dr. M. Goldsmith:

Dear Sir — In reply to your inquiry of a few days ago, asking me to state what is known at the present time as to the chemical nature of the causes producing or the products resulting from infectious diseases, gangrenous ulcers, etc., I think I can safely say that little or nothing is known as to the real and substantial causes of such morbid processes; and in reference to the nature of the products emanating from ulcers, etc., about all we know is this: the effluvia from foul and putrescent ulcers are composed chiefly of sulphuretted and phosphuretted hydrogen, ammoniacal and sulphuretted ammoniacal gases, with a little carburetted hydrogen. All of these bodies have been proved to be incompetent to induce diseases similar to those which gave rise to them.

Among the many substances which have been employed with a view to the arrest of the disease, or the checking or prevention of putrefaction, or the destruction of the noxious vapors and gases, may be enumerated both physical and chemical agents, such as charcoal to absorb, balsamic fumigations to disguise, and antiseptics to change the chemical composition of the volatile products of putrefaction — for example, chlorine, some oxy-acids (hyponitric acid, sulphuretic acid). Some salts, (nit. of lead, sulphate of iron,) again act by a thoroughly destructive effect upon the substance of the affected tissues, and destroy the integrity of the organized structure, *e.g.*, corrosive acids, caustic alkalies. Others, again, act in a milder manner, and appear only to coagulate the albuminous fluid in and about the diseased parts, *e.g.*, corrosive sublimate, nitrate of silver, etc. As an example of what we know in reference to the action of antiseptics, such as chlorine, nitrous acid, sulphurous acid, etc., I will state that they decompose the organic body giving rise to offensive and noxious emanations, and act as disinfectants and antiseptics,

1st. By abstracting water.

2d. By forming with organic matters compounds less susceptible of decay.

3d. By deodorizing the body.

4th. By destroying cryptogamic plants and infusorial animalcules.

Little, also, is known upon this subject, of a definite nature, as most of the experiments have been made with a view not to strike at the cause, but to destroy the noxious character of the products of putrid disease.

Very respectfully yours, etc.,

THOS. E. JENKINS

purpose, an amputation stump being swathed in as many layers as could be held on with the bandage. The formula ran, "Il faut mettre trop d'ouate!" This method seemed to give some satisfactory results which were attributed to firm, equable compression and immobilization of the parts by a more or less porous dressing.[7]

There was little else to show that the beginning of the third great era in surgery was at hand. An incident which happened about this time serves to show how little I myself appreciated that wonderful changes were on the eve of taking place.

Before leaving Paris I was urged to call on an American family which for several years had been resident in Paris. The members of this family formerly were patients of my father and ones in whom he had always retained a friendly interest. On paying my respects to Mrs. D., the head of the family, I found myself unexpectedly called upon to listen patiently to a long story about her "case," which she thought ought to interest a young surgeon such as I aspired to be. It appeared that the poor lady had been afflicted with an ovarian tumor and had sought in vain for some member of the French school of surgeons who would be willing to undertake an operation for its removal. It so happened that Marion Sims had been spending part of the winter abroad and had recently left Paris and was at that moment making his preparations to take passage for home. On receipt of an urgent telegram, this distinguished American surgeon returned somewhat reluctantly to Paris, and the operation was performed successfully. Mrs. D. naturally was very enthusiastic over the result and endeavored to impress upon me the great significance which her experience bore upon the future of surgery. I listened politely to her statement, as one does to the praises of the grateful patient of a brother physician. Having spent three years in Europe and having acquired, as I thought, a pretty accurate knowledge of all that the great centers of medical education had to teach, I may perhaps be pardoned for thinking of myself as an epitome of the medical science of the day. I fear, therefore, that I was not as responsive to the good lady's exhortations as the occasion demanded. As time rolled on, however, and the new

[7] The carbolic dressing of Lister was thought by many to be a physical filter or screen which protected the wound from germs suspended in the air. The sterile cotton stopper in a culture tube acts in such a manner. Alphonse Guérin developed the occlusive cotton dressing, which although not sterilized by heat was made of virgin cotton. It was left in place for fifteen days and was supposed to protect the wound from the miasms of the air. Actually, it gave protection from prying surgical fingers. The use of Guérin's cotton dressing was bitterly attacked by Le Fort, who accused its inventor of having an outrageously high mortality rate among amputees so treated [*Bull. Acad. de méd.* (Paris, 1878) pp. 649, 661]. As J. C. W. suggests, other merits of the cotton dressing resided in the firm and equable pressure it produced. Dr. Sumner L. Koch of Chicago introduced sterile cotton mechanic's waste for the same purpose. The "pressure" dressing so formed was used extensively in World War II for thermal burns.

era in surgery with all its wonderful possibilities began to unfold itself, I came to realize that I had been listening to a prophetic statement of what soon was to come about and that much of the knowledge which I had spent six years to acquire was to be discarded because it possessed only an historical value.

Some time before setting forth to revisit London, I was dining with relatives who were visiting Paris. My uncle, Dr. Charles Mifflin, asked me whether I had ever heard of carbolic acid. "I do not mean carbonic acid," he added. Even the name of this new remedy was quite unfamiliar to me. Other reports soon followed and I began to hear of the new method of treating wounds by a surgeon in Glasgow named Lister. I also heard for the first time of Louis Pasteur, who had been engaged in studying certain problems in industrial chemistry and had made important discoveries on the action of germs in the process of fermentation. It had occurred to Lister, I was told, that the changes in the fluids which accumulate in the cavity of a wound were in the nature of a fermentation, probably produced by similar organisms. He had discovered in carbolic acid an agent destructive to their life. The claim was put forward that by the use of this drug he had found it possible to make wounds heal without the usual intervening process of suppuration.

I have made no mention thus far of Nélaton, although he was easily the leader in French surgery.[8] Auguste Nélaton had reached a period when he was relinquishing the activities of school and hospital to younger men. He had acquired a world-wide reputation in military surgery by his discovery of the bullet in Garibaldi's foot after Mr. Partridge of King's College Hospital, London, had failed to do so. This he had accomplished by the invention of his porcelain-tipped instrument known as Nélaton's probe, an achievement which was regarded as a triumph for French surgery. He was also high in favor at court, owing to the successful treatment of the young Prince Imperial. The Prince, a child about ten years of age, had been suffering from a swelling on the hip which Nélaton pronounced an abscess. It was reported that when he took up his knife to operate, Napoleon instinctively stretched out a protesting arm, but the surgeon, murmuring gruffly "Pardon, sire," restrained the anxious and doubting father with one hand while he plunged the knife in and laid open the abscess. I had the privilege of seeing Nélaton on but one brief occasion while making a ward visit with another surgeon and was most favorably impressed with his refined features, courteous manner, and distinguished bearing.

[8] The warning "Toute incision de la peau est une porte ouverte vers la mort" is attributed to Nélaton.

❧ XIII

Prophets of A New Era

The time soon came for me to leave Paris, cross the English Channel, and devote the remaining months of the academic year 1868–69 to a more intensive study of surgery than I had hitherto attempted. British surgery held a high reputation and was represented by more men of world-wide celebrity than were to be found at any of the other European schools. John Erichsen, whose textbook on surgery was a standard work of the time, was still in possession of his full powers as an operator and teacher. James Paget was at the height of his career and his book, *Lectures of Surgical Pathology,* was regarded as a classic in surgical literature. Sir William Fergusson, who had been called from Edinburgh to London in the 1840's, was at the moment perhaps the most prominent operating surgeon in London. Spencer Wells's operations for ovarian tumors at the Samaritan Hospital were engaging the eager attention of surgeons the world over. Sir Henry Thompson was not only the leading surgeon in diseases of the genito-urinary system in London but an acknowledged authority everywhere and one of the pioneers in the movement to make this branch of surgery a separate specialty. Pollock and Timothy Holmes at St. George's Hospital both were men with well-earned reputations, and at the Orthopaedic Hospital, Brodhurst was an able exponent of his specialty. John Wood had devised an operation for the radical cure of hernia with which his name was identified.

Christopher Heath, then a young man, was giving courses in operative surgery which were held in high esteem, and I was fortunate to be able to enroll myself as one of his pupils. The classes were small and each student had the benefit of personal attention at every one of the series of operations. One cadaver was assigned to a pair of students, who were thus able to act alternately as operator and assistant while Heath criticized every minute detail of the technique. There was a thoroughness in his drill which I have rarely seen equalled. Heath's work on diseases of the jaw, published later in life, gave him an enduring reputation. I find Durham's name mentioned in my notes as a young man performing the operation of lithotomy at Guy's Hospital. Many years later I met him again, when he was senior surgeon of that great hospital and one of a group of distinguished visitors who attended the first meeting of the Congress of

Physicians and Surgeons in Washington. I also had an opportunity to attend Thomas Bryant's clinic and hear him lecture. He was a fluent speaker, easy in manner, and with a style well adapted to the powers of comprehension of the average student. His *Practise of Surgery* had a large circulation in this country and ran through many editions. On my return home I found it the textbook recommended for the use of students at the Harvard Medical School, and it continued as such after my appointment as a teacher. It held its place valiantly in the old guard of surgical textbooks until all such were displaced by a demand for an entirely new surgery which was to dispute with internal medicine the right to treat the interior as well as the surface of the body.

It was at Mr. Holmes's clinic that I first saw an attempt at the antiseptic treatment of wounds. My notes record that the hands and instruments of the operator were washed in a solution of carbolic acid of the strength of one part of the acid to forty parts of water and that the wounds were dressed with one part of the acid to five of olive oil.

In looking back to this period of surgery in London, I find it difficult to record operative methods in the domain of general surgery which have left a lasting impression on my mind. I find mention of the operation for cleft palate as performed by Pollock and by Fergusson. My attention had been attracted to the different methods of performing this operation in Europe because this had been a specialty of my father, who I think had a record of about one hundred operations for cleft palate. His method, which had been described in numerous published communications, was then regarded as the standard one in the United States. He preferred, however, to operate upon patients as adults, and I was much interested therefore to see Fergusson operate upon a child only three months old. This, he stated, was done in deference to the wishes of the child's parents and was with him an exceptional case.

Mr. Brodhurst's work at the Orthopaedic Hospital seemed to me to be of an advanced character and an improvement on what I had seen at home, although at this time Louis Sayre in New York, whom I had heard lecture on one occasion in Gross's clinic in Philadelphia, had already placed this branch of surgery on a substantial basis and Buckminster Brown in Boston was beginning to develop orthopedic surgery as a specialty.

Mr. John Wood's operation for the radical cure of hernia was among the novelties of the day, and I took occasion to study his method with much care. Mr. Wood was a colleague of Sir William Fergusson at King's College Hospital, and was a man of quiet, unassuming manner

but unwavering in his opinions and impressive in his sincerity. The
operation was done with care but without pretension as to style. It
was performed as follows: The scrotum on the affected side having
been pushed up into the dilated inguinal canal by the index finger of
the left hand, a large curved needle with eye near its point was passed
along the surface of the finger as a guide and then pushed out through
the anterior wall of the canal and the skin. It was then threaded with
silver wire and withdrawn. This performance was repeated, the needle
entering and emerging at the same point, and the other end of the
loop drawn down and out through the point of entrance in the scrotum. The two free ends of the suture having been twisted together,
traction was made on the wire loop in the groin and a considerable
amount of cribriform fascia was thus drawn up and held firmly in the
ring. The protruding ends of this double suture were then twisted
over a roller bandage.

This operation attracted much attention in the surgical world, especially in England and this country. "Radical cures" of hernia were
numerous at that time and consisted chiefly in the application of some
mechanical device or the injection of some drug into the inguinal
canal. Great results were freely claimed for all these methods but
orthodox surgery regarded them justly with much suspicion. A cure
based upon a well-conceived and skillfully carried out surgical operation was an entirely different matter, however, and Wood's operation
was accorded a favorable reception. I recall vividly a case in which
this operation had been performed by one of the visiting surgeons at
the MGH previous to my departure for Europe, while I was still a
house pupil. Convalescence was prolonged and complicated by suppuration and an attack of erysipelas which meandered over a large
portion of the poor man's body. Doubtless in a limited number of
cases a radical cure was effected by this operation, but it was not
until many years later when antiseptic surgery had become well established that permanent relief from hernia was obtained by operative
procedures.

The two features of surgery in London at that period which stamped
themselves upon my mind as by far the most interesting were found
in the work of Sir Henry Thompson and of Spencer Wells. I have
already referred in some detail to Sir Henry in my account of a visit
to London two years previously and shall have occasion to mention
him again. Suffice it to say here that his method of crushing stone in
the bladder seemed a distinct improvement on the customary procedure
of the period. Up to that time the pattern of the lithotrite used was
chiefly that of Civiale. The stone having been crushed as thoroughly
as the conditions of the case permitted, a considerable period of time

was allowed to elapse before a second operation was attempted. During this interval the smaller fragments were left to escape without any attempt to wash out the bladder. Clover had devised a syringe for this purpose but it had not come into general use, probably because the caliber of the tube was not sufficiently large to allow the larger fragments to pass through it. The operation for lithotrity, as it was then practiced, involved a number of repetitions, frequently was followed by cystitis, and occasionally terminated fatally. There was, if I remember rightly, a growing dissatisfaction with the operation and an inclination to resort more frequently to some of the older methods of cutting for stone.

As I have already described, Sir Henry had sought to overcome the danger of cystitis by brief and frequent operations. The work of both Thompson and Clover undoubtedly helped to improve the statistics of lithotrity but still failed to place it upon an entirely satisfactory basis. Sir Henry's personality, his skill as an operator, and his reputation as a writer and lecturer all combined to make him one of the most interesting and conspicuous medical men of his time.

Spencer Wells owed his place in surgery to very different qualities. At the time of my visit he had performed 312 ovariotomies with a mortality of 16 per cent. I recall him as a person of retiring disposition and domestic tastes. He seemed to occupy the position of the apostle of a small but distinct sect of men who were dedicated to working out the new and difficult problem of abdominal surgery.[1] He had fellow workers in the United States, among the most prominent of whom were Marion Sims, Horatio R. Storer of Boston, Gilman Kimball and Walter Burnham of Lowell, and the Atlee brothers of Philadelphia, all of whom had been followers of Ephraim McDowell, the acknowledged pioneer of ovariotomy.

[1] The early ovariotomists were in a sense specialists who limited their surgical endeavor to this one operation. With what now appears as an uncanny intuition they avoided tasks that called for anatomical dissection and the handling of septic cases. They were not mere seekers after fame or other worldly reward for undertakings which by their very nature brought grave risk to the lives of fellow beings. Note the choice of the appropriate words "apostle," "sect," and "dedicated."

The finest hour of a surgical specialty can be its early, formative phase when the conviction of a few earnest men outruns the techniques available for its expression. The apostles of the new activity in surgery are carried forward by a true creative impulse rather than driven by some less worthy and vital motivation. Then, as Alfred North Whitehead said about activities in the arts, there comes a later phase when systematic techniques exceed the conviction. The techniques can be readily acquired by the "bright boys" who lack comprehension of the significance of what they do. They display their cleverness in handling the words and touching up the ideas of their predecessors.

Some of the lesser specialties never experience this first phase or hour of conviction. The invention of some gadget facilitates a technical breakthrough into new territory and conquest by instrumentation becomes as soulless as a blitzkrieg.

I had been looking forward since my trip with Spencer Wells across the Atlantic to seeing some of his operations at the Samaritan Hospital, and on my arrival in London was given a cordial reception. I saw several of his operations and on one occasion was invited to assist him. All that I was required to do in the way of preparation was to remove my coat and turn up my shirt sleeves. I do not remember any preliminary cleansing of the hands.[2] I was much impressed with his technical skill and the rapidity and careful attention to detail with which the operation was performed. Everything had been prepared beforehand; instruments, needles and thread were all in their allotted places, and principal and assistants worked with that machinelike accuracy which comes only with daily repetition. The steps followed one another with great smoothness and rapidity. A small incision was made along the median line, the cyst was exposed, and the contents were drawn off by the trochar and cannula. A portion of adherent omentum was clamped and tied off. The stump of the cyst was held externally by a detachable clamp. Nothing could have been more satisfactory from an onlooker's point of view, but a few days later I heard from his assistant that the case had terminated fatally. That Spencer Wells had been able to attain at that time so high a measure of success was due undoubtedly to his adroit methods. The incisions were small and superficial; cysts were allowed to grow to a size which made them easily accessible; the contents of the abdominal cavity were not exposed to view, and the operation resembled, as nearly as one of such importance could, what was known at that time as subcutaneous surgery.

I found one of my Vienna fellow students in London, where he had just established himself as a practitioner. Dr. J. Frank Payne had made his appearance in our little circle two years before as an Oxford graduate who had received the award of an Elizabethan travelling fellowship. He was of a retiring disposition, and soon won the esteem and respect of all his colleagues. During my stay in London we met occasionally at the house of one of his contemporaries, Dr. Carafi, for the purpose of discussing microscopical specimens in a quiet way. I gathered the impression that there were but a few men in London at that time who were interested in the new pathology and that these men were making an effort to do pioneer work in pathological histology. Payne was looking forward to an appointment at St. Thomas's

[2] In a letter to the *Boston Evening Transcript*, Mar. 13, 1912, J.C.W. wrote:

In London I assisted Wells in one of his abdominal operations, rolling up my sleeves, and plunging into the work with my surgically dirty hands and clothing, untroubled by any notion that the condition of my hands or of Wells's endangered the life of the patient. I had indeed several times assisted American surgeons in the same type of operation, before working with Wells.

Hospital. The stately group of buildings opposite the Houses of Parliament had not then been completed, and when I saw them for the first time many years later my colleague, full of years and honors, was one of its senior physicians, already anticipating with some misgivings the approaching period of his retirement.

So far as I recall, the anesthetic in almost universal use in London was chloroform, and I do not remember having seen ether given during my three years' stay in Europe. One exception should be made to this statement and that was the occasion when I gave ether for Liebreich in Paris. Richard Liebreich occupied as prominent a position in his special field, the eye, as any man in Paris and later added to his reputation by a successful career in London. I had attended a course in ophthalmoscopy given by LaCouer and had been most hospitably received by Liebreich. After many discussions as to the relative merits of ether and chloroform anesthesia, Liebreich finally gave me the opportunity to try ether on one of his patients. It was with many misgivings and much agitation on his part that the operation was performed under these conditions. So far as I know it was only at Lyons that ether had been used as an anesthetic. With that exception, Boston was practically alone in its loyalty to etherization. There was a feeling generally expressed that complete anesthesia could not be accomplished without giving this agent in quantities sufficient to make its employment dangerous to life, and it was not until many years after, when Dr. B. Joy Jeffries, who was attending a meeting of the British Medical Association in London, carried with him a demijohn of Squibb's best ether and demonstrated our method of giving the anesthetic, that it came more generally into use.

During my stay in London I had an opportunity to attend one of the meetings of the Pathological Society. I was much struck with the large attendance and the abundant number of pathological specimens shown. The program was carried out in a very businesslike way. No member was allotted more than five minutes for his communication and when, as occasionally occurred, some enthusiast ventured to exceed his limit of time, a vigorous shuffling of feet brought him promptly down into his seat. After the meeting there was much general conversation among members upon current medical topics, and I recall vividly the comments of London surgeons upon the claims of a young man in Glasgow to be able to heal wounds without suppuration. These were received with much skepticism and were regarded as the efforts of an enthusiast to attain conditions which the practical surgeon looked upon as decidedly Utopian.

I Talked with Lister

I had engaged passage home and had but a few weeks left before my three years' course of studies abroad would come to an end. It was now the beginning of June and the beauty of English scenery was at its height. My cousin Dr. Thomas Dwight and I had received a tempting invitation to join Mr. Charles H. Joy and his family in a four-in-hand tour across the south of England. This was the "poetry of travel" in those days. In the autumn of 1855 I had been one of a family party which had made the trip from Paris to Rome in an old English travelling carriage which my father had purchased from Mr. James Davis. The postillion in saddle in front and the courier in his rumble behind combined to make a most picturesque outfit for the journey. The old posting days enabled one to enjoy scenery to an extent which has never since been equalled.

This was an opportunity to see England as I had seen France and Switzerland in my childhood days. The trip was to include an excursion through a picturesque portion of Wales. But I knew that my European sojourn would be incomplete without a visit to Glasgow to see the work of Lister; actually this visit became the crowning event of my years as a student. Dwight and I broke away from our party at Bristol and took the night train for Edinburgh, arriving on June 14th. My classmate at Vienna, Blair Cunynghamel, who subsequently rose to honor and distinction in his profession, was on hand to receive us. Through his good offices we were able to visit the Royal Infirmary and see for the first time some examples of Listerian antiseptic treatment, and also to meet Mr. Joseph Bell, Mr. John Chiene, and Mr. Patrick Heron Watson. If I remember rightly the latter succeeded Mr. Bell on his retirement from the professorship of surgery a few years later.

I have already referred to the reception given us by Sir James Simpson on this occasion [Chapter III] and his explanation of the principle of acupressure. He was the dominant figure of medicine and surgery in Scotland at that period, and it seems to me that great credit should be accorded him for an active interest in the progress of medical science, which paved the way not only for improvement in the treatment of wounds but for much that pertained to preventive medicine.

After a brief stay in Edinburgh we turned toward Glasgow, passing through the valley of the Trossachs and crossing Lochs Katrine and Lomond. We presented our credentials to Mr. Lister the same evening. As I look back upon this most interesting episode of my European life, we seemed to be leaving the teachings of the old medical world of which we were fairly up-to-date products to enter the birthplace of a new medicine and surgery, there to receive at the source an inspiration to cast off much that was old and prepare ourselves for the dawn of a science which was to revolutionize medicine.

Joseph Lister was living in a very modest house in the residential quarter of Glasgow. He was still a young man although at the head of a large hospital service. We did not receive the impression, from either his bearing or his environment, of a man who had attained celebrity. He seemed to be quietly pursuing his avocation as a practicing surgeon, absorbed in hospital service and scientific investigation. There was an air of almost puritanical simplicity and reserve, with no assumption of superiority. His manner was frank and simple, and characterized by great sincerity of purpose. There was no display of the prosperous practitioner about him; he was surrounded by neither retainers nor a group of admiring pupils. He was an unassuming doctor of a serious turn endeavoring to work out in his own quiet way a theory and system of practice which he hoped would advance the art of surgery.

Lister gave us every opportunity to see the application of his method of healing wounds. The next morning at the hospital visit dressings were shown to us with much care and detail. The group of cases in the wards was made up of compound fractures, psoas abscess, and empyema, all of which illustrated well the advantages of his dressing. His explanations were clear and concise, and he seemed to me to be possessed of much more knowledge of modern pathology than his fellow countrymen. After dinner at his home that evening, we adjourned to his study, where he showed us flasks with open but downward-curved necks containing specimens of urine which for months had remained unchanged. Although air could pass freely, the bacteria were deposited at the curve of the tortuous tube, and fermentation of the contained fluids was thus prevented. Lister also called our attention to the effects of a catgut ligature placed around a carotid artery of a calf.[1] The new ring of tissue formed about the vessel, he explained,

[1] On the 31st of December, 1868 Lister tied the right carotid artery of a calf at about the middle of the neck with two ligatures separated from each other by a distance of about an inch and a half. One was composed of three strips of peritoneum from the small intestine of an ox, twisted into a cord; the other was of fine catgut. Both had previously been soaked for four hours in a saturated watery solution of carbolic acid. The wound healed by first intention, and the

was the result of the organization of the material of which the ligature was composed. This thought gave rise to some discussion of the pre-vailing theory of the organization of the thrombus, during which Lister turned to me and said, "I do not expect my contemporaries to accept all my doctrines, but I look to the coming generation to adopt and perfect them."

The dressings he was using at that time were made of a lac plaster spread upon cambric, having much the appearance of ordinary ad-hesive plaster. It served as a vehicle for carbolic acid, the emanations of which were supposed to exert a destructive influence upon germs. The acid itself was known to be an irritant and was not brought directly into contact with an open wound. To prevent direct contact, a waterproof material known as "protective" was placed over the in-cision. The carbolized plaster was then separated from its cambric backing by the application of heat and the flexible mass was laid upon the protective layer, overlapping the latter in all directions. The vapor of carbolic acid could penetrate the protective layer with sufficient power to exert its antiseptic influence. This Lister had proved by placing protective on a fragment of beefsteak which was placed in a shallow jar and then gently pouring a solution of the acid upon the protective layer, where it remained suspended and separated from direct contact with the raw meat beneath. The emanations which penetrated this layer prevented decomposition. Discharges from the wound, as they emerged from beneath the edges of the protective, were acted upon directly by the acid and germs were thus prevented from spreading along this column of fluid organic matter into the interior of the wound. I am recording Lister's early views of his treat-ment as I heard them from his own lips, without attempting to repro-duce the antiseptic theory of that period in any detail.

I had an opportunity to see Lister perform an amputation of the breast. His method of preparing the field of operation was to wash the skin thoroughly with a weak solution of carbolic acid. Folds of skin and parts covered with hair were rubbed hard with a 1-to-5 oily solution of carbolic acid. During the operation hemorrhage was

---

calf was killed a month afterwards. [*The Collected Papers of Joseph, Baron Lister,* (Oxford, 1909), I, xxxviii; II, 93.]

In 1886 J.C.W. published a monograph of nearly two hundred pages on *The Healing of Arteries after Ligature in Man and Animals.* A lengthy review of the history of the subject preceded a section reporting the results of experiments in animals. These were performed in the physiological and pathological laboratories of the Harvard Medical School and also in the veterinary department of the University. Reference was made to human arteries in the Army Medical Museum and also to MGH material. It seems likely that the brief conversation with Lister in 1869 had stimulated a lasting interest in the subject and led to this thorough and detailed monograph by Warren.

controlled by torsion, not a single ligature being employed. Torsion was used almost universally in Great Britain for all the smaller arteries. The edges of the incision were brought together with silk sutures. Lister was studying methods of preparing catgut so that it could be used as a suture but had not yet adopted it for that purpose. Since the time he began to use the antiseptic treatment he had encountered but one complication of erysipelas and two of pyemia. "This in wards which contain on an average some sixty patients and in an infirmary which has for its site an old cholera burying ground is certainly something to boast of." At our second visit to the hospital wards we were shown a case of phimosis in which carbolized oil had been used for a dressing. Before leaving Glasgow I obtained from Lister's apothecary samples of his plaster in large tin cylinders, and carried them with me across the Atlantic.[2]

This visit to Lister left a deep impression upon me. I saw in him a surgical clinician who, unlike the majority of the men of his time, fully appreciated the practical value of scientific research to the work he had in hand. All branches of science in that day were suffering from the reproach of being more or less theoretical. The harvest time for the faithful laborers in the fields of science was still a long way off. The public looked upon a man who showed a propensity for such pursuits as one not likely to be of much value to them. This was especially true of medicine in Great Britain and in this country. I remember well the remark of a distinguished German pathologist who in conversation with Ranvier said of English doctors, "Ils font tous la clientele." That was the only kind of man a physician was expected to be in English-speaking countries. Lister, however, had an alert ear for whatever science had to offer him, and so it came about that Pasteur's researches for the wine and silk industries bore a message to

---

[2] Dr. George W. Gay in a letter to J.C.W. dated April 7, 1926 wrote:

> Dr. [Abner] Post tells me that he was surgical house officer at the MGH in 1869–70 and distinctly remembers your return from Europe with a supply of Lister dressings and also a reasonable stock of enthusiasm. Both were used at your hospital from that time on to the present and it would be fair to presume that you had not a little to do in introducing antiseptic and aseptic surgery to Boston. [MGH Archives.]

The first reported use of carbolic acid in Boston surgery appears to have been made by George Derby of the City Hospital on September 21, 1867 [*Boston Med. and Surg. J.* 77, 271 (October 31, 1867)]. George H. Gay of the MGH followed suit on October 12 (reported April 9, 1868). Other local surgeons who gave this agent an early trial were Samuel Cabot of the MGH, and David W. Cheever, William H. Thorndike, and F. C. Ropes of the City Hospital. Henry O. Marcy of Cambridge put carbolic acid to surgical use on December 19, 1867 in private practice, and later claimed American priority on the basis of having been a pupil of Lister during the summer months of 1870.

him full of meaning. The fluids accumulating in an open wound undergo chemical changes similar to those observed by Pasteur, and this decomposition must be attributable to the presence of microscopic organisms. It was in this crude form that the new doctrine was presented to us.

My stay in Glasgow was a brief one, but I had not yet fulfilled a promise made to my father that I would not fail to visit Dublin. Many years before his experience with the profession there had been so gratifying that he felt my education would be incomplete without a glimpse of Irish surgery.[3] My Berlin classmate Swanzy, later Sir Henry Swanzy, who died in 1913 after a long and distinguished career that brought him many honors, had furnished me with ample introductions. Of special interest was the Rotunda Hospital, which under the direction of Denham had gained an international reputation in obstetrics. It was a school much resorted to by medical students, and it was here that Dr. William L. Richardson obtained his early education as an obstetrician.[4] My stay in Dublin was necessarily a very brief one. Only a few days remained before the departure of the Cunard steamship *Tarifa* from Queenstown, and I can but mention the pleasant hospitality that I received at the hands of my father's and Swanzy's friends. The names of Stokes, Johnston, Butt, and Hamilton may be mentioned. A trip to Killarney fittingly completed my journeyings in foreign lands and the 30th of July found me, in company with my cousin Dr. Thomas Dwight, bound for home.

[3] In a letter to his father dated August 22, 1834 Dr. J. Mason Warren wrote: "I have seldom experienced more hospitality and good-will than during my visit to Dublin. Every one seemed to do his best to oblige me without any reserve." He continued to keep in touch with the work of his Irish colleagues throughout life. In the *Dublin Quarterly Journal of Medical Science* for November 1866 a paper by J. Mason Warren on fissure of the palate was reviewed with this comment: "Mr. Warren's acquaintance with Irish surgery might be a lesson to many at home who remain habitually ignorant of the doings of their brethren." [Howard Payson Arnold, *Memoir of Jonathan Mason Warren, M.D.* (Boston, 1886), pp. 195 f.]

[4] In 1867–68 the young Dr. Richardson studied in the School of Physic at the University of Dublin and served as externe at the Rotunda Lying-in Hospital. In April 1868 he received the degree of L.M. (Licentiate of Midwifery) and a special diploma for excellence in obstetrics. His role at the Boston Lying-in Hospital is described in a later chapter.

∾ XV

Practice on Park Street

I entered upon my professional career in Boston as a practicing physician and surgeon at the old mansion-house, No. 2 Park Street, on September 6th, 1869. There had been no material change in this street and it was still used for residential purposes. No. 2 was part of a block of four buildings which had been built by Charles Bulfinch early in the century (1805) and remained substantially unchanged. The house had been occupied by two generations of my family [1] and was well adapted to the purposes of a practitioner of medicine, not only on account of its central position in the old city but also because of its internal arrangement. The residence was spacious, with a frontage of nearly forty feet. A vestibule at the entrance opened into a large central hall, at the back of which was a winding staircase. In the four corners of the hall were four marble busts supported by substantial pedestals. To the right was an arch leading into a patients' sitting room. On the left was the doctor's study, a delightful, old-fashioned room surrounded with high bookcases which almost completely covered the walls and left space only for the fireplace and mantel. In a deep recess over the fireplace was placed a mirror reflecting the form of an old mahogany Willard clock, which droningly ticked away the hours and lent an air of repose and comfort. The windows opening on the street were somewhat larger than the original Bulfinch type (perhaps to permit more readily the entrance of students seeking sanctuary within from an indignant mob). That this actually happened once was recounted to me by the late Dr. Henry C. Perkins of Newburyport. As a student he had slept in a little dressing room at the back of the office, and was aroused one night by a group of classmates in such a predicament.

The high bookcases lining the walls were heavily laden with the accumulation of more than half a century of medical literature, a fair representation of the medical progress of the period. No expense had been spared by my grandfather, and thus my father had become the

---

[1] J.C.W.'s grandfather Dr. John C. Warren died on May 4th, 1856, and No. 2 Park Street was left to Dr. J. Mason Warren. J.C.W.'s sister Rosamond makes this amusing note in her *Recollections:* "My mother refused [to move into No. 2] until the various skeletons, fossils, pickled specimens of all kinds, and the large copy of Rembrandt's 'Lesson in Anatomy,' which hung in the hall, were removed."

possessor not only of the standard works of earlier days but also of many a rare and valuable monograph produced when no thought of expense was allowed to stand in the way of an ambitious author.[2] The room was rounded into an oval at the further end and led into what had been the dressing room or the students' bedroom. This residence was somewhat formidable for an inexperienced beginner, particularly one of youthful appearance like myself, but seemed to carry with it a certain measure of endorsement to any doubting visitor who had "expected to see an older man."

On the second floor were the family quarters. Fronting on the street were the parlor and the dining room, communicating by mahogany

[2] The bulk of the private medical library assembled by the Warrens now forms a special collection of about two thousand books and pamphlets in the Harvard University Schools of Medicine and Public Health Library. Some of the flyleaves bear the names of five Warren owners. A portion of this family collection had been given previously to the Boston Medical Library by J.C.W., and in 1928 the remainder was bequeathed by his son to Harvard.

The collection includes incunabula such as an eight-volume *Medicinae* of Celsus (1497), which had been acquired by J.C.W. A copy of the *De Custorum Chirurgia per Institutionem* of Taliacotius (1597) was brought home by J. Mason Warren, the exponent of plastic surgery. John C. Warren collected a *De Humani Corporis Fabrica* of Vesalius (1543), Pare's *Opera Chirurgica* (1582), and Harvey's *De Motu Cordis e Sanguinis in Animalibus* (1639).

The medical Warrens have long been sponsors and friends of institutional libraries. Dr. John C. Warren was treasurer and librarian of the original Boston Medical Library (1805–1826). He and Dr. James Jackson had organized the first Society for Medical Improvement (1803–?1810), which installed a collection of books at the home of Dr. John Fleet on Milk Street. This collection became the nucleus of the Boston Medical Library, which in 1810 moved to No. 49 (old) Marlborough Street, the new home of Harvard's medical school. The Medical Faculty opened its own library in 1819, after the move to Mason Street.

Warren and Jackson were among the fourteen organizers of the Anthology Society in 1805, which opened a general library on Congress Street. The trustees of this Society were incorporated two years later as the Proprietors of the Boston Athenaeum, which found its first home in Scollay's Buildings at Tremont Street. The members of the Anthology Society were voted life shares in the Athenaeum (the MGH held Share No. 95 from 1817 to 1822). The Athenaeum absorbed the Boston Medical Library in 1826.

When the latter made a new start in 1875 at Hamilton Place opposite the Park Street Church, J.C.W. was appointed to its first executive committee. He also served on the building committee set up in 1899 to erect the present building of the Boston Medical Library on the Fenway.

In 1823 the trustees of the MGH appointed a committee to "collect" a general library for the patients. Several months later Dr. John C. Warren received a deposit of $50 from a Bostonian for the purchase of religious books to be lent to patients in the wards. In 1841 Dr. Warren established what became known as the Warren Fund at the Hospital for the purchase of religious books to be *given* to patients. Three years later the trustees authorized an appropriation of $50 for the general library. In 1880 the members of the Warren family gave their consent to a proposal that the Warren Fund be applied to the general library, which was soon renamed the Warren Library. In 1900 J.C.W. gave it a large monetary gift. Present-day hospital employees as well as patients find its hospitable and well-stocked reading room a welcome sanctuary.

folding doors. The view from these rooms was an exceptional one, there being no dwelling houses intervening to block out the sky line formed by the hills of Brookline. The western sun on a winter's day gave light and warmth which penetrated all corners of the house until the very close of the day. In the rear was a finely proportioned oval library with lofty cases filled with the accumulations of two generations and surmounted by many busts and vases. The foliage of the old Granary Burying Ground immediately behind the house could be seen through an arched alcove, in which stood the bust of Dr. James Jackson, imparting, as he himself had done, a sense of refinement and dignity to his surroundings. Jackson had been a lifelong friend of the family. Between the windows a fine piece of Empire cabinet work, a relic of the old John Warren house on School Street, stood opposite the fireplace. Above the mantel hung a family portrait of Joseph Warren by John Singleton Copley.[3]

It was representative of early Boston mansions, of which few examples are left today. Naturally I had some misgivings in entering upon a career in such ambitious surroundings, but the other members of the family still being in Europe, the house was empty and at my disposal. I proceeded to carry on old traditions as best I could.[4]

[3] A more intimate description of the oval library is given by Rosamond Warren Gibson in her *Recollections of My Life for My Children* (Boston: privately printed, 1939):

> At the back, on the right of the stairs was the large oval library, running out towards the Granary Burying Ground. This room had two windows on the side looking into the yard, and a bay window at the end, on each side of which were closets containing medical books, specimens, and a skeleton in a case. During the day we were quite brave in exploring these regions, even shaking hands with the skeleton. At night, however, no one enjoyed being left in that room alone. Bookcases all around the room reached nearly to the ceiling, surmounted by busts. Crimson satin curtains decorated the windows, while an old-fashioned mahogany desk, long tables, and comfortable chairs constituted the remaining furniture. Over the mantel-piece hung a fine Copley portrait of General Joseph Warren, surmounted by two crossed swords, one of which was said to have been carried by him at the battle of Bunker Hill, while the other belonged to my grandfather [John C.] Warren as surgeon of the Cadet Corps for over forty years.

[4] A reluctance to mention personal and family affairs was a prevailing trait of J.C.W.'s generation of Bostonians. From this point on, his Reminiscences deal largely with professional matters. Two episodes related by his sister Rosamond in her *Recollections* are here inserted; one has to do with the famous Boston fire of November 1872, and the other takes cognizance of J.C.W.'s marriage. Rosamond (Mrs. Gibson) was then living at No. 137 Beacon Street.

> As my mother was in Europe, Coll was living alone at No. 2 Park Street at that time. When it looked as if the fire would spread as far as our house, he sent for me to come and remove the silver from a secret cupboard which he could not find. Many of the horses at that time were ill with epizoötic, but Lawrence Curtis secured a Kenny and Clark hack and called in the

middle of the night to take me up there. Charlie [Gibson] also said we could take his horse, which was harnessed to an express cart. On arriving, I found the silver, most of which consisted of my own wedding presents, in a large wooden and silver chest. This with other precious things, too large for the hack, was put in the cart, after having placed on top the picture of "Cleopatra Dissolving the Pearl," by Guido Reni, a family heirloom from my Grandfather Crowninshield. Having secured all we could and the cart having been sent off, we started for home in the hack. Imagine my horror, on reaching the State House, to find Cleopatra lying in the road with the chest on top of her! It seemed that someone had run into the cart and upset it, and the horse, breaking away, had run back to the stable. Kind friends, however, came to the rescue, picked up the treasures, righted the cart, and dragged it to No. 137. There, to my despair, we found that the corner of the chest had gone through Cleopatra's hand, and I trembled to think what my mother would say. Fortunately, we had it beautifully restored, but as the fire never reached Park Street after all, the picture would have been much safer where it was.

The painting of Cleopatra was purchased by George Crowninshield for his father Benjamin, J.C.W.'s grandfather, at the Zampieri Palace in Bologna, which had sponsored the school of Guido. It is described in the *Reminiscences of My Life for My Children* (privately printed, 1910) by Annie Crowninshield Warren, J.C.W.'s mother.

J.C.W. mentions the goings on during the night of the great fire in his chapter "Reminiscences of Park Street" in Robert Means Lawrence's *Old Park Street and Its Vicinity* (Boston, 1922):

The night of the Great Boston Fire in 1872 was a memorable one for Number Two. This private dwelling was then on the very front line of the residential district; and with its neighbors in the block was nearer to the seat of the conflagration than any dwelling-house of that period. The writer, being the only occupant of the house at that time, hastily summoned members of the family from their homes in the "Back Bay," and they kept open house for the greater part of the night. Old fire bags, bearing the name of John C. Warren, were unearthed from their concealment in ornamental fire buckets of the date 1816. These were filled with silver; and together with valuable paintings, were removed to the homes of relatives. This was not done until the fire had worked up Summer Street as far as Washington Street, when it was felt that the stampede of vehicles of all kinds would soon make passage from Park Street to Beacon Street impracticable.

The account of J.C.W.'s marriage as related by his sister follows:

In May, 1873, my brother was married at Emmanuel Church by Phillips Brooks to lovely Amy Shaw, daughter of Mr. and Mrs. Gardiner Howland Shaw. My mother brought her a string of pearls and a diamond cross as presents from her and Coll. She was, without exception, the handsomest person I ever saw, taking into consideration her height, carriage, and coloring, besides her golden hair, lovely blue eyes, small nose, and short upper lip. She had been greatly admired abroad and that winter in Boston everyone rushed to the window to see Amy walk by in her blue velvet trimmed with fur.

The Warrens had two sons, John and Joseph. John Warren became associate professor of anatomy at the Harvard Medical School. He published a dissecting manual in 1924 in coauthorship with his assistant, Dr. Alexander S. Begg. After he had spent eight years in the preparation of an anatomical atlas, a fatal illness cut short his contribution to medical science. The atlas was brought to completion by his colleagues, however, and published by the Harvard University

Press in 1930. Joseph Warren departed from the family tradition of medicine to become Bussey and later Weld Professor of Law at Harvard. Richard, son of Joseph, has restored the name of Warren to the rolls of surgery.

It is also of interest to sketch the subsequent history of No. 2 Park Street. J.C.W. and his wife lived here through 1874 while his mother was visiting Paris and Rome, and then moved to No. 58 Beacon Street near the foot of the Common. When business firms began to encroach on the residences of Park Street, his mother moved to Commonwealth Avenue in the new Back Bay. The old Bulfinch house on Park Street was replaced by the present building about 1877. The new structure contained the 250-seat Hawthorne Hall and also a gallery leased to the art dealers, Doll and Richards, who remained here until 1908. The Warren property was then leased to the Houghton Mifflin Company, publishers, and sold to this firm in 1939.

The Old Guard in Control

During my sojourn in Europe there had been only one noticeable change at the Massachusetts General Hospital. The old amphitheatre known as the Dome (Ether Dome) had been abandoned, and an operating theatre and out-patient department had been opened in a new wing.[1] This was still the period of what aptly has been called the "surgery of the amphitheatre" and the new building had been so constructed as to give room to a much larger class. An "etherizing" and a "recovery" room had been added and were regarded as noteworthy innovations. Handsome mahogany instrument cases lined with red cloth occupied conspicuous positions in the new theatre. They were the gift of Dr. Henry J. Bigelow, who as the senior surgeon was the dominant figure of the hospital staff.[2] There was an atmosphere of up-to-dateness about the place which seemed to augur well for the future, and I felt the old "esprit de corps" coming back with full force within me as I took my place on the benches at my first Saturday morning attendance at surgical operations.

There was no change, however, in the old-time customs. Operating gowns had not yet made their appearance and the old blue broadcloth frock coat with velvet collar buttoned resolutely around the throat still continued to be the costume of the operating surgeon. The technique of the operation and the after-treatment were the same as they had been in my student days. Possessed, as I was, with an abundant supply of Lister dressings, naturally I was eager to have an opportunity to test their value, but on venturing to propose that they be used in a sample case, I was informed coldly that the "carbolic

---

[1] The new operating building at the MGH was opened in 1868. Dr. J. Mason Warren, before his death in 1867, had been active in raising funds for its construction. Its spacious amphitheatre was officially named the Henry J. Bigelow Operating Theatre in 1890.

Following the erection of a new surgical building in 1900, the high-ceilinged amphitheatre of 1868 was put to a number of uses. The seats were removed and the large floor space was given over to Zander physical-therapy apparatus. During the influenza epidemic of 1918 beds were installed to care for navy personnel. For many years the building housed the x-ray department, and finally in 1937 the structure was demolished, together with the 1900 surgical building, to make way for the George Robert White Building.

[2] Dr. Bigelow also donated new surgical instruments which he had purchased in Europe.

acid treatment" had already been tried and discarded.[3] An occasion soon offered itself in my own practice, in a case of amputation of the breast for carcinoma. The operation was performed on October 9th, 1869, and I think it was probably one of the earliest instances of antiseptic surgery in this country performed strictly according to the directions of Lister.[4]

[3] In the autumn of 1867, under the direction of Dr. Henry J. Bigelow, "Lister dressings" were applied in two amputation cases by Henry Beach, then a surgical house pupil. "They did well. But other dressings did well also, so that the new method was abandoned." By 1876, however, Bigelow had "accepted the new doctrine with most of its details." (From a lecture on "The Modern Art of Promoting the Repair of Tissue" given by Bigelow at the Harvard Medical School in 1876 and published in the June 5, 1879 number of the *Boston Medical and Surgical Journal.*)

Bigelow's ardent support of etherization in 1846 has often been contrasted with his initial attitude toward Listerism, the former being taken to illustrate the open-mindedness of youth and the latter, the conservatism of advancing years. This is by no means the whole explanation of the matter. The result of taking a few breaths of ether vapor was immediate and obvious. Even after he had accepted the antiseptic method, Bigelow had a lingering distaste for the ritual which antisepsis brought into his practical world of surgery. To the hardheaded professor the procedures smacked of abracadabra and offended his sense of dignity. He described his own reaction with insight: "It flatters neither the vanity nor the scientific sense to exorcise an invisible enemy with something very like a censer."

It was characteristic of Bigelow not to acknowledge the part J.C.W. played in bringing the techniques of Listerian antisepsis to Boston in 1869 (see following note). He did, however, express wholehearted respect toward Lister himself. It seems likely, nevertheless, that it was largely through J.C.W.'s influence that Boston surgery and its leader kept well abreast of the field in this country.

One of the most celebrated contemporaries of Bigelow was Samuel D. Gross, under whom J.C.W. had studied while in Philadelphia. Gross was the author of a *System of Surgery* which saw many editions, and in the preface to the sixth edition (1882) Lister was praised only as the apostle of cleanliness: "It was he who first taught surgeons the importance and value of thorough cleanliness in their operations and dressings before his time so little understood and so seldom practised." But as to antiseptic methods, Gross recorded on page 346: "I have never found any appreciable benefit in such a case from the use of antiseptic dressings, although they are regarded by many surgeons as most valuable accessories."

[4] On his return from Europe J.C.W. was an ardent disciple of Lister. The following letter by him appeared in the October 7, 1869 issue of the *Boston Medical and Surgical Journal (4, 175)*:

> *Mr. Editor,* — Having recently had the privilege of visiting the wards of Prof. Lister, at Glasgow, it may prove of some interest to the readers of the *Medical Journal* to learn the latest modifications he has made in the antiseptic treatment of wounds.
>
> This subject still continues to excite considerable interest in most English cities, and has been taken up and employed successfully in some of the continental schools. Although this system has been condemned by many distinguished surgeons, it has not been by any means universally so, and still claims several enthusiastic supporters in Great Britain.
>
> It may be as well to touch upon his germ theory of putrefaction and the process of healing by scabbing, although the subject has been very clearly and

Soon after my return I received an appointment as physician to out-patients at the Massachusetts General Hospital. This I gladly

elaborately exposed by him in a series of articles which have appeared during the last eighteen months in the *Lancet* and *British Medical Journal*. The germ theory may be briefly stated thus: — suppuration in wounds is caused by an irritation produced by the presence of germs or organisms which find their way into a wound, and there multiply and cause putrefaction.

Putrefaction, then, is the exciting cause of suppuration in a wound: can this be prevented, the largest wound may heal without any secretion of pus. This process of healing, such as may take place in a large lacerated wound of the leg accompanying compound fracture, is not considered by him to be healing by "first intention," nor indeed "by granulation." It is rather an intermediate process. Given a wound sufficiently large and accompanied with sufficient loss of substance to be incapable of healing by first intention — the extravasated blood and serum cover the surface of the exposed parts and form a clot which serves the purpose of a protecting scab. Provided now that no living germ is introduced beneath or penetrates this covering, the cell formation takes place quietly in the parts below, while the clot itself becomes organized in the same manner as a thrombus in an artery. The clot or scab establishes in this way a vascular connection with the parts beneath. Meanwhile, cicatrization continues, and as the edges of the wound approximate each other the scab is compressed on all sides, and finally atrophies and comes away. If it is cut into, however, before union is complete, it will *bleed*. When a wound heals in this manner, no pus whatever is found upon the dressings. They may be stained by the escape of a small amount of serum and what is called a mucous discharge. This fluid, examined carefully under the microscope, is found to contain no pus corpuscles whatever.

The antiseptic treatment of wounds has undergone a variety of modifications since Mr. Lister first began his experiments, some two years ago. Most of these have been described at length in the English Journals, and will hardly need repetition here, especially as his present method differs from them in several essential particulars.

The dressings are now changed daily, and the tin plate and the paste have been discarded, and a very thin piece of oil silk and a lac plaster are used in their place. (The receipt as given us by the New Apothecaries' Company at Glasgow, is the following: — Take of Shellac 3 parts, Carbolic acid 1 part. Dissolve with gentle heat, and spread with machine; when spread, coat with a solution of gutta percha, 1 + 16 of bisulphate carbon.) After an operation the wound is washed with a solution of carbolic acid, one part to twenty of water, and the edges are brought together by antiseptic sutures. The nozzle of a syringe is then introduced into one end of the wound, which is freely syringed out with the same solution. A strip of very thin oil silk, rendered antiseptic by being dipped into the acid solution, is then placed upon the wound of a size just sufficient to cover it. The object of this is to protect the wound from the carbolic acid contained in the dressing next to come. This consists of the lac plaster. Before application the plaster is stripped off from its cambric, by moistening the cloth in water. This is done in order that the plaster may more easily adapt itself to the parts about the wound. The gutta-percha layer must also be rubbed off. The size of the plaster thus applied is sufficient to overlap the wound an inch or two in all directions. Above this is applied another much larger piece of the plaster, with its cambric on, and the whole is secured by a bandage.

The object which he tries to accomplish is to *blockade* the wound in all directions by dressings exhaling carbolic-acid vapor, while the wound itself

accepted as it seemed an opportunity to pave the way to a later appointment on the surgical staff. At that period there was only one

---

is not touched by the acid at all. The small amount of the acid left in the wound soon ceases to exert any irritating influence, and the wound is exposed only to the vapor of the acid which penetrates the oil-silk covering. Mr. Lister has found by experiment that the vapor of the acid which passes through a piece of oil-silk is sufficient to disinfect any animal matter which may be on the other side. Any secretions which exude from the wound and become exposed to the air are thus thoroughly disinfected before they have a chance to regurgitate. The same fate awaits any germ which tries to find its way in with them.

If there is any discharge from the wound the dressings should be changed daily. The upper dressing being removed, the lower layer of plaster, which adheres closely to the skin, is carefully peeled off from one end and with it the oil silk. As the wound is exposed it is syringed with the 1-40 solution, and this is continued until the new dressing is applied.

Plaster dressings cannot be applied in all cases, for instance on wounds about the genital organs. In such cases a piece of lint soaked in a solution of one part to five of oil is used, but this must be changed frequently.

We should not omit to add that the parts to be operated upon should be well washed with a weak solution of the acid, and if there are any folds of skin or parts covered with hair in the neighborhood, these should be rubbed hard with the 1-5 oily solution, to destroy any organisms that may be lurking about.

A word here about the antiseptic ligature and suture. A detailed account of the ligature of arteries on the antiseptic system has been given by Mr. Lister in an article in the *Lancet* of April 3, 1869, and he still continues to employ ligatures prepared in this way. This, in brief, consists in the employment of fine catgut ligatures steeped in an oily solution of the acid of the strength of one part to five, with a small quantity of water diffused through it. It has been found by experiment, that such a ligature not only does not exert any irritating influence on the parts about, but eventually becomes organized and intimately connected with the outer coat of the artery and the surrounding tissue. At present torsion is used almost universally in England for all the smaller arteries, and the writer had the opportunity of witnessing an amputation of the breast by Mr. Lister, where not a single ligature was used.

Up to the present time he has contented himself with employing silk for sutures — with one exception, however. This was in an operation for the removal of a small tumor on the forehead, where catgut sutures were used. The wound was dressed antiseptically, and the patient left for the country and was not seen for several days. On his return, the dressings were removed, and the wound was found to have healed without suppuration. The sutures remained, to all appearance, unchanged; but on seizing one of them with the forceps in order to cut them with the scissors, the external portion came away easily, leaving *no trace behind* of the part which had been buried in the edges of the wound. The same was the case with all the other sutures. He is of the opinion that in this case the deep portion of the suture had either become organized or was absorbed. He purposes to experiment further in this direction to see if this result is constant.

The antiseptic dressing has been found to be most successful in the treatment of abscesses, compound fractures, excisions of the breast, and in those wounds to which the dressing can be easily and accurately applied. He has not had uniform success in the treatment of amputations, though he has found them on the whole to do much better than when dressed according to old rules. During the last two years that he has employed this system he

occupant of the position of surgeon to out-patients. This was Dr. J. Theodore Heard, who had retired from the Service with an excellent

has had but one case of erysipelas and two of pyaemia. This in wards, which contain on an average some sixty patients, and in an infirmary which has for its site an old cholera burying ground, is certainly something to boast of.

The writer has had the opportunity of conversing at length with Mr. Lister on this system, and also with many prominent English surgeons, and can truly say that nowhere has he seen the details so carefully attended to as in Mr. Lister's wards. Most surgeons, in England at least, have contented themselves with following his directions in a general way, frequently omitting some important particular. For instance, one writer states that he took great pains to wash out his sponges in water both before and during the operation! The very thing he should have taken care not to do, unless the water had been previously rendered antiseptic.

Whatever the merits of the antiseptic system may be, it is very evident that a proper appreciation of them can never be arrived at without that scrupulous attention to detail which has so frequently been insisted upon by its originator. Very truly yours,

J. C. WARREN, M.D.

A present-day student of wound healing accustomed to thinking in terms of the reactions of living tissues may find a document such as J.C.W.'s letter totally incomprehensible as the record of an advance in surgical thinking. It can be said with good reason that it would be preferable to ignore a wound altogether rather than destroy more tissue, along with natural defense mechanisms of the body, by such zealous application of a corrosive solution of carbolic acid. The fact is that Listerism in the stage of development described in the letter is understandable only when viewed against a background of rampant cross-infection within hospitals (hospitalism). Its benefits were measurable by the reduction of erysipelas, pyemia, hospital gangrene, and the other infections carried from one wound to another. The drastic techniques described by J.C.W. could have been beneficial only in an environment of ubiquitous sepsis, meddlesome dressings and almost complete ignorance of isolation precautions.

In concept, Listerism oversimplified wound suppuration as a unifactorial event. A germ was lurking about and trying to find its way into the wound; Lister was trying to prevent it from doing so. In this sense, and as J.C.W. interpreted it, Listerism was truly *anti*-sepsis, that is, a measure to prevent the entrance of a pathogen into the wound (see note 3, Chapter I).

Listerism, as interpreted for several decades, not only failed to emphasize the effectiveness of the natural defense mechanisms of the living body; it also gave but slight weight to the factor of the dead tissue in the wound on which bacteria gain a foothold. There can be no doubt that Lister himself was aware of both factors, but the emphasis on excluding germs obscured all other considerations. His awareness of the dead-tissue factor is shown, for example, by a continued advocacy of the use of drains to prevent the accumulation of contaminated blood clot.

To intimate that surgeons before Lister expected all wounds to suppurate and pour forth "laudable pus" is to underestimate the intelligence of generations of shrewd observers over the course of centuries. Confusion on this point centers in a failure to discriminate between different kinds of wounds, a matter on which the old-time wound surgeon was clear. Hippocrates taught that dead flesh in a wound must turn into pus, but Theodoric as well as Mondeville expected *incised* wounds, in which dead tissue is customarily minimal, to heal without suppuration as a matter of course. In Lister's own century, at the Battle of Waterloo, it was generally agreed among English surgeons that if the edges of

record as an army surgeon during the Civil War. Up to the time of his appointment (1866) the surgical service of the Hospital had been provided solely by the staff of six visiting surgeons, and it was part of their duty after the morning visit to prescribe for ambulant patients seeking surgical advice or aid. During the morning hours these patients were assembled in one of the small rooms near the rear entrance to the Bulfinch Building. This duty did not consume any considerable portion of the surgeon's time, as the details of treatment were entrusted to the hands of the senior house pupil.[5] This system had been in vogue since the foundation of the Hospital up to the time of my departure for Europe. Three years later on my return, I found an out-patient department established as a separate unit of the Hospital.

The only change in the staff of visiting surgeons which had taken place was the appointment of Dr. Algernon Coolidge to fill the vacancy left by the death of my father, Dr. J. Mason Warren.

The Civil War had given a great stimulus to operative surgery quite

------

clean-cut saber wounds were drawn together by adhesive straps, healing would be accomplished without suppuration.

Historically, the period of applying the term "laudable pus" to all wounds was a brief one and coincided with the bringing together of large numbers of patients with fresh wounds under a single roof. This gave opportunity for cross-infection (hospitalism), and even the clean-cut incised wound suppurated whether made by a saber or by the surgeon's scalpel. Any break in the skin became a portal of entry for life-endangering infection.

Although surgical incisions were usually without gross contusions and dead tissue, they were oftentimes crudely made under emotional stress and hemorrhage was controlled with heavy ligatures which in addition to being contaminated usually strangled sizable masses of tissue. Operations conducted in this fashion today would be attended by a high incidence of suppuration even though they were invested with aseptic ritual and the currently approved "coverage" by antibiotics. In military surgery following Waterloo, saber cuts became rare, and as newer weapons were developed the gunshot wounds were attended by more and more destruction to living flesh. The mass casualties in the Crimea and in our Civil War were crowded into improvised shelters and cared for in almost complete ignorance of isolation techniques. Bacteria invaded all wounds irrespective of whether dead tissue was present, and erysipelas, pyemia, and hospital gangrene took an untold number of lives. At the siege of Sevastopol the Russian surgeon Pirogoff urged that the wounded be dispersed among the huts of peasants and the wounds ignored; in the Civil War the lightly wounded often had a better chance if they skulked in the bushes and avoided hospitals.

It was against this background that Lister's 1867 publication appeared, and the principles it enunciated brought sepsis arising from cross-infection under control. Listerism could not, nor did it pretend to, eliminate suppuration arising in contaminated dead tissue and infected blood clots, although explorative efforts were made in this direction. The principle of excision of dead tissue (débridement) as the initial step in wound management finally emerged in the 1914–1918 war.

[5] After 1867 six house pupils were appointed annually: two for the medical department, and four for the surgical.

independent of the stimulus provided by the development of scientific medicine. A large number of physicians scattered all over the country had received a surgical training in the army, and this department of medicine was beginning to claim a greater share of the resources accorded the healing arts. The need of a department officered by younger men became apparent at the Massachusetts General Hospital, and it was not long before the surgical staff had to be enlarged. The appointment of Dr. Charles Burnham Porter as surgeon to out-patients (1868) was followed by the similar appointments (1872) of Drs. J. Collins Warren and Henry H. A. Beach, in the order named. The duties of this junior staff were at first confined exclusively to out-patient service, for the rights and privileges of the visiting surgeons were jealously guarded. No opportunity whatsoever was given to the junior members to perform major surgical operations or to assume even temporarily the role of a visiting surgeon.

The staff of six visiting surgeons [6] was considered ample for the needs of the service, and all of the demands of that day were met by its members, some one of whom could usually be found on hand to meet an emergency. Domestic life was on a simpler basis; few of the surgeons were in the habit of living for any protracted period of time outside the city limits, and the Hospital "hack" sent in search of surgical talent rarely returned empty.[7] Prior to this, the only means of communication was a carriage ordered from a neighboring livery stable and reinforced by a hospital employee familiar with the addresses of members of the staff and adept in communicating through the night speaking-tube. As was bound to happen sooner or later, on one occasion an accident case in which amputation was required was received when no available surgeon could be found. It was obvious that a new system was needed, and from that time on the out-patient surgeon began to share in the opportunities of operative surgery. It

[6] In 1872 the visiting surgeons were Henry J. Bigelow, Henry G. Clark, Samuel Cabot, George H. Gay, Richard M. Hodges, and Algernon Coolidge.

[7] The idea of a municipal ambulance service in Boston was suggested in 1861 by a Committee on a Free City Hospital (City Document No. 34). In New York a city ambulance service, said to be the first in the world, was started at the Bellevue Hospital in 1869 by Dr. Edward B. Dalton, then Sanitary Superintendent of the Metropolitan Board of Health. The following year he became a visiting physician at the MGH, and in July 1873 the first horse-drawn ambulance of this institution made its appearance. As it was used for the transportation of physicians as well as patients, it is probably the "Hospital hack" mentioned by J.C.W. Four years later the Boston City Hospital began its ambulance service, and in 1882 the Boston Police Department acquired two ambulances for public use.

Dr. Dalton was one of the six close friends memorialized by Henry Lee Higginson in his gift of "The Soldier's Field" to Harvard University in 1890. See "The Soldier's Field Address" in the appendix to Bliss Perry's *Life and Letters of Henry Lee Higginson* (Boston, 1921).

was also found necessary to ensure the presence in the city of at least one member of both staffs at all times day and night. Specialized surgical skills could not be brought in contact with the great problems of surgery with the ease characteristic of the present day. It was not until some years later that through the generosity of that public-spirited member of the profession, Dr. Charles G. Weld, a new building was added to the Hospital in connection with the out-patient department, giving the first opportunity for the development of special departments.[8]

In abandoning the old amphitheatre in the Dome, it had not occurred to the Hospital authorities that a great opportunity existed to preserve the memory of the greatest of all the contributions of the Massachusetts General Hospital. Here was the home of as momentous and dramatic an event as any that had occurred in the history of surgery up to that time. It was not until the closing years of the century that the significance of this old surgical landmark was fully appreciated. No better use was found for it in 1868 than to turn it into a store room. Later, the seats having been removed, it was partitioned into seven rooms and used as a dormitory for female employees.[9] Finally, when the preparations for the Jubilee of Anaesthesia in 1896 were being made and the members of the visiting staff of the time of which I am writing had nearly all passed away, the historic importance of this old deserted chamber became manifest and an effort was made to restore it as nearly as possible to its original condition. The seats were replaced, and the various objects which had lined the walls and which still could be identified in the old daguerreotype of "the first operation under ether" were collected so far as possible and placed in their original positions. These included the statue of Apollo which had been moved to the new amphitheatre, the Egyptian mummy which had found a temporary home in the Boston Museum of Fine Arts, and a skeleton concealed in its case by drapery curtains. The

[8] This building was the George H. Gay Ward, erected as a two-story wing on the south side of the first Surgical Building and opened on January 1, 1884. Every room was lighted with gas.

[9] The "Ether Dome" served as a female dormitory from 1873 to 1889, then as the nurses' dining room until 1892. In that year the room partitions were removed, the seats were restored, and the amphitheatre was used thereafter for lectures and clinical demonstrations. A more complete restoration was accomplished in 1930 through a gift of Mrs. William Whitworth Gannett.

After 1868 the amphitheatre in the Dome was no longer used for surgical operations. On June 8 of that year the Massachusetts Medical Society assembled in the new operating theatre of the Hospital and listened to the Annual Address given by Henry Grafton Clark, visiting surgeon. He referred in round numbers to the eight thousand operations performed in the old amphitheatre during the first half century of the institution. By way of comparison, during the single year 1955 over twelve thousand operations requiring anesthesia were performed in the various operating rooms that now carry on the surgical work of the Hospital.

old operating cases had unfortunately disappeared but new ones, formed as nearly as possible to imitate their predecessors, were put in the accustomed places and served as receptacles for the first sponge used in administering ether, the mouth-piece of the apparatus which Morton himself had used at the historic operation, and many surgical instruments of the same period.[10]

The Hospital of the early 1870's was as fine a representative of the surgery of the day as could be found in the country. It was also quite on a par with the best that was to be found in Europe. Dr. Henry Jacob Bigelow, the senior surgeon, was now nearing the height of his career, and was a recognized authority throughout the country. Hospital practice, however, was unchanged so far as the scope of the surgery which had developed following the advent of anesthesia was concerned. Surgery was still "external medicine" with the exceptions of the operations for trephining the skull for depressed fracture, tapping the chest to remove fluids from the pleural cavity, and the relief of strangulated hernia and stone in the bladder. No attempts were

[10] J.C.W.'s depth of feeling about the Hospital and the discovery of ether anesthesia is revealed in the peroration to his presidential address before the American Surgical Association on May 4, 1897:

> Gentlemen: The old Massachusetts General Hospital stands as it did in 1846, with its sightly Bulfinch dome and granite columns. From a scientific standpoint it seems an antiquated structure in comparison with the modern pavilion wards, laboratories, and operating-theatres which surround it, but it will never be torn down. It will always remain one of the conspicuous landmarks of this wonderful century — as a shrine of surgery sacred to that moment "when the fiercest extremity of suffering was steeped in the waters of forgetfulness, and the deepest furrow in the knotted brow of agony was smoothed away forever."

Convictions that spring from intimate emotional involvement are likely to sway practitioners of a useful art and sometimes make them blind to a frank and open scrutiny of procedures. Dr. E. Amory Codman, skeptic and fearless critic of all things surgical, related in 1939:

> I remember that after getting through the hospital I wrote a paper on anaesthesia giving the results of my personal experiences and that of the hospital in general during my term as House Officer. In the paper I reported so many deaths and complications that when I submitted it to Doctor Coll Warren I was advised against printing it because it was too truthful and might make people more afraid of anaesthetics. [Letter, Codman to Henry K. Beecher.]

It is of more than passing interest to complete the cycle by recording that Dr. Henry K. Beecher, chief of the department of anesthesia at the MGH, was recently criticized in a surgical journal for "disservice to anesthesiology and to the patient" by a group of sixteen, mostly clinical, practitioners of the art. The accusation was made because Beecher and Todd had published data pertaining to the death rate attending anesthesia. As Beecher and Todd state in answer to the criticism, "If it was a disservice to publish them, then the only possible conclusion is that a 'service' would have been to suppress them." [Beecher and Todd *vs.* Abajian *et al., Annals of Surgery 142,* 138 (July 1955).]

made to extend surgery into the major cavities of the body. Much attention was paid to the technique of operative surgery, and courses were illustrated by operations on the cadaver, which included amputations, joint resections, and ligatures of arteries. While these exercises were supposed to cover all the ground with which the students should be familiar, their chief value lay in the opportunity offered to acquire a familiarity with and a certain dexterity in handling the knife and other surgical tools. Apart from the work of the ovariotomist, whose operations were still regarded by the leading authorities as unjustifiable, there had been little change in the scope of general surgery. Progressive steps were being taken by pioneers in the various special departments of surgery, but as yet their work had not begun to bear fruit. The remark made by a physician to his former pupil, my classmate Dr. J. Orne Green, illustrates well the attitude of the older school towards the new branches of medicine. On being informed by Green that he had devoted himself in Europe exclusively to the study of aural surgery, the physician remarked, "Oh! diseases of the ear? Well, they are one of two kinds: those that cure themselves and those that can't be cured."

Not long after I had become well established as a practitioner, my colleague Dr. Thomas Buckminster Curtis returned from Paris, where he had concluded his brilliant career as an undergraduate in the École de Médecine. He also received an appointment on the surgical out-patient staff (1875), and his training and erudition at once placed him in the position of a recognized authority on the surgical literature of the day. It would have been hard to find an obscure or puzzling type of disease for which Curtis would not be able to find an explanation by placing his finger upon a monograph which covered the whole ground. His talents found quick recognition by Dr. Bigelow, with whom he became a great favorite. Curtis was familiar with the leaders of the French and English schools and was able to furnish much information to his chief and to argue out many a knotty question with him. I recall these discussions on the great surgical problems of the day as being among the most valuable assets in my store of surgical knowledge. And so it came about that when one day the conversation turned to the methods of Sir Henry Thompson in crushing for stone, the interest of Dr. Bigelow was immediately aroused, and many and long were the discussions on Sir Henry's practice of multiple sittings to which I have already referred. Thompson's method, it will be remembered, consisted in performing as many as twenty or thirty "crushings" in some cases. This was expounded by Curtis as the most up-to-date method of treating stones in the bladder and as a distinct advance over the older method of lithotrity. The mortality of the old operation, attributable to cystitis, was by no means small, and the new method was designed to avoid this complication by reducing the injury to the bladder to a minimum.

It was not long after one of these discussions that Dr. Bigelow invited us to witness an operation for stone. We were much startled to see him occupy the better part of an hour in its performance. This was in total disregard of Sir Henry's advice to limit the time during which the instrument remained in the bladder to the briefest possible period. When Dr. Bigelow's operation was completed, however, every particle of stone had been removed with the aid of his newly invented evacuator and the bladder thoroughly washed out. To our surprise no ill effects followed this performance and the patient made an unusually rapid recovery. Shortly after this I turned over a patient with stone, who came into my wards, to Dr. Bigelow. It turned out that there were a large number of stones of very small size, all of which he was able to remove through his new evacuator without resorting to a previous crushing. I called his attention to the fact that in this particular case he had performed neither lithotomy nor lithotrity and that it was necessary therefore for him to invent a new name. "Something that means evacuation," he replied, and so the word "litholapaxy" was added to the medical dictionary.[11]

[11] Dr. Bigelow's contribution to lithotrity was the demonstration of the tolerance of the bladder to prolonged operation provided the fragments of crushed stone were thoroughly flushed out by the "simplified evacuator" which was his invention (see note 2, Chapter I).

A Trickle of New Ideas

It is not my purpose to attempt to describe the various phases of the development of surgery under the new method of antiseptic treatment, for that is a matter of historical record. I shall confine myself to a reference to such salient features in the development of this great change in surgery as came within the scope of my personal experience. As Lister had predicted in 1869, the changes came slowly and were worked out by the generation of surgeons and scientists who were at that time about to enter upon their professional careers. The older men who had control of the practice of surgery assumed that the new method consisted of the employment of a single drug and that the virtues of this drug were exploited by building up a plausible theory as a scientific background. Many years were to pass before these men of the older generation began to realize that carbolic acid was not an essential part of the new concept. Meanwhile, old traditions and methods continued to prevail and hospital practice underwent no material change.

I was given an opportunity from time to time to apply Lister's dressings and did the best I could in the role of a subordinate. It was but natural that unconvincing results should follow, and it is not surprising that even thoughtful men failed to appreciate at its just value a system of treatment based on a theory which was as yet imperfectly understood. It is true that the "germ theory of disease," as it was then called, had for many years received considerable attention by the medical writers of the day, but this theory was still regarded as belonging to the speculative problems of medicine. Bacteriology as a science had not yet come into its own. Wounds did not heal by first intention often enough to arouse much enthusiasm in the minds of the older surgeons, who had seen many a much-vaunted panacea come, have its day, and go. The minute detail which was essential to the success of such a sweeping change as antisepsis was known to only a limited number of men, and even in their hands the details were often imperfectly worked out, as was bound to be the case when the most enthusiastic followers of the system could be classed as novices in the art of the new surgery. Failures were only too frequent, and few men cared to bring forward statistics that could be turned against them by some opponent with a conservative mind. It was

clear that the new art, involving as it did a revolution in the habits
and the training of both the surgical chief and all his subordinates, including the entire personnel of a hospital service as well as surgical
assistants, could become firmly established only in the fulness of time.
The new knowledge had to trickle down from the chief at the apex of
the pyramid through the ranks of a large and motley following in
order to develop the smoothly working machine with which all who
have to do with surgery today are familiar. The older men of that
day are therefore hardly to be blamed for not at once becoming
proselytes of the new cult. It is interesting, however, to look back upon
that period and recall the reluctance with which some of the leaders
in surgery received the new doctrine. Thoughtful men of intellectual
attainment failed to grasp its true significance, and many months and
even years rolled by before any systematic attempt was made to
organize operative surgery along the new lines.[1]

[1] At the Cincinnati meeting of the American Surgical Association in 1883,
Dr. B. A. Watson of New Jersey commented favorably on the results of applying
Lister's methods. A pack of conservatives took up the hot trail in full voice.
What was said from this point on is worth quoting in full. Henry E. Sigerist re-
produced this discussion in his Hodgen Lecture [*J. Missouri Med. Assoc. 32*, 169
(May 1935)] to portray the state of emotion that still blocked the acceptance of
antisepsis sixteen years after Lister's first publication on the subject.

Dr. J. H. Packard, of Philadelphia, Pennsylvania: If I understood the
essayist correctly, I must take exception to his statement that the majority of
American surgeons have adopted Listerism. Certainly, on behalf of the
surgeons of Philadelphia, I feel warranted in saying that it has not in their
hands yielded such results as to induce them to adhere to it.

Dr. Alfred Post, of New York, N. Y.: I think I can say the same in regard
to the surgeons of New York; I do not think that any of them now use the
method.

Dr. A. Vanderveer, of Albany, New York: I can say the same with
regard to the surgeons of Albany and vicinity. In 1878 I published one
of the first papers in this country on the death of a patient from poisoning by carbolic acid in a case of ovariotomy. And I desire also to call
attention, in connection with Dr. Watson's statement with regard to the
value of carbolic acid, to the fact that it occupies one of the lowest positions in the list of antiseptic agents, much inferior, for instance, to corrosive
sublimate.

It is the through drainage that is the important factor in the treatment
of wounds.

Dr. T. G. Richardson, of New Orleans, Louisiana: There is not a surgeon
in our State who uses the Lister method.

The power of carbolic acid to control inflammation is, I think, very
slight.

Dr. C. H. Mastin, of Mobile, Alabama: I wish to state that there is
not a surgeon in the State of Alabama who uses the Lister method now.
We have ceased to use it entirely.

Dr. T. A. McGraw, of Detroit, Michigan: I had the misfortune some
time ago to lose a patient from following out the Lister system; a loss
which I ascribed to the poisonous effect of the carbolic acid.

The case was that of a boy, on whom I performed an amputation at

It was not until well into the seventies, if my recollections serve me rightly, that systematic attempts were made by the surgeons of the

---

the knee-joint. I used a two per cent. solution of carbolic acid. After the operation I dressed the wound with adhesive plaster, then wrapped it in cotton and applied a bandage. I employed the method in detail. I left my patient in a good condition, free from pain, and resting well, with no fever, and the pulse good. In the morning I found him in a condition of coma, with contracted pupils, and a rapid, feeble pulse, and from that time he sank, and in two days died.

Dr. W. W. Dawson, of Cincinnati, Ohio: You are, Mr. President, the apostle of antisepsis. You have taught, and still teach, that it is cleanliness. Listerism is still upon its trial. Is the better success we have the result of the use of the germicides, or does it come from enforced cleanliness? One of our surgeons, Dr. Dandridge, has practised Listerism in all its completeness, and I doubt whether his success has been greater than that of surgeons who were ever watchful as to drainage, to ventilation, and disinfection.

To Dr. Markoe we are all indebted for the most thorough drainage. Under what is known as Markoe's "through drainage" wounds heal with unwonted rapidity. This is doubtless a step in advance.

Dr. H. F. Campbell, of Augusta, Georgia: I believe that the action of the carbolic acid spray has the effect of retarding the suppuration in a wound, but I do not think that it is due to the influence of carbolic acid upon germs. I think that it arises from its effect on the reflex relations between the blood-vessels and the sensitive nerves.

Dr. David Prince, Jacksonville, Illinois: In my opinion, we cannot be too thankful to Mr. Lister for directing the attention of the profession to the method of treating wounds so as to avoid the influence of those agents which we know float in the air. But the Lister system is so complicated in its details that it is doubtful whether it can retain its hold in practice when it is found that other and simpler methods will do as well. We cannot too much honor the man who stood at the head of the reform in the management of wounds that is now universally adopted not in detail but in general practice. If Listerism means the detail of the dressing of wounds, doubtless it is short-lived, but if Listerism means the principles which are involved in antisepsis, Listerism is immortal. We know, Mr. President, that the open dressing of wounds, so that they shall be antiseptic, is as good as the closed method. The great end is to prevent putrefactive processes, and whether you attain this end by the use of carbolic acid, salicylic acid, iodoform, or corrosive sublimate, it is the same.

Dr. R. A. Kinloch, of Charleston, South Carolina: I wish to express my faith, to a large extent, in the Listerian principles and the use of carbolic acid. It seems to me that we are here to-day, as American surgeons, expressing opinions which will not be received very generally by surgeons throughout the world. As American surgeons it would appear from the discussion which has taken place that we are almost forced to say, that Lister had introduced a system capable of doing not much good, but a great deal of harm.

Dr. C. B. Nancrede, of Philadelphia, Pennsylvania: Having expressed my views on the subject of Listerism at the last meeting, I will not now occupy the time of the Association further than to say, that, having tried the method, I had abandoned it to ascertain whether my results were really attributable to the superiority of the dressings. My results were so much worse than with Listerian dressings, that I returned to it; besides, I have seen indisputable proof of the superiority of Listerism in the practice

Hospital staff to carry out the antiseptic system. Dr. Bigelow had become interested in the so-called Callender dressings, devised by the well known English surgeon. His method consisted, as I remember it, in the application of sheet lint saturated with carbolized oil as a surgical dressing. The method seemed more simple and practical than that of Lister and was generally adopted throughout the Hospital. Soon after this came Lister's "spray," by means of which the air in the immediate vicinity of the wound was rendered antiseptic.[2] This was

---

of one of my colleagues. I think that Dr. Packard is under some misapprehension when stating that no one in Philadelphia believed in the principles or adhered to the methods of Lister. Besides myself, there are a number of surgeons who either in some special operations or in all are Listerians.

Dr. B. A. Watson: It seems to me that the gentlemen have mistaken entirely the tenor of my paper, as they do everything that relates to Listerism. They appear to infer that the paper relates to the use of carbolic acid alone. The paper does not refer to the use of the acid alone, or to the use of any other single agent, but to the peculiar treatment which was perfected and introduced by Mr. Lister. Although carbolic acid may be condemned, yet the system which was introduced by him must be saved. Again, I think the gentlemen are mistaken in asserting that I said all the surgeons of the United States are advocates of the system. On the contrary, I know that Listerism in America has made but little progress; but, nevertheless, the present system of surgical practice has been modified to a very great extent by the introduction of the Lister treatment, and we find scarcely a wound treated in the United States to-day but what some part of Listerism is adopted. It is contended that some parts of it are good and some bad.

Thorough drainage was never practised to any great extent prior to the introduction of Listerism. Further, the great care and attention that is paid to cleanliness was not thought of until Mr. Lister came forward with his system and practice. And when we object to this and that part of the Lister system, it seems to me that we are not objecting to Listerism as a whole. Some aim their darts at the spray and think that is the whole of the system; but the great objections come not from those who have tried Listerism, but from those who are willing to raise their hands and thank God that they have neither witnessed its application nor used it. [*Transactions of the American Surgical Association 1*, 219 (1883).]

[2] As noted before, Dr. Bigelow had tried and abandoned Lister dressings in 1867. He made a second trial eight years later: "The evidence had so accumulated that I set fairly to work to try the experiment again, beginning with what seemed the most reasonable. I thoroughly washed ulcers and wounds in a carbolic solution, covered them with a cloth similarly wet, and then with rubber cloth to hinder evaporation. They did better than before." (Bigelow's 1876 Lecture at the Medical School.)

Dr. Bigelow described the Callender dressings in his Second Lecture on "The Modern Art of Promoting the Repair of Tissue" given at the Medical School in 1878. He had seen these dressings applied in the wards of Mr. George W. Callender at St. Bartholomew's in July of that year. The Lister spray had been introduced at the MGH in 1877.

A report on antiseptic surgery as practiced in the east wing of the Hospital on the services of Drs. Bigelow, Hodges, and Beach was published in the *Boston Medical and Surgical Journal* for July 14, 1881, and a further report appeared in *The Physician's Magazine* for March 1886.

effected by the employment of an atomizer driven by an alcohol lamp which threw a cloud of carbolized vapor over a space several yards in diameter enveloping the patient's wound and the surrounding attendants. I well recall the contempt with which this innovation was received by one of the old ward tenders to whom fell the additional duty of keeping the new apparatus in good working order. "That won't last long," was his somewhat cynical but prophetic comment.

This extension of the method was based upon the prevalent theory that access of air to the wound was a dangerous source of infection. How difficult it was to remove from men's minds the teachings of a lifetime! At first the spray method seemed to bring with it a confirmation of the theory that contact with air caused infection, for the very thorough drenching of everything which came in contact with the wound helped to overcome the many breaks in the antiseptic chain which were a prominent feature of the practices of those early days. There were many inconveniences and disadvantages, however, in the working of the spray technique. It was a source of frequent annoyance that the apparatus would fail to work properly at the appointed time, and the surgeon's patience was often severely tested by the unavoidable delay. Lister had laid down the rule that no break should be allowed to occur in this detail of the operation, as the life of the patient might be jeopardized if the wound were allowed to be exposed even for a moment to the unsterilized air.

The free use of powerful chemical antiseptic agents in the hands of those who did not yet fully understand their action upon the human body brought with it many unforeseen risks. This was true not only of carbolic acid and iodoform but especially of that much older antiseptic, corrosive sublimate. Carbolic acid seemed to pervade everything and everybody who came in contact with the surroundings of the operating table. Hands and wounds were washed with a 1-to-40 and sometimes a 1-to-20 solution. Dressings were saturated with it and the air of the space in which many persons were crowded together was redolent with its fumes. New groups of symptoms began to appear, not only in the patients operated upon but in the surgeon, who occasionally found himself the subject of an idiosyncrasy which made him susceptible to this drug. The effect of carbolic poisoning of the kidneys seriously interfered with many a surgeon's labors and a puzzling series of nervous symptoms following operation were finally traced to absorption of carbolic acid into the system. Cases of carbolic gangrene produced suits at law and caused much anxiety and distress both to the patient and to the surgeon. This agent, like ether, left its mark upon the unfortunate operator for the rest of the day in the form of an aroma which could not have been grateful to the olfactory nerves of those with whom he came in contact. All these disagreeable qualities seemed to culminate in the new agent — iodoform — which presently appeared.[3]

At first iodoform was used in quantities which would startle practitioners of today. Cavities of a wound were packed freely not only with iodoform gauze but also with the powder in large quantities. Dire were the effects upon the nervous system of the patients, many of whom were permanently affected, and the practitioner's belongings became so saturated with its odors that they had to be relegated to the trash heap. Corrosive sublimate solution was used as a douche or local wash in a strength which not only interfered with the normal process of repair but produced local irritation and symptoms of mercurial poisoning.

Progress was slow, results were uncertain, and advocates of the new methods continued to be looked upon by the authorities of the day as idealists who were striving for impracticable standards. For working out the problem each surgeon on a service had a system all his own, and the system was usually discarded by his successor. Thus no systematic effort was made to train the personnel of the several services in routine methods which might establish a higher grade of surgical cleanliness throughout the hospital on an enduring basis. New methods of bacteriological investigation began to throw light on the sources of surgical infection, and increasing attention was paid to that part of the technique which preceded the operation. The work of Koch [4] in Germany had given a great impetus to the study of the habits of bacteria, and German surgeons had begun to realize that cleanliness played a more important role in the successful solution of their daily problems than the use of any particular drug. German surgeons were among the first to appreciate the importance of the use of the razor and the thorough scrubbing process with the nail brush,

---

[3] Iodoform was discovered by Georges Serullas in 1822. A pharmacological work on this compound was published by Rhigini in 1862. Iodoform was used in the treatment of syphilitic sores and later in gynecology; Von Mosetig employed it in tuberculous wounds about 1880, and soon Billroth began to use it as a general wound antiseptic. His results were reported by Johann Mikulicz in *Wiener Klinik* (January 1882), and this report was incorporated into a little-known book published in Boston in 1888 by Otis K. Newell, surgeon to out-patients at the MGH, entitled *The Best Surgical Dressing . . . with a Consideration of Beach's Principle of Bullet-Wound Treatment.*

[4] In 1878 Robert Koch published his book on *Aetiologie der Wundinfectionskrankheiten,* and in 1881 his papers "Zur Untersuchung von pathogenen Mikro-Organismen" and "Ueber Disinfection." His description of the microörganisms responsible for the infection of wounds gave substance to the theoretical foundation of Lister's methods. His studies supplied evidence that could be seen by the humblest worker; no longer would Dr. Bigelow have to "exorcise an invisible enemy."

at first generally regarded as unnecessary exaggerations of the new cult.

Renewed interest was aroused by the introduction of many details of this nature, and the followers of the new surgery who had struggled along against the handicaps of its many imperfections began to see a prospect of the culmination of their hopes. It was from such a beginning that aseptic surgery was gradually developed. Antiseptic dressings lingered for a long time and much influence on the healing of the wound was attributed to the agents which they contained.

❧ XVIII

The Aneurism of William Young, Mechanic

To illustrate the methods of surgery at the Massachusetts General Hospital in 1876, when Dr. J. Collins Warren was appointed a visiting surgeon, the case of William Young, who was admitted on August 25th of that year to the service of Dr. Warren, is here transcribed. The record of this case begins on page 99 in Volume 173 of the West Surgical Records. Despite the use of carbolic acid, the tragedy of post-operative infection terminated in a fatal secondary hemorrhage.

J. C. W.	William Young	33
Aug. 25	Mechanic	N. Y.
1 year	Popliteal Aneurism	Plainville.

On the 13th of Dec. 1862 at the Battle of Fredricksburg P't was wounded by a musket ball. The ball entered the calf of left leg a little to the inside of the median line and came out on the inner surf. of knee. The wound healed well but the patient says that on recovery he noticed a bunch as large as the end of his thumb under the knee. After recovery there was only limited motion of knee joint. The lump would grow larger at times and then, he thinks, go away entirely. One year ago he says it was all gone. Then it reappeared again and has never disappeared since. It grew more rapidly than ever before, and, four months ago, it began to push over on the inside of knee until now on the inside of knee the tumor is larger than beneath knee.

Circumference of right knee	13¼ inches
"　　　　　" left　"	18　　"

There is a rounded tumor occupying concavity of knee joint and running up on inside almost to patella, and extending up on inner surface of leg to a point 11 inches below ant. superior spine of ilium. Pulsation, thrill and murmur are present. Pt. complains of intense pain in leg. Foot raised by pillows. ℞ Morph. Sulph. gr. ⅓.

℞ Morph. Sulph. gr. ⅓. House Diet. Appetite fair.
℞ Morph. Sulph. gr. ½ in night for pain.

Aug. 27. Morph. Sulph. gr. ii ⅔ given during day for great pain. Bandage to leg, and cannon ball applied to Femoral Art.

Aug. 30. Operation Dr. Warren Ether

Knee measured 19 inches. At 9.20 A.M. Tourniquet applied to femoral artery. Two tourniquets were used during the operation, being placed as

163

near together as possible, and being used alternately to apply pressure. The pressure was kept up for 12 hours. The tourniquets were changed every 15 minutes for 4 hours. Every 20 minutes during the rest of the time. Pulse increased from 84 till it reached about 100 at 5 P.M. and 116 at 9 P.M. Now going above 120. 2 pounds and a half of Ether were used. At 12.45 P.M. a slight pulsation was detected during change of tourniquets. No pulsation after that. At 2.55 P.M. Brandy ℥ ss. Beef tea ℥ i were given per rectum.

At 6.10 Beef tea ℥ ss. Brandy ℥ iv given by mouth and Beef tea ℥ i. Brandy ℥ ss given by rectum.
At 8.10 P.M. Brandy ℥ ss by mouth.
At 8.20 P.M. urine drawn.
At 9.30 P.M. tourniquets removed. No pulsation in tumor. Cotton batting placed over tumor and bandage applied. On coming out of ether P't has great pain in leg. At 10.30 P.M. Morph. Sulph. gr. ⅔. Some relief. At 11.15 P.M. Beef tea ℥ i. At 11.30 Morph. Sulph. gr. ⅓. No pulsation in tumor. At 11.30 P't went to sleep.
Aug. 31. At 7.45 A.M. Pulsation detected in tumor. P't had had Morph. Sulph. gr. ½ at 12.15 A.M. Quite quiet but uncomfortable all day. Pulsation growing stronger in tumor. Takes only liquid food . . .

Sept. 1. Since 12 o'clock last night has had Morph. Sulph. gr. ii. Pulsation stronger but not quite as bad as before operation.

Sept. 4. C . . . H . . . splint applied. Morph Sulph. gr. i.

Sept. 6. Less p'n than usual. Morph. gr. ⅜ during day.

Sept. 10.   Operation   Dr. Warren   s̄ Ether

At 8.10 A.M. Pressure applied to Femoral as before. Pressure kept up sufficiently to stop pulsation in aneurism till 4 A.M. of the next day. Partial pressure kept up for next three days. During that time the aneurism was observed to pulsate whenever the pressure was removed from Femoral . . . The tourniquets were changed every twenty minutes . . .
Sept. 11. At 1 P.M. P't partook of a bowl of House Soup, some bread and a bottle of ale.

Sept. 19. During the past week Morph. Sulph. gr. vii were given for pain. 1 Bottle of ale a day and extra Diet.

Operation   Dr. Warren   Ether

The sac was laid open by a long incision; a large amount of fresh clot was scooped out and the interior sponged dry. The popliteal artery was found and ligatured at the point where it entered the upper extremity of sac.
After a fruitless search for a large vessel at the lower extremity of the sac, a fresh incision was made on the posterior aspect of the tumor and the popliteal artery again found and ligated just at its bifurcation. Towels soaked in Carbolic wash 1 to 40 were laid over the wounds and bandage applied. The operation lasted two hours and a half.
One grain and one half of Morph. given during the P.M. and evening for pain in leg. Two provisional ligatures were placed, one at each extremity of w'nd.

Sept. 21. Dressings removed and reapplied; wound looking well. Morph. gr. iss during the day.

Sept. 23. Drainage tube introduced into lower opening. P't complains of odor of Carbolic acid. Dressed with Potass. permang. Morph. gr. i ⅓.

Sept. 27. A chill at 4 A.M. At visit a blush about w'nd extending up to groin. P't feels very weak. A.M. P 105 T 102.5 P.M. P 110 T 104.4. Morph. gr. ⅔. ℞ Tinct. Cinch. Co. ℥ ss. t.d.

Sept. 28. Blush spreading down leg. P't weaker, no appetite. Drainage tube out. W'nd syringed daily with Permang. of Potass. sol. Morph. gr. ⅔. ℞ Quin. Sulph. gr. ii t.d. Tr. Cinch. stopped. A.M. P. 115 T. 103.2. P.M. P. 110 T. 103.

Sept. 30. Blush extending over ankle, whole lower leg and knee swollen and very tender. Not so much discharge from wound. Poult. applied to leg. ℞ Quin. Sulph. gr. ii every two hours. Brandy ℥ i t.d. P't very weak, great p'n in leg. Morph. gr. i ⅔. A.M. P. 115. T. 100.9. P.M. P. 110 T. 102.

Oct. 2. P't has less pain; feels better tho' there is quiet delirium at times. Blush less. Swelling less. More disch. fr. wound . . .

Oct. 3. At four o'clock P.M. Violent hemorrhage came on suddenly from the upper point of ligature. Pressure over the Femoral by means of a cannon ball was at once applied by a nurse which partially but not wholly controlled the hemorrhage. On arrival of the House Pupil the p't was found blanched and pulseless. A tourniquet applied at once checked the bleeding. Brandy ℥ ss. Laudanum gtt. xx were given: the foot of the bed raised: heaters applied to the feet, and blankets thrown over p't. Brandy ℥ i was given in divided doses. The pulse of the patient was then found to be 115 and tolerably strong. At 5.15 P.M. the pulse failing again. Ether M. xxx were given subcutaneously. An attempt was made to tie the provisional ligature but it came away at once.

The p't growing steadily weaker was further stimulated by Brandy M. xxx subcutaneously. Ether M. xv subcutaneously and Brandy ℥ iv. The pulse became imperceptible, and at 7.10 P.M. the patient

Died.

Records of Autopsy, Page 25.

Dr. Warren reported this case as that of W. Y. in the Proceedings of the Boston Society for Medical Improvement, *Boston Medical and Surgical Journal* 95, 535 (November 2, 1876). The following paragraph is taken from this report.

Dr. Fitz showed the specimen, which consisted of the aorta from its origin, the left femoral, and a portion of the aneurism in continuity. The fatal haemorrhage had resulted from the sloughing of the walls of the artery at the upper end of the aneurismal sac, where the ligature had been applied. There was no alteration of the inner surface of the femoral artery, but the fibrous tissue was indurated around it, corresponding with the region where compression had been applied. The entire inner coat of the thoracic aorta was thickened, wrinkled, elevated in patches, of an opaque grayish-white color, and the canal was dilated, especially that of the arch. Just above the coeliac axis these alterations ceased abruptly, the interior of the abdominal aorta being smooth and yellow, its walls evidently in a normal condition. The specimen was particularly interesting from the absence of changes at the point of compression and the presence of chronic inflammatory conditions of the thoracic aorta, such as are associated with the formation of aneurisms, in a young man in whom a popliteal aneurism had arisen, directly or indirectly from a traumatic cause.

✍ XIX

A New Generation
at the Old Hospital

I was appointed a visiting surgeon at the Massachusetts General Hospital in 1876. The promotion of Dr. Charles Burnham Porter to the visiting staff had taken place the year before, and it was not long until Dr. H. H. A. Beach's name was added to the list. When Dr. Samuel Cabot retired a few years later (1882), Dr. John Homans' name was first on the list of candidates to fill the vacancy. In age Dr. Homans was senior to all three of the new appointees. At the outbreak of the Civil War he was a surgical house pupil at the Hospital, and he saw active service as a surgeon in both the Navy and the Army. After serving for a short time as pathologist at the Hospital, he accepted an appointment to the out-patient surgical service at the Boston City Hospital. His brother Dr. Charles D. Homans was already a member of the visiting surgical staff at that hospital, and there appeared to have been some question raised as to the propriety of two members of the same family holding such positions in a city institution. John Homans later applied for and received an appointment to the out-patient surgical staff at the Hospital [1876, following that of J. Collins Warren]. He was a man of great self-reliance and full of enthusiasm for his calling. Having acquired much practical knowledge during his military career, he made a prolonged visit to the centers of medical education in Europe, and returned home late in 1866 determined to devote himself exclusively to the practice of surgery. He had seen and profited by the work of Spencer Wells and other pioneers in abdominal surgery, which at that time was for all practical purposes confined to the operation of ovariotomy. The very unfavorable results [1] which hitherto had attended operations of this kind presented no terrors for John Homans. The technique of ovariotomy had been greatly im-

---

[1] At least nine ovariotomies were performed during the first five decades of the Hospital, and all the patients died except one. The exception was a patient operated upon on May 30, 1869 by Dr. Samuel Cabot, who covered the incision with "cotton soaked in Carbolic oil" (West Surgical Records, vol. 136, p. 246). It is not always clear in the Records whether a given operation was performed inside the Hospital or in nearby lodgings obtained by the Hospital for the purpose (see note 3).

proved, and the new antiseptic system held out new hopes for success.[2]

Thus it came about in Boston that Dr. John Homans soon began to assume the role of a leader in this new field of surgery, which was still regarded by older heads as an experiment which had not yet passed beyond the doubtful stage. This was the situation when Homans became a candidate for the vacant position of the visiting staff of the Hospital. Much doubt existed as to the propriety of making such an appointment, for it apparently meant the introduction of abdominal surgery into the Hospital. Nothing could better illustrate the attitude that then existed toward the new surgery than to note the condition to which the new appointee was obliged to submit: he was not to bring any of his ovariotomy patients into the Hospital.

On Dr. Bigelow's resignation in 1886, which followed closely that of Dr. Hodges, the surgery of the Hospital passed into the hands of a new generation, and the question of whether abdominal surgery could be recognized as a legitimate field for hospital work was reopened. A few years before, a certain number of patients with ovarian tumors had been admitted to an extemporized ward in the immediate vicinity of the Hospital and several operations had been performed.[3] But the results did not appear encouraging enough to justify the performance of such operations within the Hospital. The feeling was very strong at that time that the atmosphere of surgical wards made it quite out of the question to attempt extensive operations which involved opening of the peritoneal cavity within the walls of a general hospital. So the recognition of abdominal surgery was abandoned for the time being.

These were anxious days for the members of the new staff upon

[2] Dr. John Homans performed five ovariotomies between 1872 and 1877, and all five patients died. In his sixth case (1877) he used the carbolic spray and the patient went on to recovery. During the following year he did six ovariotomies with antiseptic precautions, and only one patient died. Many of his later operations were done at St. Margaret's Infirmary in Louisburg Square on Beacon Hill, a well-known private nursing home.

[3] Dr. Norton Folsom, Resident Physician (superintendent) of the Hospital, addressed the following letter to the visiting committee of the Trustees on November 30, 1874:

Gent.[n]

Dr. [Samuel] Cabot is about to perform the operation of ovariotomy upon a patient now in the House.

The Surgical Staff agree that the chances of saving the patient would be much greater if a room were obtained *outside of the Hospital* for her.

A suitable room would not cost more than $8.00 per week and would not be needed many weeks.

I would respectfully request the authority to engage it *at once*, and charge the cost to "Contingencies."

The private room was obtained, the operation was performed, and Dr. Cabot's house patient was discharged "well." (Letter in MGH Archives.)

whom was placed the responsibility for the future policy of the Hospital. The younger men who had been trained in the new surgery from the beginning of their careers were becoming numerous and it was becoming clear that a great hospital could no longer set its face against the rapidly expanding field of abdominal surgery. Surgeons today cannot fully appreciate the difficulties of this problem as it presented itself to those who had responsibility for advising the Trustees as to the propriety of this important new department. The contrast between conditions then and now is difficult to apprehend. Antiseptic and aseptic surgery were still in a state of imperfect development, while the undertakings required in the name of surgical aid were of a very formidable character. The field of morbid growth had up to that time been practically untouched by the surgeon's knife. It was a vast domain abounding with problems which were trying to the conscience of the pioneer. Tumors which had been left to reach maturity existed in numbers unknown to the practitioner of the present day. The senior surgeons of the new staff had been brought up in the old school, but it now became their duty to assume the role of leaders and to demonstrate the practicability of making aseptic surgery a legitimate part of the scope of hospital work. Many a surgeon of middle life had to relearn his art, under conditions far more difficult than may ever exist again.

It was in 1887 that Professor Harold C. Ernst suggested to me the use of sterilized cotton for surgical dressings. This material was used in his laboratory work: why should it not be equally suitable at the bedside? Tin boxes were prepared to hold sufficiently large amounts of cotton, and Bunsen burners provided the necessary heat. The cotton thus prepared was used as material for dressings in all the wounds encountered on my service that year but, as I have already stated, each surgeon was addicted to his own particular whim and the new method, undoubtedly carried out with many imperfections, attracted no attention from my colleagues. It is an interesting commentary upon the shortcomings of the four months' service [4] then in

[4] The system of divided responsibilities and privileges, based on discontinuous periods of service for all staff members of the MGH, started in 1835. Prior to that time Dr. John C. Warren held the simple position that "there should be a head to everything." From 1835 until 1911 the discontinuous system described by J.C.W. prevailed. In 1911 the post of surgeon-in-chief was created for Dr. Maurice H. Richardson, and largely through the efforts of Dr. E. Amory Codman a reorientation of the surgical services was achieved. The announcement of the new plan in the *Boston Medical and Surgical Journal* for August 31, 1911 clearly states its purpose.

> Under the old method of divided services, no one man was ever able to study a group of cases or a given disease over an extended period of time. With the development of scientific clinical research the opportunity

vogue that when I went on duty again in the following year I found among the new set of house pupils and nurses not a single person who could give me any information as to where my sterilizing apparatus could be found. Later the tin boxes were discovered in a scrap heap. Not even a memory of my early efforts with aseptic dressings had survived. Thus an opportunity had been missed by the Hospital to introduce aseptic surgery in this country.

In 1889 the Bradlee Ward (E) was opened for clean abdominal surgery.[5] It was isolated from the surrounding buildings as thoroughly as possible and equipped with an entirely independent outfit of instruments and dressings. Although a few selected patients had been taken into the Hospital for abdominal surgery before this date and patients in private practice were constantly increasing in number, the occasion of opening this ward marked, as it were, the official recognition of the new surgery in this part of the country. The new operating theatre in the Bradlee Ward became the prototype of its successors of today. An asphalt floor, tiled walls, and an adjoining sterilizing room were in striking contrast to what had been thought good enough up to this date. It became an object of interest to visiting members of the profession from other cities and doubtless served as a model for many other institutions.

The old operating theatre, named the Henry J. Bigelow Operating Theatre in 1890, was still in use for general surgery. Scarcely more than two decades before, it had been looked upon as the most up-to-date creation of its kind but, as was the custom of the period, it served many purposes. In the early morning hours it was devoted to clinical instruction and as such was the gathering point of patients from the wards and the out-patient department. There was much coming and going of students and teachers, and the building was

---

to do this has become essential to medical progress; and hence has arisen the principle of continuous service, now generally recognized and already established in many large hospitals. A hospital is no longer to be regarded solely as a place for getting so much work done and caring for so many patients, but as a laboratory for the furtherance of medical knowledge.

[5] On February 21, 1889 J.C.W. performed the first operation in the new operating room of the Bradlee Ward (E). He described it in a letter sent February 12, 1920 to Miss Minnie S. Hollingsworth, an 1897 graduate of the MGH Training School for Nurses.

I happened to be the surgeon on duty who had an abdominal operation to perform at that moment. The case was one of hysterectomy and the operation consisted, as was the fashion then, of putting a wire clamp around the base of the protruding organ and cutting off the uterus leaving the stump exposed outside the abdominal wound. It involved a very painful convalescence and fortunately the method soon gave way to a more scientific procedure. [MGH Archives.]

so centrally situated that it became a thoroughfare connecting the various outlying departments of the Hospital. Its dingy wooden benches and dusty floors showed evidences of rough usage by the time the surgeon on duty appeared to carry on his daily task. In the following decade much-needed alterations were brought about. Operative surgery was given new facilities and the necessary isolation. Lectures and demonstrations were relegated to other quarters and the old-time type of amphitheatre so familiar to students of my generation disappeared forever.

Drs. Arthur T. Cabot and Maurice H. Richardson were added to the visiting staff in 1886. These surgeons had been trained in the new teachings from the beginning and, as their subsequent careers have shown, no more able exponents of the new cult could have been chosen. With the staff thus reorganized, the Massachusetts General Hospital was able completely to maintain the high traditions of its history.

I shall not attempt to trace the further progress of the new surgery in detail. The experiences which I have described as following one another at the Hospital were doubtless those of many another medical center in this country during the rise and development of aseptic surgery. So far as my own personal recollection goes, it was in the wards of the Johns Hopkins Hospital that I saw the first carrying out of asepsis as it exists today. Credit should be given to Dr. William S. Halsted for the elaboration of a technique which is in all its minute details so characteristic of American surgery today.

It will be seen that the transitional period during which the development of the new system took place extended to a date which was at least two decades after Lister's first announcements. The prediction Lister made in 1869, when he foretold the attitude of the coming generation toward the new surgery, was thus fully borne out so far as my own personal observations were concerned. In giving this account of the rise and growth of a third era in surgery, I am impressed strongly with the feeling that it has been but a preparation for another and still more marvellous epoch.

An account of this period of the Hospital activities would not be complete without some reference to the work of Dr. Reginald H. Fitz, who, though not himself a surgeon, has perhaps contributed as much to the enlargement of the field of surgery as any other one man. Dr. Fitz, on his return from European studies (about a year later than mine), brought with him much knowledge of pathological anatomy and enthusiasm for its study. He came home with a reputation already made, his career as a student and his work abroad in the German schools having impressed the members of the Medical

Faculty of Harvard. After a series of rapid promotions, he was made professor of pathological anatomy in 1878. His work stimulated interest within the Department of Medicine, which was undergoing rapid changes and needed the efforts of a man trained in modern methods of investigation to keep it abreast of the times. This increased activity in the Department of Medicine brought about a change in the organization of the Massachusetts General Hospital. As a result a new hospital department was created, and an appropriate building was erected and equipped with all the necessary appointments for the performance of post-mortem examinations and for carrying on more efficiently the laboratory work of the Hospital. In the fulness of time the outlay then made was destined to reap a rich harvest, for it was in these new and congenial surroundings that Dr. Fitz worked out his great contributions and gave to the world a new name for the medical dictionary.

The term *appendicitis* was presented in his classic paper published in 1886, and this was followed by an enormous increase in the number of operations performed. The "surgery of the amphitheatre" flourished in a corresponding degree. The great master of surgery now, more than ever before, gauged his title to fame by the number of operations performed in a single morning rather than by contributions to surgical knowledge. The rapid expansion of the field gave its hard-worked practitioner little time to do more than consider how he might qualify himself for the ever-increasing number of new techniques. Suffering humanity for the time being served as "material" upon which these new problems were to be worked out. The welfare of the individual patient was somewhat lost sight of amid the exigencies the surgeon had to face in his daily tasks.

But while all this wonderful progress was being made in the operating theatre and at the bedside, work in the laboratory went on without interruption. The spirit of scientific research which I had first witnessed as a student in the centers of European learning had found its way to these shores. Like the art of surgery, it was undergoing a rapid, though at first unnoticed, development. A new generation of workers was growing up, trained to observe and think for themselves concerning the problems of normal health and of disease. The years of patient labor, often unappreciated and frequently unrewarded, now seemed to have reached the point of beginning to bear fruit.

Events such as the creation and growth of the Rockefeller Institute, and the development of a fresh point of view regarding the role of the surgeon as expounded by such men as Harvey Cushing and George W. Crile, have since opened up a new and fascinating field

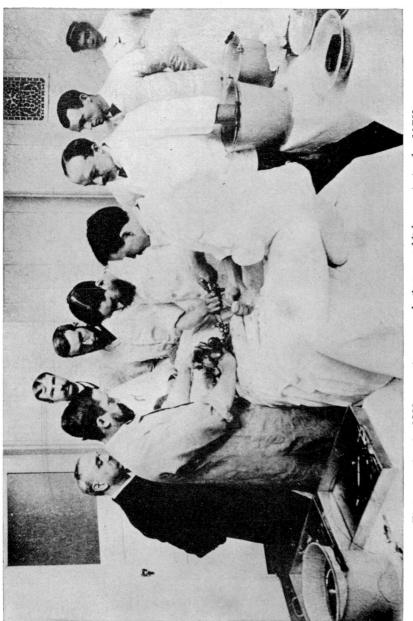

First operation in 1889 operating room, built to establish asepsis in the MGH. Dr. Warren is second from left, assisted by Dr. Samuel J. Mixter.

of work for the future. The appealing aspect of this new trend is the kindly concern for the patient and the feeling engendered that he has finally come into his own. Each patient becomes a special problem worthy of the time and thoughtful consideration of the brightest intellects. The human frame, with its wonderful mechanism and its complex vital processes, comes to be regarded as an intricate machine, each component of which must be taken into account in reaching a diagnosis or seeking a remedy. The operator comes to realize that surgical interference must be accompanied by eternal vigilance as the price of success. It does not seem to be too extravagant an expectation that this new biological surgery is destined to open up another era full of aid and comfort to suffering humanity.

❧ XX

A New Generation
at Harvard

On my return from Europe in 1869, nothing in the medical world struck me more forcibly than the inadequacy of the facilities for medical education at home as compared with those of European medical schools. The old-time curriculum handed down from previous generations still prevailed at the Harvard Medical School. I have described the go-as-you-please arrangement of lectures, the lack of a graded curriculum, the absence of system in the course of study, and the inadequacy of standards in the requirements for the degree. Fortunately the Medical Faculty was not made up solely of representatives of the old regime but contained a number of younger members who were alert to the necessities of the time. A radical change was in the air.

The clinical instruction was of good quality and presided over by teachers of well-earned reputations, but the hospital wards did not furnish opportunities for studying any of the "specialties" and the facilities for laboratory instruction were completely lacking. This was in strong contrast to the advantages existing abroad, which I had come to look upon as necessities. The Medical School building on North Grove Street contained little beyond three lecture rooms and the museum.[1] There was a small, semidetached dissecting room and a chemical laboratory where Dr. Calvin Ellis gave occasionally

[1] By 1870 the North Grove Street school building had seen nearly twenty-five years of hard use and undoubtedly looked antiquated and shabby to J.C.W. and his contemporaries. In contrast, the older generation for whom the school had been the center of a life's work were bound by sentimental ties to the building. It was about this period that Oliver Wendell Holmes described the structure in *The Harvard Book* (Cambridge, 1875), I, 239:

> The Massachusetts Medical College . . . is lofty, well lighted, and, as contrasted with the immediately contiguous edifices, of an almost imposing architectural aspect. The ground-floor is devoted to the working laboratory for students and the janitor's apartments . . . On the floor above are the Medical and Chemical Lecture-Rooms and the Library. A formidable flight of thirty-two steps leads to the second floor, where are the Museum Hall, the Anatomical theatre, the Professors' and the Demonstrators' rooms . . . Beneath the seats of the Anatomical theatre is a spacious but obscure and irregular crypt, chiefly occupied by the Professor of Anatomy.
> The Warren Anatomical Museum occupies a hall extending through the whole depth of the building. The main collection was presented by the late

some elementary instruction in the use of the microscope. No facilities were provided for research work; indeed a strong feeling existed at that time that a medical school was designed for teaching purposes only.

Description of rodent ulcer as recorded by Dr. Warren in personal ledger, September 30, 1870.

During my second and third years in Europe I had devoted a large part of my time to laboratory work and had made some special studies in surgical pathology. My interest had been aroused to the point that I desired to continue this type of work at home. Realizing that a young practitioner was bound to have many leisure moments, I decided to fit out a table with a microscope and some chemicals in a corner of my study and to avail myself of every opportunity to continue my studies on the pathology and classification of tumors. This was a subject which was attracting much attention at the time. After receiving an appointment at the Hospital, I was

Dr. John Collins Warren, and was accompanied with the gift of six thousand dollars for its preservation and increase . . . It is well known to all who have watched the growth and improvement of the collection, the care with which the specimens have been preserved and displayed, the order which has been introduced into their arrangement, the labor which has been expended upon individual preparations, the constant additions which have been made without any formal presentation, that the time and energies of one man have been devoted to the Museum . . . To Dr. J. B. S. Jackson the Museum owes more than to all others, except its founder.

able to obtain material from time to time for this purpose.[2] As an illustration of the increased interest in scientific medicine, I may mention a private course of instruction which I gave in 1870 on the microscopical appearances and classification of tumors. This was offered in my improvised laboratory to members of the profession. The class was organized by no less a personage than Dr. David W. Cheever, who was then adjunct professor of anatomy. As a by-product of these activities I was able to produce a Boylston Prize Essay on the "Anatomy and Development of Rodent Ulcer," an ailment imperfectly understood at that time.

In 1871 I was appointed instructor in surgery, and several months later a vote of the Corporation permitted instructors to sit as members on the Medical Faculty. A prominent feature of the work assigned to me as a teacher was a course on surgical pathology. Dr. Henry P. Bowditch and Dr. Reginald H. Fitz had recently returned from their European studies, the former to become assistant professor in charge of the new department of physiology,[3] which had been separated from anatomy. Dr. Fitz came home with a reputation already made as an able student with a strong bent for scientific research. He immediately received an appointment as instructor in morbid anatomy, as it was then called. For these innovations in the course of instruction suitable laboratories had to be provided, and this meant a new departure for the Medical School. An addition was built on the roof of the North Grove Street school building for three laboratories — two for physiology and one for microscopic work. Thus laboratory instruction became a permanent feature of the medical curriculum. This is but a single example of the many changes that were taking

[2] In May 1870 J.C.W. began to record pathological observations in a private ledger, which he entitled "Microscopical Examination of Tumors." This is still preserved at the Hospital. The specimens were furnished mostly by staff surgeons of the Hospital, and the reports made by J.C.W. were afterwards copied by the house pupils into the Surgical Records. His studies in the great laboratories of pathology on the Continent had enabled him to bring fresh knowledge and enthusiasms to the surgical work going on at home. Apparently his services in this regard supplemented those of the duly appointed hospital microscopist, then Calvin Ellis.

[3] Josiah Stickney Lombard is listed as assistant professor of physiology from 1866 to 1870, but the subject did not gain the dignity of recognition as a separate discipline at Harvard until 1871. Then with the assent of Holmes, who had held the title of Parkman Professor of Anatomy and Physiology, departmental status was accorded physiology and Henry P. Bowditch was appointed assistant professor. This was one of the long-overdue actions effected by Charles W. Eliot. In 1868 the University Council of Great Britain had refused to recognize the medical degree of Harvard because there was no professor of physiology. The dereliction of the Medical Faculty in this matter can be documented by the career of John Call Dalton, Jr., of Chelmsford, Massachusetts, a graduate of Harvard College in 1844 and of the Medical School in 1847. He was

place in medical education at the time. It was the beginning of an era not only for surgery but for many departments of medicine as a whole.[4]

---

apothecary at the MGH during the eventful year of 1846 and a surgical house pupil in 1847. Three years later Dalton prepared himself to become the pioneer American physiologist by study with Claude Bernard in Paris. He was the first in America to introduce experiments and demonstrations on living animals under the influence of ether, and sacrificed medical practice for teaching and research. Dalton was not called to Harvard, but held the chair of physiology in several medical schools, beginning at the University of Buffalo in 1851 and taking up his major appointment at the College of Physicians and Surgeons in New York City in 1855.

John Call was the brother of Edward Barry Dalton, mentioned in note 7, Chapter XVI. The Dalton Scholarship Fund at the MGH, a memorial to John and Edward, was founded by their brothers in 1891 to promote investigation in the science of medicine. One of these brothers was Charles H. Dalton, president of the Corporation of the MGH.

[4] J.C.W. does not mention the work of Dr. Robert Amory in his Reminiscences. He did, however, write a brief sketch for the 1913 Report of the Secretary of the Class of 1863, Harvard College. It is transcribed here because of the light it throws on the endeavor of a young medical scientist of the period.

> When Robert Amory was a practitioner in Longwood [Brookline], having settled there after his marriage [1864], he was not content to be simply an ordinary medical practitioner, but had a decided taste for research.
>
> Like many young men who had seen the imperfections of medical education in this country at that time, he had a keen interest in the advancement of medical science, and was one of the founders of the Boston Society of the Medical Sciences. This Association was composed principally of young men who did not have an opportunity to take part in the discussions of their elder brethren in the meetings of the then established societies, which were devoted chiefly to the report of cases coming within the observation of the members.
>
> Little was done in those days in experimental medicine. The use of the microscope had only just begun. The young men who were interested in these studies felt they would have a more appreciative audience by forming an association amongst themselves. Dr. Amory took a prominent part in this undertaking, and the early meetings of the Society were held in the house on La Grange Street [Boston] which belonged to him. This was probably one of the first scientific medical laboratories established in this country.
>
> Robert Amory was a physician, and consequently was interested more in medical than surgical research, and more especially in the physiological action of drugs. Bromide of potassium was a remedy first brought to notice at that time, and his researches on the action of the drug gave him a well-earned reputation as an investigator. In fact he was known at one time as "Bromide of Potash Amory."
>
> The substantial support thus given to the young association by one of its members helped greatly to establish it on a permanent basis, and not a few of its members (many of whom are men who have since earned a national reputation) received some of their first inspirations in the little laboratory on La Grange Street. Later, Dr. Amory established a laboratory in a small building on his own place in Longwood.
>
> He had the mechanical gift to a marked degree, and this was of great value to him in pursuing his researches. It led him often to topics and

Harvard University was beginning to feel the effects of the new policies which had followed the inauguration of Charles W. Eliot as President in 1869.[5] At the time of my appointment the new three-

fields other than purely medical. Some of the very earliest work on the transmission of sound over the electric wire was done in this laboratory in connection with the Hubbards, who were so intimately associated with Graham Bell in the studies which produced the final development of the telephone. It was the privilege of our Society to witness some of the very earliest attempts of the transmission of a message from Dr. Amory's laboratory to the parlor of his house, where we were assembled on that occasion.

Later, as Professor of Physiology at Bowdoin College, Amory was able to give a course of lectures which had the merit of laying before the students the very latest researches in this branch of science, in which he himself bore a prominent place. But eventually the increasing cares of practice prevented him from continuing the pursuit of medical science on a scale in accord with his ambition. He, however, never relinquished his investigations even after he had retired from the practice of medicine. During the last years of his life he employed his leisure moments in the perfection of an apparatus for sterilizing surgical dressings by means of electricity as a heating agent, which promises to be a valuable help to the surgeons' armamentarium.

In all this work Amory conducted himself with modesty and discretion, well aware of his own limitations and of the enormous difficulties to be overcome in getting results from observations, such as those in which he was engaged. Great courtesy, geniality, and patience were marked characteristics of the man; but as he looked back upon the enormous strides that had been made since he began his medical career, it must have been a great satisfaction to him to have felt that he was one of the first to see the great advantages to be derived from a devotion to the scientific side of his profession.

[5] On March 10, 1869 the Overseers of Harvard University held a meeting at the Medical School on North Grove Street to approve the granting of degrees to about seventy medical students. Charles W. Eliot, then a member of the faculty of the new Massachusetts Institute of Technology, attended as one of the Overseers. During the meeting the door of the room opened and the Reverend George Putnam appeared and called Eliot outside. The latter was then informed that the Harvard Corporation wished to elect him to the presidency. Would he accept?

Charles W. Eliot had been a classmate of James C. White at Harvard College (1853). Dr. White's education in Vienna has already been briefly mentioned (note 9, Chapter VI). Eliot studied chemistry and educational methods in Europe in the years 1863–1865 and returned home to become professor of analytical chemistry in the newly established Massachusetts Institute of Technology. He went again to Europe in 1867–68, spending fourteen months there. The following year he became president of Harvard at the age of thirty-five.

At the meeting of the Medical Faculty on November 1, 1869 Dr. White presented a resolution asking that the new president be invited to attend all future meetings. No president had ever known to attend a meeting of the doctors of the Medical Faculty in Boston. Mr. Eliot seized the initiative in his reply:

Dear Sir,

I have the honor to acknowledge the receipt of your note of Nov. 2nd informing me of the wish of the Medical Faculty that I preside at their meetings.

year graded course of study in the Medical School had been established. The younger members of the Faculty, headed by Dr. James
C. White and under the leadership of President Eliot, had worked
strenuously to break away from the old proprietary system and to
bring medical education up to an equality with the standards which
existed in European schools. Harvard was already a conspicuous
leader in the new movement in this country, and all departments
of the Medical School were responding to the stimulus. It soon became evident that the new course of study, lengthened to occupy
the full academic year, was quite a different affair from the brief
course of winter lectures of the old system. The elaboration of additional courses of study which the new plan entailed made it

---

I had proposed to attend those meetings in accordance with the Statutes
of the University, and it will be doubly agreeable to me to do so in response
to the cordial invitation of the Faculty itself.

May I beg you to send me notice of the Faculty meetings by mail a
few days in advance?

Very truly yours
CHARLES W. ELIOT

Dr. Calvin Ellis
Dean of the Medical Faculty

[Letter in Harvard Medical School Library; quoted by Reginald Fitz in
"President Eliot and Dr. Holmes Leap Forward," *Harvard Library Bulletin 1*,
212 (Spring 1947).]

The story leading up to the reform in medical education that was begun
in 1870–71 at the Medical School is both dramatic and amusing. The struggle
between the liberals (White, Ellis, Bacon, Jackson, and Cheever, led by the new
president) and the conservatives (Holmes and Clarke, captained by the redoubt-
able Bigelow) went on for about four months. Mr. Eliot recalls the climax:

At last, one night he [Holmes] voted against Dr. Bigelow, who was advo-
cating standing still in all respects, to my great surprise and to Dr. Bigelow's
greater. The Faculty soon adjourned . . . As I was standing by the centre
table in the parlor Dr. Holmes came up to me and said, "Mr. President, you
have undoubtedly seen what is the matter with me." I could not say that I
had. Screwing the ball of his thumb round on the top of the table, Dr.
Holmes went on: "I have been under Dr. Bigelow's thumb so long, that I
have not been able to get out from under." [C. W. Eliot, "Oliver Wendell
Holmes," *Harvard Graduates' Magazine* (June 1923); reprinted in Eliot, *A
Late Harvest* (Boston, 1924), p. 37.]

Eliot showed great wisdom in adapting educational patterns observed in Europe
to American needs, employing safeguards not observed by some of the German-
ophilic reformers who were to come later. A letter written to his mother on
October 30, 1864 shows his insight into the matter:

A German University would suit the 150 young men who enter Freshmen
[at Harvard] every year, about as well as a barn-yard would suit a whale
. . . The system is utterly inapplicable with us, for the reason that we could
only copy its looseness without being able to imitate its restrictions. [Henry
James, *Charles W. Eliot, President of Harvard University, 1869–1909*
(Boston, 1930), I, 136.]

evident that even more ample accommodations for teaching purposes must soon be forthcoming. Those of us who had become familiar with the more advanced standards of foreign lands were thus given much food for thought. Many were the discussions held by Dr. Bowditch and myself on the problems which were presenting themselves with great rapidity.

The Medical School Moves
to Boylston Street

I recall vividly the decision that a new plant was required for the Medical School. I also remember a conversation with Dr. Fitz in his office on Boylston Street when I asked him for his coöperation in a proposal to raise funds for a building more suited to our needs. The resolve became then and there crystallized that an effort should be made to acquaint the public with the importance of a proper accommodation for the study of a branch of learning so important to the welfare of the community.

It was felt that an appeal for funds to help the cause of medical education would meet with a ready response. The legacy of financial burdens left by the Civil War was no longer bearing so heavily upon the nation as it had during the past decade. Times were beginning to be prosperous.[1] Large sums were being given to worthy undertakings by generous men and women. Harvard College as well as many other institutions of learning had been presented with stately memorial buildings, and it seemed highly probable that an appeal by the Faculty of Medicine would not be disregarded.

The first step in the campaign was the call for a meeting, which was held at No. 2 Park Street on October 20th, 1874. A memorandum listing those present on this occasion gives the names of Calvin Ellis, James C. White, Oliver F. Wadsworth, Reginald H. Fitz, Henry P. Bowditch, William L. Richardson, and Thomas Dwight. President Eliot was unable to be present, owing to a Faculty meeting in Cambridge. As a result of the Park Street meeting the following circular was issued:

MEDICAL EDUCATION
. . . . .
Boston, October 20, 1874

Dear Sir:

A meeting of persons interested in the erection of a new building for the
HARVARD MEDICAL SCHOOL
will be held in the Lower Horticultural Hall, on Thursday, October 22, at

---

[1] The impression created by J.C.W.'s description of economic good times needs qualification. After the Panic of 1873 hard times and unemployment continued into 1879. The "Great Railroad Strike of 1877" was the first of a long series of clashes between capital and labor.

10:30 A.M., to consider the best method of obtaining money necessary for that purpose.

Hon. J. H. Clifford will preside; and addresses will be made by President Eliot, Dr. Edward H. Clarke, Dr. Oliver Wendell Holmes and Rev. Edward E. Hale.

You are earnestly requested to be present.

JOHN A. LOWELL	NATHANIEL THAYER
J. INGERSOLL BOWDITCH	RALPH W. EMERSON
MARTIN BRIMMER	CALVIN ELLIS, M.D.
HENRY L. PIERCE	BENJ. E. COTTING, M.D.
HENRY P. KIDDER	CHARLES E. WARE, M.D.

It would have been hard to improve upon this list of names at any period of Boston history. An issue of the *Boston Transcript* of the above date says:

The meeting presented the most notable assemblage that has been witnessed in this city since that to promote the Agassiz memorial, including some of the most eminent gentlemen in literature and the practice of medicine in this vicinity, together with others who are well known in the mercantile world — all graduates of Harvard, and devoted to the promotion of the welfare of their alma mater.

The Honorable John H. Clifford of New Bedford, the Governor of Massachusetts, presided over the meeting, an indication that the movement was a matter of public concern, and not only of interest to the medical profession. It seems worth recording, as showing a change of habits and customs, that although the meeting was held at a seasonable hour and convenient locality only one woman was present. This fact was impressed upon my memory by the greeting of the Chairman, who addressed the assembled company as "Lady and Gentlemen." The lady was the daughter of the Reverend Edward Everett Hale and sat on the platform by her father's side.

The first speaker was President Eliot, who identified this movement as the sequel to the complete change in the methods of instruction at the Medical School which had taken place a few years before.[2]

---

[2] In 1856 Eliot had taught a class in chemistry at the Medical School and could speak from personal knowledge concerning the low average level of attainment among its students. Dr. Henry J. Bigelow appears to have overlooked this fact when he was resisting the changes proposed by the young president, which he thought would wreck the Harvard Medical School. "He actually proposes," said Bigelow, "to have written examinations for the degree of Doctor of Medicine. I had to tell him that he knew nothing about the quality of the Harvard Medical students; more than half of them can barely write. Of course, they can't pass written examinations."

President Eliot described the old methods of instruction in remarks made at a meeting of the Boston Society for Medical Improvement on March 5, 1900:

It was thirty-five years ago that I was a lecturer in the Harvard Medical School for one winter; at that time lectures began in the school on North

He contrasted the old methods of instruction with the new, and pointed out the necessity of endowment if a high standard was to be maintained. In the course of his remarks President Eliot made the following interesting statement: "The whole endowment of that school, which has done such a work in this community for ninety years, is less than $100,000, including the building. No department of the university is so poor in money, buildings and in all the appliances for instruction." [3]

Grove Street at eight o'clock in the morning and went on steadily till two o'clock — six mortal hours, one after the other, of lectures, without a question from the professor, without the possibility of an observation by the students, with no interchange of thought between teacher and student, none whatever, just the lecture to be listened to, and possibly to be taken notes of. Some of the students could hardly write, so that the taking of notes was difficult for them. Can you imagine such a misapplication of force as that? It seems as if it must have been contrived before the invention of printing; but it was still going on centuries after that invention. We have got a good way from that now; and I would not have you suppose that there were not some good doctors made in those days. There were, by a kind of miracle, and not in the lecture-room.

It is of more than passing interest to note that in his talk Mr. Eliot referred to Professor Langdell's development in Cambridge of the case method of teaching in law, and complimented Walter Cannon's proposal that cases in medicine be made the basis for instruction in an analogous manner. Eliot was most emphatic in explaining the need to select the important cases and present them in proper sequence. Unless this selection were done with insight and good judgment, the instruction would be neither comprehensive nor systematic and the case method would fail. He envisioned, of course, "the inductive method applied to medical education," and in fact the transcript of his remarks as printed in the *Boston Medical and Surgical Journal 142*, 557 (May 24, 1900) is so entitled.

The development of the clinical clerkship as launched by Osler at the Johns Hopkins obscured this point, and the clerkship is sometimes described as the "case method" of teaching. Certainly it is not that envisioned by Eliot, because the case-taking activities of a student clinical clerk are shaped by the admission of patients to hospital. This is of course random with respect to the importance of the case and the sequence in which it is encountered. The experience of the clinical clerk smacks more of the old apprenticeship than it resembles learning by scientific induction. The episodic nature of the case taking to which a clinical clerk is exposed is in fact a very slow method of acquiring generalizations and one that would not be countenanced by educators in a more scientifically advanced branch of knowledge.

[3] President Eliot explained in one of his annual reports: "So long as medical schools are conducted as private ventures for the benefit of a few physicians and surgeons who have united to form a corporation or faculty, the community ought not to endow them."

The reason for the lack of endowment for medical education throughout the country also seemed clear to Frederick T. Gates when he explored the subject for Mr. Rockefeller in 1893. In his private memoirs Gates wrote:

While other departments of science, such as astronomy, chemistry, physics, geology, etc., had been endowed very generously in colleges and universities, *medicine, owing to the commercial organization of medical colleges, had*

Dr. Oliver Wendell Holmes, the next speaker, presented the situation from the point of view of a member of the Medical Faculty and of the profession. His plea was made not only for a building which would house the belongings of the School safely from the hazard of fire, but for the endowment of professorships and scholarships. Conditions were needed, he said, that would permit the Faculty to insist upon some respectable amount of preliminary education as a prerequisite for admission to the Medical School. Only by such means could this department of the University be placed on an equality with the academic branch. Dr. Holmes gave a graphic description of the environment of the old building at the head of North Grove Street, saying that not only was the condition of its neighborhood such as greatly to increase the danger from fire, but the region which the visitor contemplated from its portals was of such ignoble aspect and so hopelessly given over to baser uses that the graduate of any well-ordered medical institution in Europe or America could only exclaim, "O star-eyed Science, hast thou wander'd there!" [4] His remarks closed with an eloquent tribute to the life of sacrifice which the physician cheerfully accepts and a citation of the importance of his work to the welfare of the community.

The exercises were closed by Dr. Edward H. Clarke and the Reverend Edward Everett Hale. On the motion of the Honorable Martin Brimmer a committee of fifty were appointed to carry into effect the object of the meeting. This committee organized itself with Governor Clifford as chairman and Mr. George Higginson as treasurer. An executive committee was appointed, composed of the following: President Charles W. Eliot, Mr. George Higginson, Hon. Martin Brimmer, and Drs. James C. White, Henry P. Bowditch, William L. Richardson, and J. Collins Warren (secretary).

The campaign which followed had for its object the raising of $200,000, an amount which was regarded then as a very ambitious sum and quite as much as we had any reasonable expectation of

---

rarely been endowed [italics by the editor], and research had been left to shift for itself, dependent altogether on such chance time as a rare spirit, without facilities, might steal from his practice.

It became clear to me that medicine could hardly hope to become a science until medicine was endowed, and qualified men were enabled to give themselves to uninterrupted study and investigation, on ample salary, entirely independent of practice. To this end, it seemed to me an institute of medical research ought to be established in the United States. And here was an opportunity for Mr. Rockefeller to do an immense service to his country and perhaps the world. ["The Memoirs of Frederick T. Gates," *American Heritage, The Magazine of History* (April 1955), p. 72.]

[4] From Thomas Campbell's "Pleasures of Hope" (Part I).

securing.[5] President Eliot had been able to announce at the meeting of October 22 the gift of a parcel of real estate on Brimmer Street valued at $20,000. This gift, at first recorded as anonymous, was later revealed as a memorial given by the parents of George Woodbury Swett, who had graduated from the Medical School in 1868 and had planned to devote his life to scientific research. Young Swett was a pioneer in what was then a tiny world of laboratory activities in the School but what is now so conspicuous and important a feature.[6] An early death cut short his promising career, and the house which was to have been his residence became the first contribution to the new medical school undertaking. A medallion of the young student is preserved among the memorial collections of the School.[7]

It is not the plan of this narrative to enter upon a detailed account of the ensuing campaign. The sum which it was estimated the Swett gift would realize was a most encouraging beginning. The members of the committee whose names accompanied the initial appeal were men prominent in the community and with a reputation of great public spirit. From the outset it was evident to the small band of active workers that they themselves would be high upon the list of benefactors. The treasurer's reports of the following years bear testimony to the generous response made by the leading citizens of that day. Colonel Henry Lee, himself a large giver and prominent

[5] The relative magnitude of this 1874 goal of $200,000 is apparent from the estimate that a total of $531,300 was donated in 1876 by private citizens in Boston for charitable purposes. Justin Winsor, ed., *Memorial History of Boston* (Boston, 1880–81), IV, 668.

[6] How tiny the world of laboratory activities in medicine actually was can be illustrated by the fact that a campaign to raise money for a new medical school could be launched with so little mention of the benefits which were to flow from medical research in the coming decades. All emphasis was on the training of the doctor for practice.

The same focus on practice is found pervading the lectures and writings of the period. A sentence from Henry J. Bigelow is typical: "The mass of work must be performed by the . . . practitioner, who has been educated with the view of turning his acquirements to immediate practical account, and whose business so occupies him that he contributes comparatively little to the absolute advance of knowledge." ("Medical Education in America," the Annual Address before the Massachusetts Medical Society, June 7, 1871.)

The new view that was to guide the medicine of the future was championed by James C. White. In the introductory address to the winter course of lectures on November 2, 1870 he spoke as follows: "Until we renounce the theory that medicine in America is to be taught, not as a science as elsewhere, that only so much of it is to be served up to the student as will make him a good practising doctor, and that he has no share in its future progress as an independent worker in its deep places, we need not hope for better things."

[7] The physiological laboratory fitted up for Dr. Henry P. Bowditch in the attic of the Medical School building on North Grove Street was in part paid for from the estate of George Woodbury Swett.

in all enterprises in which Harvard University was interested, once said that the great charities of Boston were mainly supported by a list of about eighty individuals. Spectacular donations were not characteristic of that period, nor were the gifts comparable in size with those with which we are familiar today, but it is none the less true that without the unfailing support of this small group of citizens the great educational institutions which have made Boston and New England famous would never have reached their present stage of development. The share of their incomes which in other cities would have gone to meet personal wants and provide the luxuries of life was dedicated to the annual needs of the community for public service.

The campaign for a new school building continued with much ardor until a sum of about $125,000 had been obtained. This was regarded as highly satisfactory, but of course was not sufficient to constitute an adequate building fund. As no definite plans for the future expansion of the School had been formulated, it was felt that the sum acquired would have time to grow in value while the Medical Faculty set itself to study the problem and select a suitable locality for the new building. The conflicting interests of the two great hospitals situated at opposite ends of the city made this by no means an easy task. The School had been in close proximity to the Massachusetts General Hospital since 1847, but the foundation of the Boston City Hospital in 1864 and its subsequent growth had given identity to another group of physicians and surgeons, actively interested in professional work of high standards and keen to take part in the teaching of students. The spectre of a rival school again arose, as it had on former occasions, to disturb the Faculty but, as in the past, a way was found to adjust conflicting interests. Only a short time before, in the reorganization to which the Medical School had been subjected, the talent of both hospitals had been combined in the composition of the teaching staff of the School to everyone's satisfaction.

Under these conditions it was natural for a policy to be formulated that a new medical school building should not be intimately associated with either hospital to the possible exclusion of the other, and that the interest of each institution should be duly consulted in the final selection of location. At one time negotiations were started for a parcel of land in the rear of the Home for Aged Women on Revere Street at the north end of Brimmer Street. This was thought to have the advantage of being close to the old site and yet on a line of communication toward the City Hospital. For the reasons just mentioned, this idea was abandoned.

Meanwhile the Faculty, being absorbed in the development of

its new course of study and the expansion of its teaching body which this necessarily involved, postponed from time to time taking any definite action upon a new site. The problem was finally solved in 1880 when the Faculty voted to accept President Eliot's proposal that a lot be selected on the corner of Boylston and Exeter Streets, in the undeveloped section of the Back Bay. The lot was in the center of a large open square, which was not to be cornered with buildings until years later. It seemed a somewhat remote spot, but it had the merit of being about half way between the two hospitals and thus equally accessible from either.

The Boylston Street location appealed to me as one which would place the School more conspicuously in the public eye than it had been up to that time. Dr. Holmes, with his neatly turned phrases, had brought out the disadvantage under which the School was laboring in the obscure and unattractive surroundings of the North Grove Street site. The public at large and especially that class to which the Faculty might look for the most substantial financial support did not seem to be aware of the fact that the Medical School was even in existence.

The location having been chosen, the next step was to decide on the type of building most appropriate to the needs of that period. Ware and Van Brunt [later Van Brunt and Howe] were selected as architects and a committee of the Faculty proceeded to the study of this problem. In the minds of the Faculty the most important innovation was a large chemical laboratory. The course in chemistry had recently been made an essential part of the curriculum and the work had been farmed out temporarily in other institutions. There was also to be a fine physiological laboratory in which Professor Bowditch and all his colleagues could take pride as exemplifying the new scientific spirit of the time. A railroad microscopical laboratory was planned for the upper floor near an excellently arranged dissecting room and did duty for both the histological and pathological departments. It was in an adjacent suite of rooms that Professor Charles S. Minot began his embryological collection. One room only was assigned to Dr. Fitz for research work in pathology and, although thought by all at the time to be ample for such a purpose, was soon found to be quite inadequate.

But the crowning glory of the building when completed was, in the minds of the older members of the Faculty, the anatomical amphitheatre. Its walls were adorned with portraits and busts of distinguished surgeons and anatomists, and it became the central point for large gatherings on more or less public occasions.

The material comforts of the student body were not entirely forgotten and spacious quarters were set aside for a reading room which the members of the classes might look upon as their own personal domain. Full liberty for rest and relaxation was given on a thoroughly independent basis. Although these quarters were of modest proportions from a present standpoint, they were the beginning of the recognition of the social side of medical student life, which still is much in need of a sympathetic development.

The building itself was designed as a substantial structure of brick and terra cotta with little external adornment except for tablets carrying the names of men noted for their standing in the world of medical science. The list of names was prepared by Oliver Wendell Holmes.

When the architects' plans and estimates were submitted to the Faculty in 1881 it was found that the cost was much beyond the sum remaining in the treasurer's hands after the purchase of the site. The cost of the new structure was placed at $200,000 — nearly double the amount of money then on hand. At a meeting of the Faculty held for the purpose of receiving the architects' report there was much doubt and hesitation as to the propriety of going ahead with the undertaking. Finally it was suggested that the Faculty adjourn for two weeks and that the campaign committee see in the interval what could be done in the way of raising additional funds. The financial period through which the country had recently passed was a cycle of depression following the great inflation after the close of the Civil War. It was only about this time that resumption of specie payment had taken place, but the business market was now responding favorably to new conditions and the moment seemed an opportune one to appeal to State Street for help. With the auspicious beginning of a gift of $25,000 we carried on our money raising with much enthusiasm and when the Faculty met at the appointed time, nearly the full amount had been subscribed. Asking for an adjournment of one week more, we were subsequently able to report the sum of $103,000 obtained in the three weeks. The Faculty had no further hesitation about the propriety of recommending the new plans. Building operations began forthwith.

Preparations were made for the inauguration of the new building in the spring of 1883 so that it might be ready for occupancy in the autumn at the beginning of the academic term. Before the mechanics had been banished from the building and while the painters were still at work, a fire broke out one evening in the chemical lecture room on the second floor. The cause of the fire was probably a spontaneous combustion of some material left by the workmen on leaving for the day. Fortunately, owing to the slow-burning construction material which had been employed, the fire was confined to the room in which it originated, and although the rows of wooden benches were destroyed and the heat thus developed must have been extreme, the walls remained uninjured. It so happened that no doors had as yet been placed in position and so, although the conflagration never left the lecture room, the beautiful fresh coats of paint on the walls of the interior of the building were converted into masses of blackened soot. If I remember rightly, the damage paid by the insurance companies amounted to $18,000, by far the largest item being the injury to the fresh paint.

The inauguration ceremonies were to have occurred a fortnight later, and had to be postponed, but another date was selected which coincided with the one hundredth anniversary of the foundation of the Medical School. Accordingly, exercises were held on October 17th, 1883, soon after the opening of the fall term. The program was divided into two parts. Formal ceremonies were held in the Huntington Hall of the Massachusetts Institute of Technology and consisted of an address by President Eliot and an oration by Dr. Holmes. In the course of his remarks President Eliot made the following statement, which summarizes the work accomplished since the original public meeting in the Lower Horticultural Hall in 1874:

The School has received by gift and bequest three hundred and twenty thousand dollars in ten years . . . it has paid about two hundred and twenty thousand dollars for a spacious, durable, and well-arranged building; it has increased its annual expenditure for salaries of teachers from twenty thousand dollars, in 1871–72, to thirty six thousand dollars, in 1882–83; its receipts have exceeded its expenses in every year since 1871–72, and its invested funds now exceed those of 1871 by more than one hundred thousand dollars. At the same time, the School has become a centre of chemical, histological, and sanitary research, as well as a place for thorough instruction.

President Eliot then called attention to the better education which the medical students brought with them to the School, owing to the increased requirements for entrance, and the prolongation of the period of medical study which would prepare them "to enter, not the overcrowded lower ranks of the profession, but the higher, where there is always room." The President appropriately closed his remarks as follows:

With thankfulness for the past, with reasonable satisfaction in the present, and with joyful hope in the future, the Medical Faculty celebrate this anniversary festival, welcoming their guests, thanking their benefactors, and exchanging with their colleagues, their students, and the governing boards mutual congratulations and good wishes, as the School sets bravely out upon its second century.

No public medical gathering could ever be regarded as satisfactorily staged without the participation of that most genial and talented of all professors, Oliver Wendell Holmes. This was an asset the possession of which the profession was duly proud. It was a golden age of medical eloquence which went far to offset the weakness of a still imperfectly developed medical science. It was with great satisfaction that the Centennial Address was committed into his keeping, and I commend for the perusal of those interested in the early history of their Alma Mater the little memorial booklet which contains his eloquent pronouncement.[8] I shall give one quotation, however, which has always clung to my memory as a characteristic ebullition of the author's style of wit. It may appropriately find a place here in these Reminiscences. In referring to the spacious quarters of the new building, so far superior to those in which he had labored for thirty-five years, he reminded his audience that

You will enter or look into more amphitheatres and lecture-rooms than you might have thought were called for. But if you knew what it is to lecture and be lectured to in a room just emptied of its preceding audience, you would be thankful that any arrangement should prevent such an evil. The experimental physiologists tell us that a bird will live under a bell-glass until he has substituted a large amount of carbonic acid for oxygen in the contained air. But if another bird is taken from the open air and put in with the first, the new-comer speedily dies. So when the class I was lecturing to was sitting in an atmosphere once breathed already, after I have seen head after head gently declining, and one pair of eyes after another emptying themselves of intelligence, I have said, inaudibly, with the considerate self-restraint of Musidora's rural lover, Sleep on, dear youth; this does not mean that you are indolent, or that I am dull; it is the partial coma of commencing asphyxia.

At the conclusion of Dr. Holmes's address, his portrait by Alexander was presented by Dr. Francis S. Minot as a gift of many alumni in token of their gratitude for the great services rendered to generations of pupils. Continuing, Dr. Minot said: "By his eminent scientific attainments, his sound method of teaching, his felicity of illlustration, and his untiring devotion to all the duties of his chair, he inspired those who were so fortunate as to come under his instruction with the importance of a thorough knowledge of anatomy, the foundation of medical science."

Dr. Holmes not only was willing to shine in public on grand occasions like this but was always ready with a fund of sympathy and encouragement for budding poets and young authors of scientific medical papers or committees engaged in some philanthropic task. I had an opportunity to come in personal relation with him on several occasions of this kind. In one instance, I had been urged by the ladies in charge

[8] This memorial booklet is entitled *Addresses and Exercises at the One Hundredth Anniversary of the Foundation of the Medical School of Harvard University, October 17. 1883* (Cambridge, 1884).

of the solicitation of funds "to save the Old South Church" to approach Dr. Holmes. Their hope was to garnish a final appeal with one of the doctor's characteristic poetical efforts. His good will had been sorely tested by the energetic efforts of zealous ladies repeated many times in the course of this campaign and often with success, and no one of them now dared to approach him again. Having finally consented to perform the offices of a forlorn hope, I received from him the following response:

296 Beacon Street, Nov. 22, 1876.

My dear Dr. Warren,

I *must* excuse myself. I have given what I could spare to the "Old South" Fund. I have written a poem, — some verses, at any rate, — printed in the *Daily Advertiser* under the title "A Last Appeal," to stir up people as much as I knew how to. And now I have ground my tune and taken my hand-organ on my back, I cannot make up my mind to come back to the same doorstep and begin grinding again. Seriously and absolutely, you must call some other street musician.

Always truly yours,
OLIVER WENDELL HOLMES

The formal program of the inauguration exercises was brought to a close by Dr. Samuel A. Green's presentation of the bust of Dr. Henry Jacob Bigelow by Launt Thompson. The company then adjourned to the new building, where short addresses were made by Dr. Henry W. Williams and Colonel Henry Lee. The latter spoke in behalf of the benefactors, and a more typical and worthy representative they could not have had. The head of an old and honored family, and a prosperous merchant, he was always at the fore in public-spirited movements of his day. He filled the role of a leading citizen as well as benefactor. The University was already in debt to him for assistance in the current developments of its various departments. His greeting to the Medical Faculty and the public was delivered with grace and ease, and rounded out the exercises of the day in a dignified manner.

And so the Faculty became comfortably established in new quarters, but with the era of greater prosperity came new financial burdens. In the old building a janitor's salary and a weekly washing bill had been the principal expenditures in the treasurer's accounts. Opportunity was now offered for special lines of research which previously could not be carried out because of the absence of proper laboratory accommodations, and a small world of laboratory men was being assembled who could not look to the practice of their profession as a means of support, as had hitherto been the case with teachers of medicine. The weekly payroll became an item which had to be reckoned with, and this naturally turned the thoughts of the Faculty to an adequate endowment for so rapidly expanding and changing an institution.

An appeal had already been made in the columns of the *Daily Advertiser* the previous winter with an editorial from the pen of Dr. Holmes, which was appended to the report of the exercises of the One Hundredth Anniversary. It was pointed out that increased requirements for admission had diminished the number of students, and that a preliminary examination had already been established. In addition, a voluntary fourth year had been added to the curriculum. As usual, Dr. Holmes had performed his task with a master's hand and caught the ear of the public with neatly turned phrases which stamped themselves upon the memory. Referring to the group of benefactors who had done so much for Boston institutions, he said:

The Old World motto is *Noblesse oblige.* Our generous men of wealth are changing the phrase to *Richesse oblige,* and thus becoming recognized as our untitled nobility. It is only necessary to show them in what way their beneficence will do the most extended and the most lasting good. The foundation of five or six professorships will carry the names of their founders down to a remote posterity, and call them to honored remembrance when the stately buildings around us are replaced by other and still nobler structures.

The first response to this appeal came from the Faculty itself in the shape of a bequest from one of its most talented and progressive members, Dr. Calvin Ellis, whose death occurred in December of 1883. By a provision of his will the School eventually received his entire fortune, which amounted to nearly four hundred thousand dollars and which is now known as the Calvin and Lucy Ellis Fund. In setting so notable an example of public spirit Dr. Ellis was the pioneer in a series of benefactions of which the School became the fortunate recipient.

ॐ XXII

A Transition Period

One of the Medical Faculty ventured to remark that before another period of time equal to that which had been passed in the North Grove Street building, the new quarters on Boylston Street would be found as unsuited for the purposes of the School as its old home had become. The use of the old building had covered a period of nearly forty years, and such an estimate of the capacities of the new one seemed absurdly inadequate. Not forty but merely twenty years were to pass before the wisdom of this judgment became apparent.

The number of students in the School during the year 1883–84 was 243. Ten years later it had increased to 560 and in the academic year 1900–01 it rose to 605. This showed quite conclusively that in spite of increased entrance requirements and a lengthened course of study the improved facilities for obtaining a high-grade medical education had been appreciated. It indicated also the necessity for further development along the same lines in order to be able to meet the popular demand which had expressed itself in so tangible a form.

The removal of the School from close proximity to the Massachusetts General Hospital seemed to bring home to the Faculty the interdependence of the two institutions, and this feeling was further strengthened by an incident which occurred in 1886. Dr. Robert T. Edes having resigned from the Jackson Professorship of Clinical Medicine, the question arose as to the advisability of making a selection of his successor from some other clinical center. After some discussion it was generally agreed that such a move was not practicable owing to the inability of the School to provide any clinical facilities for a teacher who was not already a member of a local hospital staff. Shortly before, the University of Pennsylvania, which had a hospital of its own, had been able to appoint William Osler to a professorship of medicine, calling him from McGill University. A few years later, when the faculty of the new Johns Hopkins Medical School was being organized by President Gilman, the same favorable combination of a university-controlled hospital enabled that institution to select the most able talent wherever it happened to be found and so attain world-wide celebrity.

At Harvard the necessity for a more intimate understanding between school and hospital was felt more strongly by the Medical Faculty as time went on, and the desirability of establishing a school of medicine on this foundation became obvious. President Eliot, in his Report for 1888–89, recommended a more intimate union of school and hospital,[1] and subsequently the Medical Faculty appointed a committee (of which I was a member) to find a way of accomplishing this end. Negotiations were opened with the Trustees of the Massachusetts General Hospital early in 1890. It was pointed out that the Hospital had had its origin in a demand both for the relief of the sick poor and for the advance of medical knowledge. The old building at the head of North Grove Street which the Medical School had vacated seven years earlier had been turned over to the Harvard Dental School, but, standing as it did on ground that was practically a part of the Hospital enclosure, it seemed naturally to belong to the latter institution.[2] It was suggested that the University donate the building to the

[1] President Eliot wrote in his Annual Report for 1888–89 that when a vacancy occurred in a clinical department of the Medical School

> the question before the Governing Board of the University is — not who is the best man for the place in Boston or elsewhere — but who is the most available man as a teacher among the Boston practitioners already holding cognate hospital appointments given by other Boards of Trustees, who in making their selection had teaching not at all in mind. More than once this limitation of choice has proved unfortunate. More than once the School and the community have lost an important medical reinforcement because the School was not in a position to offer to the desired person an adequate hospital appointment as well as a professorship.

[2] The old Medical School on North Grove Street always brings to mind the murder of Dr. George Parkman on November 23, 1849 and the famous trial, conviction, and execution of Dr. John W. Webster, Erving Professor of Chemistry. The following letter of Dr. Jacob Bigelow [quoted in F. A. Washburn, *The Massachusetts General Hospital: Its Development 1900–1935* (Houghton Mifflin, Boston, 1939), p. 49] suggests that the Parkman murder may have been a turning point in the development of the Harvard Medical School, particularly in its subsequent geographical relation to the Massachusetts General Hospital:

Boston, Oct. 12, 1850

S. A. Eliot, Esq.
Dear Sir:

During the erection of the Mass. Medical College in Grove Street, and at various times afterward, I visited the premises in company with the late Dr. George Parkman. He stated to me in many conversations his intention to lay open a square in front of the College by removing the whole block of old buildings which now encumber the ground. He was not able at once to effect his liberal purpose in consequence of the claims of certain parties to whom he had sold on mortgage, but he was confident that the estates would revert to him in a short time, so that the claims of the persons interested could be settled without difficulty. He then expressed the intention to remove the whole, and actually began by pulling down the building nearest to the college, of which he had the whole fee. Dr. Parkman further expressed

Hospital in exchange for the privilege of a nomination for a Hospital appointment in connection with the organization of the academic departments of medicine and surgery. After lengthy deliberation, the Trustees of the Hospital were unable to come to a favorable decision on a matter involving so radical a change, and the Faculty had to abandon this plan.[3]

---

his intention to make a passage from the college into Bridge Street [North Anderson Street], to remove the bowling alley from the opposite side, and to cause to be cut off the end of the Foundry which projects into the street. I have no doubt that, but for his lamented death, he would have fully carried out these designs, which in connexion with the rest of his generous donation, so honorably associate his name with the cause of medical learning, and which constituted a favorite object of his anticipation during life . . .

Respectfully,
JACOB BIGELOW

Charles Dickens had met Professor Webster in 1842, and on another trip to Boston in 1868 he wrote in a letter to Lord Lytton:

Being in Boston I went over to the Medical School at Harvard and saw the exact localities where Professor Webster did that amazing murder and worked so hard to rid himself of the body of the murdered man. They were horribly grim, private, cold, and quiet. The identical furnace, smelling fearfully (some anatomical broth in it, I suppose), as if the body was still there; jars of pieces of sour mortality standing about, like the forty robbers in Ali Baba after being scalded to death; and bodies near us ready to be carried in to next morning's lecture. [Edward F. Payne, *Dickens Days in Boston* (Boston, 1927), p. 211.]

By 1908 many of the unsightly structures mentioned in Dr. Bigelow's letter had been acquired by the Hospital and pulled down. In the following year the old medical college building, located at what is now the approach to the George Robert White Building, was vacated by the Dental School and turned over to the Hospital. In 1911 it was demolished in preparation for an ambitious building program.

[3] On January 10, 1890 the Trustees of the MGH received a communication from Drs. James C. White, J. Collins Warren, and Frederick C. Shattuck, committee of the Medical Faculty of Harvard University, proposing a more complete union between the two institutions. The matter was referred to a small committee which subsequently (February 14, 1890) was requested to consult with the Resident Physician, i.e., the superintendent, and the visiting physicians and surgeons.

On May 16 the "Chairman for the Committee on the new Clinical Ward and Lecture Room proposed by the Committee of the Harvard Medical School" reported that action on the proposal was declined. The Trustees accepted the report.

The rights to periods of active service at the Hospital were jealously guarded by staff members who had attained such rights over many years during which they had served the Hospital and achieved promotion by rigid seniority selection. This is shown by the following entry in the minutes of the Trustees for October 17, 1890:

A communication was received from Dr. Pratt [Resident Physician], enclosing the vote of the Visiting Physicians of the Hospital on his proposition to give the Professor of Clynical [*sic*] Medicine in Harvard University a

The Faculty committee then considered the feasibility of establishing a hospital under complete control of the School. In November of 1890 the committee reported favorably upon the project, but the magnitude of the undertaking, involving as it would an early removal from the new quarters on Boylston Street and the raising of funds to establish a hospital of adequate proportions, made it seem advisable to the Faculty to consider the possibility of accomplishing its ends in some other way.

About this time the keen eye of Dr. Bowditch, the dean of the Faculty, discovered a possible solution of the problem of clinical facilities in the will of Peter Bent Brigham, who had died in 1877. A large sum of money had been left by him for a hospital for the sick poor of the city of Boston. The will provided that this money should be held by the executors for twenty-five years, and it was estimated that by the end of this time the funds would be sufficiently large in amount to carry out the intention of the testator. The expiration of this twenty-five year period seemed far distant but, inasmuch as any scheme would involve preparation of an entirely new plan on a very extended scale, the element of time did not constitute a serious obstacle. After careful consideration the Faculty became convinced that there was nothing impracticable about it, and during the following decade, while watching with keen interest and satisfaction the development of the various departments of the School along modern lines, they kept steadfastly in mind the possibility of taking another and much more ambitious forward step.

Meanwhile the expansion of the laboratory side of the school work had gone on apace, and a new generation of younger men was identifying itself more or less exclusively with scientific medicine. Hardly a decade earlier, to have been referred to as one possessed of a scientific bend of mind would have been regarded a term of reproach. It was taken to mean that there was something impractical in one's makeup, a quality likely to interfere with ultimate success as a practitioner. But now a new point of view was replacing old standards and the scientific worker was becoming a recognized member of the medical world and one for whose activities proper provisions should be made.

The demand for suitable accommodations for those engaged in

---

continuous service in the wards of the Hospital of eight months annually and recommending instead of Dr. Pratt's plan "the addition for this year of three months' service to the Professor of Clinical Medicine as offered by Drs. Richardson, Whittier and Cutler," one month each, "from their respective terms of service." *Voted* that the Board accept the suggestion of the Visiting Physicians, and authorizes the three months' change to be made accordingly.

laboratory instruction and research work was yearly becoming more pressing, and in 1889 was met by a generous response from a recent graduate of the Medical School, Dr. Henry F. Sears. His gift of $35,000 enabled the Faculty to build a valuable addition to the School on a portion of the unoccupied land on the Boylston Street lot. The Sears Laboratory, opened in December of 1890, gave for the first time sufficient space for the work of the departments of bacteriology and pathological anatomy. Bacteriology thus came into its own as a department of medicine, sufficiently well recognized to occupy a conspicuous position in the Medical School plant. Here, under the able supervision of Dr. Harold C. Ernst, the pioneer in this branch of medicine in this country, many problems were worked out which have contributed so much to the efficiency of city and state hygienic laboratories.

The department of pathology was given space to expand to dimensions somewhat more in keeping with the rapidly increasing respect in which it was held by the educators of the period. Years of painstaking laboratory research were beginning to bear fruit of very practical value and basic to the teaching and practice of medicine. In 1892 Dr. William T. Councilman was called from Johns Hopkins University to fill the vacancy caused by the transfer of Dr. Reginald H. Fitz to become Hersey Professor of the Theory and Practice of Physic. Dr. Councilman was duly installed as Shattuck Professor of Pathological Anatomy.[4] This appointment, together with that of Dr. William H. Howell as associate professor of physiology, may be said to have marked the inauguration of a new policy by which the University was attempting to place the Medical School on a par with its other depart-

---

[4] In writing of William T. Councilman in *Science* (June 30, 1933), Harvey Cushing recalled:

> Accustomed as a second-year student to the formal lectures then in vogue at the Harvard Medical School, the writer well remembers what an impression was made by the addition in 1892 to a somewhat austere faculty of this breezy informal pipe-smoking man, unmistakably sloping toward the sunny side, who was said to have been the first "outsider" ever appointed to a professorial chair in the School. Accustomed to work elbow to elbow with others, those of us who cared to do so and knew enough to take advantage of the opportunity were welcome to a chair and a desk and a problem in his laboratory.

In the following year (1893) William Townsend Porter was called from the St. Louis Medical College to become assistant professor of physiology. Although Councilman and Porter were the first "outsiders," it has been noted that in 1883, when the Bostonian Thomas Dwight was appointed to the Parkman Professorship of Anatomy, "careful inquiry had been made both in Europe and the United States for available candidates among anatomists of reputation." [F. C. Shattuck and J. L. Bremer in S. E. Morison, ed., *The Development of Harvard University . . . 1869–1929* (Cambridge, 1930), p. 564.]

ments where the selection of a new professor was not confined to local talent.

The School was now reaching a position in which its medical science departments were given a much broader scope, and Dr. Bowditch felt obliged to retire from the position of dean of the Faculty to devote more time to research in the physiological laboratory. Under his guidance the School had experienced a period of prosperity unprecedented in its existence and was rapidly growing in both the number of its students and the extent of its reputation. The office of the dean was entrusted to Dr. William L. Richardson, under whose efficient and capable management the affairs of the School were to be placed on a thoroughly modern basis.

During the transition period the requirements for admission and the standards required for graduation had steadily increased. An entrance examination had been established for the first time in 1877, and the standards of this examination were raised in 1885 and again in 1893. An optional fourth year had been added in 1879 and was made compulsory in 1892. The number of students was constantly increasing and a demand for more ample accommodations was coming from every department. The chemical laboratories, which had been planned to accommodate 210 students, had to provide for 350. In the pathology department 150 men were crowded into a room built for 60. The modification of the methods of instruction which this laboratory expansion had made desirable could not even be started without increased floor space.

The laboratories of the Hospital afforded a measure of relief but these were far away, and the conviction had gradually become established that, once having entered upon a policy of expansion in keeping with the spirit of the age, there must be no holding back. The Medical Department of the University, in spite of what had already been accomplished, needed a vastly more elaborate system of laboratory accommodations and most important of all an intimate association with hospital facilities of a varied character. With these thoughts now uppermost in mind, the attention of the Faculty was again called to the Brigham Fund. The date assigned by the testator for the employment of this large bequest for the building of a hospital was growing nearer. In a few years' time a Board of Trustees would be created and the intent of the will carried out. It became therefore a matter of paramount importance to study the problem of an active coöperation of the School with a hospital under the limitations which would apply to the two institutions. A union of school and hospital was a combination with which the public, in this part of the country at least, was not familiar. Any attempt on the part of a great educational institution seemingly to appropriate for its own uses a charitable bequest of many millions of dollars intended for the sick poor of Boston would be regarded with suspicion. It would be necessary to enlighten the public at large and the governing bodies of both institutions as to the enormous benefits to be derived from close coöperation.

I have already touched upon the advantages that accrue to a school which possesses the right of nomination of appointees to a hospital service. The faculty is thus enabled to place its clinical instruction on a par with its laboratory instruction and to organize the clinical departments of the school on the same standard of efficiency as that existing in the other departments. Suitable candidates can be selected regardless of their locality. The whole world may be canvassed in the search for the incumbent of some particular chair. The dimension of the inducement offered is the only basis on which it is possible for outside talent to consider the question of responding to an invitation. From the standpoint of the hospital, by such an association it not only obtains the services of men of the highest reputation but, when instruction is made part of the functions of the hospital, is enabled to give the sick more careful, constant, and thoughtful attention than when no such instruction is given. Dr. John S. Billings, in his address at the opening of the Johns Hopkins Hospital, dwelt upon this point and called attention to the stimulating influence of the students upon the work of the teacher: "Keen eyes will note every error in diagnosis, every failure in results of treatment." The very act of teaching clarifies the teacher's knowledge, and those patients who are the subjects of discussion in the lecture room receive the best treatment. Not the least of the benefits of such a system is its value to the community in turning out highly trained physicians. Were some benefactor or founder of a great hospital to contrast such an inspired teaching-hospital service with the old-time municipal charity institution, there would be little doubt as to the conditions of the bequest which he would leave to posterity.

The period during which the Medical School occupied the Boylston Street building saw many important changes in the hospitals of Boston. The City Hospital was constantly increasing in size, and its department for contagious diseases, opened in 1895, came to be unequalled in this country.[5] A great change also took place at the Massachusetts General Hospital, where a pathological laboratory was built in 1896 and endowed with money obtained by members of the Staff.

[5] The Pathological Building at the Boston City Hospital was formally opened in December 1895, ten months before the corresponding event at the MGH. Its activities were supervised by William Councilman, who had been appointed visiting pathologist to the city institution in 1892.

Although a laboratory is now recognized as an essential part of any well-organized hospital, this laboratory was then a new departure and when completed was more extensive and better equipped than that of any other hospital either in this country or in Europe.[6]

A new building for the Massachusetts Charitable Eye and Ear Infirmary was opened in 1899 to replace the structure which for half a century had stood on Charles Street just south of the approach to the old West Boston Bridge.[7] The new Infirmary was an example of modern hospital construction and one of the first of its kind. Land had been purchased from Mr. George Parkman, the owner of a lot adjacent to the Massachusetts General Hospital. By this development, unhygienic surroundings were removed from almost within the grounds of the Hospital and a highly desirable neighbor, from both a medical and a hygienic point of view, was acquired. By an arrangement between the Trustees of the Hospital and the Board of Managers of the Infirmary, a portion of land was transferred from the Infirmary to the Hospital for a new out-patient department.[8] The funds for the

[6] The cornerstone of the Warren Building at the MGH was laid in 1955 and the building itself dedicated in December 1956. The name was chosen as a tribute to members of the Warren family in recognition of their contributions to the medicine and surgery of the New World. This building houses the James Homer Wright Pathological Laboratories, moved from the 1896 building on Allen Street and named in honor of the man who for so many years made the old building the scientific center of the Hospital.

A research building opened in 1951 provides two floors for the J. Collins Warren Laboratory, devoted to cancer research. This activity was moved to MGH from Huntington Avenue and Shattuck Street with the Collis P. Huntington Hospital function in 1943.

[7] The following statement appears in the 74th Annual Report of the Massachusetts Charitable Eye and Ear Infirmary for 1899:

The Infirmary has suffered a great loss in the resignation of the President, Dr. J. C. Warren, who, having seen the new building, due so largely to his efforts, completed, equipped, and in successful operation, felt, after eleven years' service, that his many other duties called him away.

The vote passed by the staff follows: —

Resolved, That the Surgeons of the Massachusetts Charitable Eye and Ear Infirmary have heard with regret that Dr. J. Collins Warren has resigned the presidency of the Board of Managers. They desire at this time to express to him and place upon their records their high appreciation of his services. During his presidency the Infirmary has been reorganized in all its departments, has become possessed of a modern hospital building so complete in its appointments as not only to fulfill all the requirements of a modern surgical practice, but also to serve as a model for similar institutions, and has in addition been placed on a much firmer financial basis. They feel that to him the greater part of the credit for these many improvements is due, and desire to tender him therefor the sincere thanks of the professional staff.

[8] Dr. Frederic A. Washburn wrote in his history of the Hospital (p. 200):

The land . . . was purchased from Mr. George Parkman in 1898. It is said that the [MGH] Trustees bought this land through the agency of the

new Infirmary had been obtained partly by subscription and partly by aid from the State, the Legislature appropriating $100,000 for that purpose. It had been the policy of the Trustees of Boston's principal medical charity not to seek state aid, owing to the possibilities of political entanglements, but in the case of the Infirmary the State had been in the habit of referring affections of the eye to its care and thus avoided the necessity of establishing a state hospital for such a purpose. It was one of the few privately administered charitable institutions which received annual appropriations from the Legislature.

The erection of the new Eye and Ear Infirmary in close conjunction with the Hospital was a move in the direction of enlarging the sphere of medical charitable work in the West End of Boston, and this was further promoted by enlargements and improvements in the Boston Lying-in Hospital, which was a near neighbor on McLean Street dating from 1873. About the year 1890 the two buildings occupied by the latter institution were renovated and an operating room was added. To accomplish this, the sum of $100,000 was raised by appeal to the public. The character of the work done in obstetrics was of the highest quality under the able leadership of Dr. William L. Richardson. On returning from his European studies in 1869, Dr. Richardson had found this institution in a dormant state. After securing the control of it, he proceeded to build up a department of obstetrics which has become one of the most valuable assets of Boston.[9]

Massachusetts Eye and Ear Infirmary, which was to put up its new building on the western end of this parcel, as they though it unwise to approach Mr. Parkman direct. Their fear was that he might have feeling against the Hospital because of the murder of his father [Dr. George Parkman] by Professor Webster in the Harvard Medical School [1849]. The Medical School building was a near neighbor, and the institutions were closely related, as the staff of the Hospital and the faculty of the School were composed of much the same persons. This fear was proved groundless when Mr. Parkman's will, probated in 1908, and dated twenty-one years previously, showed that he had bequeathed the land to the Hospital. How the old gentleman must have chuckled as he saw the Hospital acquire by indirect ways land he intended to give to it.

[9] The following entry appears in the records of the trustees of the Boston Lying-in Hospital under date of January 26, 1921:

Thirty years ago when the money was being secured for the alterations in the old buildings which constitute the present hospital [on McLean Street] Dr. Warren was largely instrumental in securing the $100,000 that was then necessary. His interest and active work continued and he has been zealously soliciting funds to enable us to build a new hospital building.

J.C.W. served on the consulting staff of the Lying-in Hospital, and his sister Mrs. Rosamond Warren Gibson was said to have regarded this institution as "the chief among her many charitable interests."

The Lying-in moved to its present location on Longwood Avenue early in 1923. The Richardson House there is a memorial to Dr. William Richardson for his contributions to Boston obstetrics.

But in spite of all these hospital activities in the West End,[10] the fact still remained that the Medical School was trying to work out its salvation on an antiquated system of personnel selection, and that so long as it remained in its location on Boylston Street, isolated from all hospitals, there was no prospect of placing the School in a position to compete with the other leading medical teaching institutions of the world and thus to work out what seemed to have become its manifest destiny.[11]

[10] Other medical activities were to be found in the overpopulated West End. The House of the Good Samaritan (1860) at No. 6 McLean Street pioneered in the care of women and children with chronic diseases, and here Dr. Buckminster Brown conducted an orthopedic ward. The Harvard Dental School (1868) began at No. 54 Anderson Street and moved two years later to No. 50 Allen Street. The Channing Home (1857) for female "incurables" moved from South Street to No. 30 McLean Street in 1870. The Boston Training School for Nurses was opened in 1873 at No. 45 McLean Street and three years later moved into the "Old Brick" at the MGH. Several young Harvard clinical instructors conducted a dispensary for women and children (1873) at No. 18 Staniford Street. The North End Diet Kitchen (1874) moved to No. 34 Lynde Street and other local addresses before finally joining the outpatient department at the MGH. The Associated Charities, designed to coördinate the numerous agencies of Boston, was created in 1879 at the Charity Building on Chardon Street; the City Physician was installed in the same building. The West End Nursery and Hospital for Infants (1880) was established on Blossom Street under the leadership of Dr. Thomas Morgan Rotch, who became Harvard's first professor of pediatrics, and J.C.W. served on the consultant staff. The Sisters of St. Margaret (Episcopal) founded an infirmary at Louisburg Square (1882) and St. Monica's Home for sick Negro women (1887) at No. 45 Joy Street. A group of female doctors opened the Trinity Dispensary (1885) in St. Andrew's Church at No. 38 Chambers Street; this developed into the Vincent Memorial Hospital (1890) at No. 44 Chambers Street, named for Mrs. Mary Ann Vincent, a charity-minded actress of the old Boston Museum Stock Company. This hospital, after a sojourn on South Huntington Avenue, moved to the grounds of the MGH in 1947. The Mt. Sinai Hospital Society set up an outpatient branch on Chambers Street in 1902, and in the same year the Elizabeth Peabody House (1896), a pioneer settlement, set up Boston's first pasteurized-milk station for infants at No. 87 Poplar Street.

[11] Laboratory instruction had forged ahead so that well-organized courses became available in anatomy, physiology, pathology, bacteriology, hygiene, and chemistry before reform showed itself in clinical teaching. Leaders in the medical sciences showed a better comprehension of educational requirements and methods than did the practitioners, most of whom clung to master-and-apprentice training methods that passed on the fruits of experience rather than scientific principles and systematized knowledge. William H. Welch described the situation in a nutshell during his address on Founders' Day at the Peter Bent Brigham, November 12, 1914. "The time has gone by," he said, "when the great clinicians, those who stand before the community as the great consultants, can at the same time be the heads of departments in the schools and hospitals. Theirs is a different career."

The readjustments occasioned by this change have caused many heartaches and led to bitter misunderstandings. The changes are still being vigorously contested in some localities, but the trend forecast by Dr. David Edsall in his Aesculapian Club address in 1912 (see Appendix III) and by Dr. Welch has progressed too far to be reversed.

❧ XXIII

The Great Undertaking on Longwood Avenue

In 1899 the leaders of the Faculty made up their minds that plans must be made to secure a plot of land which would be sufficiently large to accommodate a group of buildings for the School and to provide room for one or more hospitals which might be induced to find for themselves a new home within the same area.[1] A plant of this description, as Dr. Bowditch pointed out, would call for a series of buildings similar in general plan to those which existed in some of the most recently organized German medical schools. The scheme envisioned a group of more or less detached "institutes" devoted to anatomy, physiology, and the other great departments of medicine. Such an arrangement would provide for laboratory accommodations on a far larger scale than had ever before been attempted in this or any other school in this country. An undertaking of this magnitude would involve a very large sum of money; indeed, to many members of the Faculty the difficulties surrounding an attempt to raise the necessary funds seemed an insuperable obstacle. Not only would a broad tract of land have to be purchased but the erection of several

[1] At a meeting of the Medical Faculty on June 3, 1899 Dr. Henry P. Bowditch presented this resolution:

> That the Faculty express hereby its appreciation of the great value of the *endowments for the medical school recently voted by the Corporation,* and also its opinion that the interests of both the proposed new Laboratories and of the present medical departments will be best met by concentration in one locality, by which teachers will be helped, students stimulated, loss of time prevented and a great diminution of expenses secured both for the plant and for maintenance.

> That the above be communicated to the President and Fellows and that they be requested to take immediate measures to *secure a lot of land adequate in size and situation for the accommodation of all the departments of the Medical School, the Veterinary School, the Dental School, the Graduate School of Comparative Medicine, and also for a hospital to be connected with the Medical School.*

This resolution was defeated by a vote of 12 to 6. But the following year on May 5 the Medical Faculty unanimously resolved to "recommend that the Francis Estate between Longwood Avenue and Francis Street . . . is most desirable for the location for buildings under charge of the Faculty of Medicine."

203

large buildings, each one of which would be the size of the one now occupied by the School, would represent a very formidable sum of money. Those who remembered the long period which had elapsed before the necessary funds had been obtained to enable them to move into their present quarters began to look upon the project as somewhat Utopian.

From my own point of view, however, which was based on no inconsiderable experience, there did not seem to be any inherent impracticability in the proposed undertaking. The School possessed at the turn of the century a permanent endowment of nearly one million dollars. There was also the Boylston Street building and land, the value of which had steadily increased during the seventeen years of occupancy and which, at a conservative estimate, amounted to half a million dollars. These assets were substantial enough to justify a beginning which, if necessary, could be left to our successors for completion.

The problem of an appropriate site for this large group of buildings seemed quite as perplexing as the financial problem. In order to meet the terms of the Brigham will the site had to be located within the limits of the city of Boston; [2] unless this stipulation could be met there would be no possibility of inducing the Trustees of the Brigham Hospital to become our neighbors. Unfortunately, several attractive sites did not meet this important condition. The advantages of the large vacant tract on the north bank of the Charles River which has since been occupied by the Massachusetts Institute of Technology were carefully considered by a committee appointed for this purpose. To me, an ideal site was that adjoining the Soldier's Field in the city of Cambridge [sic] on the left bank of the Charles River, immediately opposite the site of the Freshman dormitories. This situation offered a wonderful architectural opportunity. A group of buildings similar in imposing dignity to those which constitute St. Thomas' Hospital on the bank of the Thames River opposite the Houses of Parliament would offer artistic possibilities and also bring the great advantage of close proximity to the other departments of the University. This locality would also provide space for an indefinite extension of hospital facilities. As all of this region was outside of the Boston city limits,[3]

[2] The Brigham will stipulated that the hospital was to be built within the County of Suffolk, which includes Boston, Chelsea, Revere, and Winthrop.

[3] At this point J.C.W.'s memory seems to have been hazy. The vicinity of Soldier's Field, south of the Charles River, lies not in Cambridge but in Brighton, which was annexed by the City of Boston in 1873, four years before the death of Peter Bent Brigham. J.C.W. was referring probably to the site now occupied by the Harvard Graduate School of Business Administration (1926), which looks across the river directly at the old Freshman dormitories.

the question arose again whether, after all, it might not be better for Harvard to build a hospital of its own and thus become independent of all other organizations.

Under the skillful management of Mr. Robert Codman and, after his death, of his son Mr. E. D. Codman, the funds of the Brigham estate had increased enormously and passed the five million mark. It seemed foolish to abandon the proposal to associate two such prosperous institutions in a common cause and thus more than double the usefulness of each. It was with reluctance that the plan to bring the Medical School into closer touch with the University was abandoned.[4]

Prior to the erection of the Charles River Dam at Leverett Street in 1908, the vicinity of Soldier's Field was flooded every spring as a consequence of thawing snow, heavy rains, and high tides. Shattuck and Bremer inserted the following footnote in their chapter on the Medical School in S. E. Morison, ed., *The Development of Harvard University . . . 1869–1929* (Cambridge, 1930), p. 570:

> The geographical separation of the Medical School from the College is regretted keenly by many in the School. Had the Charles River dam existed in 1900, it is probable that the present site of the Business School, which is included in Suffolk County and thus meets the requirements of the Brigham will, would have been preferred by the committee.

[4] The ever-increasing importance of the natural and biological sciences to medicine has made the geographical separation of the preclinical scientists on Longwood Avenue from their many colleagues in Cambridge a matter of real concern. If the decision of 1900 were to be reconsidered today, it is not at all likely that the Faculty of Medicine would be willing to place its science laboratories so far from the University area in Cambridge, or indeed that the rest of the University would concur in such a move.

The University of Chicago has gone further than striving for geographical unity; it has welded medicine into the university structure. First, the preclinical sciences were established as "university" rather than "medical school" departments and thus kept within the framework of the scientific activities of the University. With the creation of a division of the biological sciences in 1930 the clinical as well as the preclinical departments were incorporated. The University of Chicago thus avoided the creation of a medical school in the sense of a self-governing unit with its own dean.

This trend at the University of Chicago can be traced back to the influence of Dr. Franklin P. Mall, who also helped plant the seed of full-time medicine at the Johns Hopkins. Mall had been a student of the physiologist Carl Ludwig at Leipzig, and looked upon medical education as an integral part of a university — not as vocational training. On February 28, 1902, subsequent to Harvard's decision to continue medicine in splendid isolation from the rest of the University, Dr. Lewellys F. Barker, then professor of anatomy at the University of Chicago, defined the university hospital clinic as one staffed by men who should, "like other university professors, give their whole time and energy to the work of the university, to teaching and to investigating in the hospitals." [I. Veith and F. C. McLean, *Medicine at the University of Chicago, 1927–1952* (University of Chicago Press, Chicago, 1952), p. 4.]

President Eliot, on the other hand, appeared to be thinking more in terms of an independent medical research institute similar to the Rockefeller Institute, founded in 1903. This can be illustrated by an anecdote related by Frederick T. Gates in his private memoirs:

The tract of land finally recommended by the committee was a part of the estate of the late Ebenezer Francis, and at one time had formed

---

One day I chanced to be walking down Broadway with President Charles W. Eliot of Harvard. We were talking about the Rockefeller Institute and I ventured to confess to him that to me the institute was the most interesting thing in the world. "Nothing," said I, "is to me so exciting, so fascinating as the work the institute is doing."

Dr. Eliot stopped short in the street and turned to me and said with emphasis and emotion, "I myself feel precisely so. The Rockefeller Institute is to me the most interesting thing in this world."

That statement from him is significant. Of course, Dr. Eliot could know little, if anything, of the technique of the work. Certainly it was not the technique that interested him; it was those great, underlying, general considerations which give peculiar value to medical research and which make an irresistable appeal to a layman, even though he can know nothing of the technicalities of the daily experimentation. ["The Memoirs of Frederick T. Gates," *American Heritage* (April 1955), p. 73.]

J.C.W. describes the Longwood Avenue plan as envisioning "a group of more or less detached 'institutes' devoted to anatomy, physiology, and the other great departments of medicine" (Chapter XXIII).

As for Harvard's assuming ownership of a hospital, time has shown the wisdom of leaving this function to independent corporations that accept the care of the sick as their primary responsibility. There was ample reason toward the end of the last century for the Medical Faculty to be annoyed by the roadblock which independent ownership of hospitals placed in the path of the reform of medical education. The Faculty was unable to control personnel appointments for clinical instruction. By exercising a little patience, however, Harvard established with the principal hospitals a system for the joint appointment of key personnel without becoming itself financially liable for the bedding and boarding of patients. Those universities elsewhere that undertook hospital ownership in order to secure control of personnel have had ample cause to regret having done so. The care of the sick is a family responsibility or is properly financed by taxation and philanthropy. It is not a natural function for a university.

The University rightly placed great weight on the necessity for having a dominant voice in the nomination of a professor to a chair in a clinical subject. When the University was without this voice, eligibility for the chair was limited to the hospital staff doctor who had attained control of a teaching service by promotion based on seniority as the compelling consideration. The position of the University was well stated by President Lowell in his Annual Report for 1909–10.

The University has no desire to manage, the [Brigham] Hospital, nor have the Trustees of the latter an ambition to manage the School. But it is essential to the efficiency of a Medical School that its clinical instructors should have positions in hospitals, and hence an eminent surgeon or physician cannot be called from a distance to a chair in the School unless he can be offered at the same time a clinic in a hospital. This is impossible unless the appointments in both institutions are made jointly. On the other hand, the Trustees of the Hospital believe that the welfare of their patients will be promoted by having at their disposal the scientific resources of a great school, and by the ability to call to their service the best man from any part of the country by a joint offer of a chair and a clinic. The two institutions are convinced, therefore, that the interests under their charge coincide, and can be attained only by an unbroken mutual understanding in the matter of appointments.

the site of a country residence on the shore of the original Back Bay. It met the important requirement of being within the city limits and was situated in a quarter where it could supplement the work of the City Hospital in the South End and the Massachusetts General Hospital in the West End in purveying to the wants of the poor. The lot contained twenty-six acres, or more than one million square feet, and was held at a valuation of fifty cents a foot. Before the Medical Faculty could decide to purchase the lot it was necessary to have some certainty that funds would be obtained for the erection of buildings. On the other hand, money could not be obtained readily for this purpose unless the benefactors could be assured that land had been obtained on which to build. This dilemma was overcome by a plan devised by Major Henry Lee Higginson, who had from the beginning taken the greatest interest in the planning and had given his full sympathy and support. According to Major Higginson's plan a memorandum of agreement was drawn up between certain trustees and twenty gentlemen,[5] who subscribed a sum amounting to over $500,000 for the purchase of the land. The tract was to be held by the trustees for five years, during which time it could be purchased by the University at the original price plus interest and taxes. If at the end of the five years the Faculty could not carry out its plan, the land would be sold and any profit made thereby would accrue to the original subscribers. This happy solution was reached in the summer of 1900.

At a meeting of the Triennial Congress of Physicians and Surgeons

---

Harvard has never owned or operated a major hospital for the teaching of its medical students. In 1892 a friend of the Medical School offered to give the sum of $5,000 toward a fund for the maintenance of a hospital "virtually under the control of the Medical Faculty." At a subsequent meeting of the Harvard Corporation it was voted to decline the offer "as the Corporation is not prepared to commit the University to such an enterprise" [T. F. Harrington, *The Harvard Medical School: A History, Narrative and Documentary* (New York, 1905), III, 1080].

For several years the University had some twenty beds available to the public for the treatment of cancer in the small Collis P. Huntington Memorial Hospital (the building is now occupied by the School of Public Health). These beds were turned over to the Trustees of the MGH in 1942, just in the nick of time to avoid the increased costs of operating a hospital as well as the doctor and nurse shortages that came with World War II. The Huntington had been operating in the red for some years, and the wisdom of the change cannot be questioned.

[5] The trustees were Francis L. Higginson of Boston, Thomas N. Perkins of Westwood and Henry B. Cabot of Brookline. The "twenty gentlemen" were Henry L. Higginson, Francis L. Higginson, Arthur A. Carey, Arthur T. Lyman, Alexander Cochrane, W. Sturgis Bigelow, David Sears, Joseph Lee, W. C. Cabot, C. W. Amory, Augustus Hemenway, Charles G. Weld, N. Thayer, T. Jefferson Coolidge, Joshua M. Sears, Eben S. Draper, H. H. Hunnewell, David P. Kimball, John L. Bremer, and George F. Fabyan.

held in Washington the previous spring, I had an opportunity to explain to some of my colleagues our aspirations for the future. Dr. William B. Coley of New York, a graduate of the Harvard Medical School (1888), had in this manner been made acquainted with the details of the undertaking. Occupying as he did at the time the position of medical advisor to Mr. John D. Rockefeller, he was able to express the opinion that the gentleman would undoubtedly be interested in our endeavors to raise the standard of medical education. The advancement of medical science was a field of public service toward which this great philanthropist was beginning to turn his thoughts. In spite of vigorous efforts on the part of members of the Faculty and the cordial and active coöperation of Dr. Coley, months passed by without positive results. Mr. Rockefeller's interest seemed gradually to wane and finally to cease. In looking back at this period of his interest in medical affairs, it seems to me that he was unable to decide on a far-reaching policy and was still casting about for the most effective way to make a beginning. It was not until Mr. J. Pierpont Morgan came to the front later as a backer of the undertaking that Mr. Rockefeller seriously considered taking an active part.

Meanwhile, in the autumn of 1900, a committee of the Faculty was busily employed in planning the details of the buildings and their relations to one another in the general group. Much time and effort were spent upon this preliminary work, and specific problems were referred to special committees for solution. From the suggestions of Professors William T. Porter and Charles S. Minot a standard-sized unit was designed from which estimates could be made of the space to be allotted to each department and its various subdivisions. The principle thus established was to allow for subsequent alterations by a regrouping of these units in accord with the purpose intended. The general plan upon which each of the departmental buildings was to be constructed was also made the object of special study.

The architectural plan finally adopted provided for buildings facing upon a quadrangle, with the central portion of each building to contain a lecture room on the ground floor and a departmental library above it. From the main body of each building two wings projected backwards; one wing was to contain laboratories for class instruction, and the other was divided into floors for the teaching staff and for special forms of research work.

The idea of having departmental libraries was looked upon by the laboratory scientists as a distinct advance and much better adapted for quick reference than one central library. Experience seems to have shown, however, that under this system the student may not be tempted to use the library as freely as when a central locality encourages him to avail himself of its facilities. With the gradual change in the system of instruction, a resort to original sources of information and a familiarity with current medical literature is deemed a more essential part of undergraduate medical education. On the other hand, the grouping of departmental library facilities in a common center deprives the investigator and the teacher of conveniences which the exigencies of intensive research make almost a necessity. Doubtless this conflict will be solved by a central "circulating" bureau which can provide equal convenience to students and teachers alike.

The question of the total amount of floor space needed also had to be carefully considered. The number of students in the School had reached its highest point (605 in the academic year 1900–01). The increase had been a steady one ever since the occupancy of the Boylston Street building. The scale on which the new plant would be planned was therefore fixed at a figure thought sufficiently high to meet any possible demand for many years to come. Each lecture room was arranged to accommodate a class of two hundred and fifty, and the laboratory space made to correspond. With all the care thus laboriously expended on planning, unfortunately no provision was made for the accommodation of much larger audiences on special occasions. In the past the lecture rooms had always been considered of sufficient size to meet all demands that might be made upon them. Experience has since shown that such a group of buildings should have embraced a large auditorium. The growing demand for series of lectures on popular subjects pertaining to the welfare of the community and designed for nonprofessional audiences, and the demand for a large hall as the meeting place for medical and scientific gatherings, are examples of the new functions thrust upon a medical school. Many other questions of similar importance were threshed out by the building committee, and it was not until the academic year 1900–01 was nearing its completion that the Faculty placed a detailed statement of the amount and arrangement of the required floor space in the hands of the architects, Shepley, Rutan, and Coolidge.

During the phase of planning the new school there had been no further attempt to improve the financial situation. Although the Faculty had an abiding faith in its ability to work out a solution of the problem with the resources already at hand, it seemed evident that it would be a slow and tedious process. Unforeseen obstacles which might place the School in an embarrassing position must be anticipated and avoided.

The winter of 1900 had been one of unusual national prosperity and many large business undertakings had been carried through successfully. The climax seemed to be reached when the great banking house of J. P. Morgan succeeded in uniting the steel industries of the country into one gigantic corporation. Was not this the moment for which we had been waiting so long? Might it be possible to take advantage of this flood tide of prosperity, as had been done in the early eighties when an amount sufficient to finish the Boylston Street building had been raised in a three-weeks' campaign? These thoughts crystallized into a decision to carry the campaign beyond the limits of Boston and interest friends of the University in the great financial center, New York. We had several friends who might arrange a hearing with Mr. Morgan himself, and it was the advice of Major Henry Lee Higginson, to whom we had turned for counsel, that we should aim directly at a personal interview. Through the assistance of Mr. E. Rollins Morse, whose visits to New York were frequent, Dr. Henry P. Bowditch and I were able to secure a favorable moment for an interview, and we found ourselves on a certain morning towards the close of a busy week in March 1901 at No. 23 Wall Street. Mr. Morgan had not yet arrived but we were most hospitably received by Mr. Robert Bacon, who was one of his partners and also an old friend of ours. Thus we had an unexpected opportunity to explain our plans in more detail than we had dared to hope, and no more genial or sympathetic a listener could have fallen to our lot. Mr. Morgan would soon arrive and the object of our mission would then be laid before him.

We estimated afterwards that the whole interview with Mr. Morgan himself lasted about two minutes — certainly not more than three.

Sustained with such aspirations as could be gathered from this experience, we hurried home to report the result of our first effort in the new campaign. Mr. Charles A. Coolidge then visited New York with the architectural plans and estimates but brought back no new indications as to the success or failure of our expedition. Not long afterward we learned that Mr. Morgan had departed on his annual journey to London. There was some comfort in hearing that on the day of his departure a memorandum referring to the Medical School was on a list placed in his hand.

Mr. Bacon was in daily communication with his chief by cable, and as Commencement Day drew nigh I ventured to suggest that this of all days in the year would be the one most effective for the announcement of a gift to the University. A few days later on returning home I found the following cablegram on the hall table:

Dr. J. C. Warren, Boston, Mass.
  Referring our conversation and plans submitted I am prepared erect centre pavilion and two buildings new Medical School, Harvard University. Said buildings to be known as and designated Memorial Halls in memoriam Junius Spencer Morgan, native of Massachusetts, formerly a merchant of Boston, and at time of his death a merchant of London, England. You can announce this.

JOHN PIERPONT MORGAN
London, June 21, 1901

The estimate of the cost of these three buildings was $1,083,202. The addition of the connecting terraces brought the amount of Mr. Morgan's gift to $1,135,000.

It was Class Day and President Eliot was about to leave his home to take part in the social duties of the day when I handed him the message. After a brief consultation, it was agreed that the announcement would best be postponed until Commencement Day, when it could be made by President Eliot himself in his annual address to the Alumni. As he penned an immediate answer to Mr. Morgan, I recognized again that the University had in him a guardian to whom such a great benefaction could safely be entrusted.

Great gift received. Beneficent results immeasurable. Announcement next Wednesday afternoon to assembled Alumni.

This was probably the largest single gift that the University had ever received. Its announcement on Commencement Day was followed by extensive notices in the Boston and New York papers, together with an attractive sketch of the proposed group of buildings. It so happened that Dr. William B. Coley received a visit from Mr. John D. Rockefeller, Jr. at his office the same day. Mr. Rockefeller inquired with lively interest about the correctness of the announcement in the papers, and Dr. Coley was able to point to photographs of the new designs on his mantlepiece. Fortunately these had been forwarded to him. Realization that the Faculty had actually made a brilliant beginning in their campaign on behalf of medical education and research seemed to reawaken Mr. Rockefeller's interest, and he announced then and there his intention to reconsider his position in the near future.[6]

Subsequently a request was received from Mr. Starr J. Murphy, Mr. Rockefeller's representative, for an appointment to inspect our plant and obtain complete information for a report on the educational standing of the Medical Department of the University. Although it was in the middle of the vacation season, we succeeded in rounding up a fair percentage of the heads of departments for Mr. Murphy's visit. We soon learned that the methods used by Mr. Morgan to satisfy himself as to the standing of the recipient of his bounty were quite different from those of Mr. Rockefeller. The time occupied by Mr. Morgan's inquiries could be measured in minutes, whereas the investigation proposed by Mr. Rockefeller's agent was of the most searching character. Accordingly, after this preliminary trip to Bos-

---

[6] It is recognized that in his text J.C.W. did not always distinguish with clarity the opinions and actions of Mr. Rockefeller from those of his son, Mr. Rockefeller, Jr., or identify what may have been joint decisions of father and son.

ton, we were informed that a second visit would be made when all the members of the Faculty and the President of the University himself had returned to their duties and would be able to explain the character and scope of their departments.

This second visit was made early in the term of the academic year 1901–02, and then a further request was received for detailed information regarding the organization of other medical schools, including those of Europe, in order to measure more accurately the scale upon which the new undertaking should be framed. A report of some fifty typewritten pages was prepared, and estimates were forwarded by President Eliot indicating the increase of the annual expenditures of the Medical School in its proposed new buildings.

After these elaborate investigations, which extended over a period of many months, Mr. Murphy handed his report to Mr. Rockefeller, Jr., which gave a detailed description of the current organization of the School, the reasons more room was required, and also the reasons "for locating such a plant at Harvard." This report was favorable throughout in its appraisal of the academic standing of the institution, but the argument that appeared most likely to influence Mr. Rockefeller's decision was the statement, "As the result of my examinations I am satisfied that Harvard is one of the best managed institutions in the country." President Eliot had put forth the forcible argument that an institution which had never lost a fund and in whose hands bequests had remained undiminished through centuries was deserving the confidence of its benefactors.

It was hoped that after the very thorough inquiry into the standing of the Medical School and its plans for the future, Mr. Rockefeller might give a favorable response to the appeal for aid, but we did not dare hope for a gift comparable to that made by Mr. Morgan, who had the pleasure of taking the initiative in this new movement. The gift of a single building, or the endowment of a research fund or professorship, was as much as we had a right to look for at this stage of the campaign. When, on January 30th, 1902, Dr. Coley telegraphed that Mr. Rockefeller would contribute one million dollars the news came as a great surprise. It is impossible to describe our pleasure. Obviously we had not taken into account the point of view of the multimillionaire. In his mind it is not the amount of money but the inherent merits of the case which has weight in the final decision.

Mr. Rockefeller's formal announcement contained his customary proviso that the gift would be made on condition that a certain sum of money be raised in addition. This sum was estimated provisionally at one-half million dollars, but the determination of the exact amount could be delayed until a careful review had been made of the financial situation. No restrictions were laid down regarding the purposes for which the money might be used. It was available for land, buildings, or endowment as future developments might indicate.

In compliance with the condition laid down by Mr. Rockefeller, the Faculty bent itself immediately to computing the cost of the new undertaking on the projected scale, which now involved five buildings, and taking an inventory of resources on hand or pledged. Meanwhile an appointment was made for a conference between Mr. Rockefeller and a committee of the Faculty consisting of President Eliot, Dr. Henry P. Bowditch, and myself, to be held on February 13th, 1902.

This occasion was a notable one in the history of our campaign, for it gave us an opportunity to communicate directly with our benefactor and to obtain an impersonal judgment regarding our enterprise. A trip to New York also would make it feasible to make an effort to interest other "captains of industry" in this great financial center. Enlisted as we were in the cause of raising the standard of medical education throughout the country and thus favoring an advance in its material prosperity, we felt that we might with propriety bring the undertaking to the attention of those who had a large stake invested in their country's welfare.

Our first duty on reaching New York was to call upon Mr. Morgan at his house on Madison Avenue and express our thanks for his magnificent gift made at the very opening of the campaign. A visit was arranged for ten o'clock in the morning, an hour at which Mr. Morgan received visitors by special appointment before going to Wall Street. The flavor of this reception was that of a semiofficial interview, the memory picture of which still remains vivid and centers in the two dominant personalities — the great financier and the distinguished educator. Both were striking individuals of strongly contrasting types. As we took our departure I felt satisfied with the manner in which we had been able to express our thanks, owing to the contribution of President Eliot to the demands of the occasion.

Our steps were next turned toward No. 26 Broadway, the home of the great Rockefeller interests. One of the older New York office buildings, it presented few of the characteristics of the modern "skyscraper." A spacious and roomy structure, it appeared to have an atmosphere of repose and one might almost say emptiness, quite out of keeping with the busy surroundings. A special elevator service awaited us, and after wandering through deserted hallways and corridors we were finally ushered into a large, almost warehouse-like apartment overlooking New York harbor and the Statue of Liberty. Many windows gave an ample and unobstructed view. A massive table was surrounded by chairs, evidently forming the basis of a conference room for meetings such as ours. Here we were received by Mr. Murphy, and after a considerable interval a door at the farther end of the room opened and a young man of serious mien and dignified bearing came forward to greet us. It was Mr. John D. Rockefeller, Jr., here as usual to represent his father. The interview which followed was a thoroughly businesslike one. Every detail of organization was considered with care, and it seemed to us that at no other time had the magnitude of our undertaking appeared in so glaring a light. After a prolonged conference during which negotiations were conducted principally by President Eliot and Mr. Rockefeller, the final decision was reached that in order to obtain the Rockefeller gift of one million dollars it would be necessary to raise the additional sum of $765,000.

A letter from Mr. Rockefeller, Jr. to President Eliot of the same date gave in compact form the financial situation as it existed at that time:

26 Broadway, New York,
February 13th, 1902.

Dear President Eliot: —

The following are the figures arrived at in the interview held in my office this morning between yourself, Doctors Warren and Bowditch, Mr. Murphy and myself: —

Cost of the new Harvard Medical Plant, complete,

Land	$ 300,000	
Five buildings	1,800,000	
Furnishings for the same	50,000	
Endowment	2,800,000	
Total		$4,950,000

Funds available: —

Pledge of Mr. Morgan	$1,135,000	
Pledge of Mr. Rockefeller	1,000,000	
Present endowment	1,000,000	
Sale of present medical buildings	600,000	
From Pierce endowment fund	350,000	
From Billings endowment fund	100,000	
Total		4,185,000
Leaving a balance to be raised of		$ 765,000

✿   ✿   ✿

Upon the basis of these figures I enclose a letter of pledge from my father.

Allow me to congratulate the University upon the splendid plans which it has prepared for its new medical plant, the carrying out of which I feel confident the friends of the University will make possible with little, if any delay. My father is very glad to have even a small part in this splendid work.

With expressions of esteem, I am

Very truly,
JOHN D. ROCKEFELLER, JR.

President Charles W. Eliot,
Harvard University, Cambridge, Mass.

The two endowment funds referred to in this communication had already been placed at our disposal by the Corporation. The Henry L. Pierce Fund was a large bequest, half of which had been assigned to the Medical Department of the University. The Robert C. Billings Fund was another bequest placed at the disposal of the Corporation, and this active Department again reaped the benefit. Fortunately a considerable portion of the sum made conditional by Mr. Rockefeller had already been secured. Before leaving Boston for this eventful visit we had received pledges amounting to $310,000.

An active canvass among a few of the great financiers of New York resulted in our obtaining the sum of one hundred thousand dollars from an old friend of the College and the founder of its infirmary, Mr. James Stillman. It was specifically directed that this sum be used for the endowment of a chair of Comparative Anatomy.

Again we returned to Boston filled with a sense of elation but sobered by great responsibilities. The goal of our ambitions still appeared to be a distant one and Boston now seemed a small place in which to obtain money. But our success in New York seemed to arouse a spirit of generous rivalry, and the substantial welcomes received not only from friends of the Medical School and members of the Faculty but from many a good old stand-by of the University, soon convinced us that success would crown our efforts.

A gift of $30,000 came from two members of the Medical Faculty, well known to their colleagues for frequent acts of loyalty to the cause of medicine. The George Higginson Professorship of Physiology appropriately bore the name of our treasurer in the first campaign for the Boylston Street building, an upright and public-spirited citizen whose sons have since been conspicuous friends of the University. David Sears's subscription to the guarantee fund was now added to this list as a permanent gift to the School, a sum to which later a very large addition was made. A gift of $25,000 also came from an old Bostonian, and to this was later added a large sum for the endowment of the Warren Anatomical Museum, now known as the Henry Jackson Fund. Many other old friends again proved their devotion to public service by coming to our aid and the subscription list rose to a very substantial sum. But there still remained the better part of two hundred thousand dollars to be secured before the amount specified by the Rockefeller deed of gift would be reached.

As the result of a conference with Mr. Charles H. Tweed, a graduate of the University of high rank and one of her most loyal sons, Mrs. Collis P. Huntington's attention was drawn to the needs of the Medical School in its struggle for better education. Mrs. Huntington had but recently returned from Europe, and her interest had not as yet been engaged in other worthy but rival causes. Through the good offices of her confidential advisor this public-spirited lady decided to give one of the two remaining buildings as a memorial to her husband. With this timely gift, the amount necessary to secure Mr. Rockefeller's million was not only reached but far exceeded, and Dr. Bowditch and I were able to write the following announcement to the Corporation:

> Harvard Medical School, Boston, Mass.,
> March 7, 1902

To the President and Fellows of Harvard College,
Gentlemen: —
We take great pleasure in forwarding the enclosed letter just received from Mrs. C. P. Huntington offering $250,000 for the erection of a building to be called, in memory of her late husband, the Collis P. Huntington Laboratory of Pathology and Bacteriology. This generous gift taken in connection with previous subscriptions already reported, more than completes the sum of $765,000 required to secure Mr. J. D. Rockefeller's gift of $1,000,000 for the enlargement and endowment of the Harvard Medical School, and thus ensures the realization of our great project.

Congratulating the University [7] on this successful result of our efforts, we remain,

> Yours very respectfully,
> J. COLLINS WARREN
> H. P. BOWDITCH

Notwithstanding that the goal was already passed so early in the campaign, the impetus which the movement had received was not yet spent, and numerous other gifts followed in rapid succession. Although there was no longer any question as to the propriety of carrying out the plans as originally designed and constructing the full group of five buildings, it was beginning to be realized that as four of the buildings had been presented by citizens of New York City, none of the new group as yet bore a Boston name. Fortunately this was made possible by the generosity of Mr. David Sears, whose original gift of $25,000 was increased tenfold. Mr. Sears had contemplated enlarging his subscription to a size sufficient to endow a professorship, but at the suggestion of Professor James Jackson Putnam, the sum was finally raised to a figure which enabled the Faculty to dedicate the remaining building to the memory of three generations of an honored Boston family.

It is not within the purpose of these Reminiscences to record in further detail the incidents of this successful campaign for the improvement of medical education; it is sufficient to say that in addition to these large gifts many others of generous dimensions combined to swell the rapidly growing fund. Among gifts for special purposes were

[7] The Corporation in turn voted "That the President and Fellows congratulate Drs. Warren and Bowditch on their successful efforts, and thank them therefor in the name of the entire University."

those assigned as additions to the endowments of the Jackson Professorship of Clinical Medicine, the Shattuck Professorship of Pathological Anatomy, and the George Fabyan Professorship of Comparative Pathology. Mention might also be made here of a gift of $50,000 for original research, one of the first of its kind, to be known as the Proctor Fund for the Study of Chronic Diseases.

The plans and estimates were carefully reviewed during the following season. A moderate portion of the twenty-six acre lot was set apart for the site of the Medical School, leaving by far the larger part for the construction of such hospitals as might decide from time to time to become components of the new medical community. As the architectural plans of the new laboratories began to take shape, the question of a final decision as to the material which should be used in construction became more and more urgent. The original designs had specified the use of brick and sandstone. A proposition came from the contractors (The Norcross Bros. Co.) that they were prepared to substitute a certain grade of marble which they had on hand at a figure which not only would involve no increase of the original estimates but even would mean an actual saving of $70,000. No time was lost in accepting this offer, and final preparations were made to break ground in the summer of 1903.

The financial campaign, which had ended so satisfactorily, may be said to have begun with the interview with Mr. Morgan in March 1901 and to have terminated in the same month of the following year with the gift of Mrs. Huntington, showing a net result of about three million dollars. But to this sum should be added the many gifts already mentioned which came from time to time in the shape of endowments to swell the amount as the great medical undertaking approached completion.

Although the buildings were not ready for occupancy until the beginning of the academic year 1906–07, they were sufficiently far completed the previous June for the Faculty to extend an invitation to the American Medical Association to an open-air reception and inspection of the new plant.[8] This was in the nature of a "house warming" and was a notable occasion not only from an educational but from an aesthetic point of view. A pavilion was placed in the center of the courtyard for an orchestra, and tables were spread along the marble terraces. The total attendance was reported as somewhere between six and seven thousand, and the scenic display produced by the great and gaily dressed company in such picturesque surroundings left an impression not easily forgotten. President Eliot, writing of

[8] This was on the occasion of the 57th Annual Session of the American Medical Association, June 5–8, 1906, held in Boston.

the effect produced on this occasion by the vista of the new buildings, said: "The great throng of interested persons found them spacious, handsome, well-set and of noble aspect. They were pronounced good, not only for our School, but for the cause of medical education and progress in general . . . In every sense of the word it is a monumental success."

A full account of the formal ceremonies at the dedication of the new buildings on September 25th and 26th, 1906 and an historical sketch of the development of the individual departments of the Medical School were prepared by the Faculty under the editorial supervision of Professor Harold C. Ernst. An attempt to describe that occasion would entail needless repetition. The ceremonies on the first day were held in the quadrangle, and propitious weather with a large concourse of guests seated in the classic surroundings provided an atmosphere of unusual dignity. Short addresses were given by members of the Faculty,[9] and the President of the University pronounced the final dedication in the following words:

I devote these buildings, and their successors in coming time, to the teaching of the medical and surgical arts which combat disease and death, alleviate injuries, and defend and assure private and public health; and to the pursuit of the biological and medical sciences, on which depends all progress in the medical and surgical arts and in preventive medicine.

I solemnly dedicate them to the service of individual man and of human society, and invoke upon them the favor of men and the blessing of God.

[2] The opening address at this ceremony was given by J.C.W. on "The Enlarged Foundation." His final words were:

To you benefactors all I stand here to-day, in behalf of my colleagues, to say that from the bottom of our hearts we thank you, and that we appreciate what you have done for us, and we would pray for good-will and sympathy from you in our work, for does not Scripture tell us, that "where thy treasure is, there will thy heart be also."

Appendices

Drs. Henry P. Bowditch (seated) and J. Collins Warren.

Biographical Supplement

On the 4th of May 1902, Dr. Warren was to reach his sixtieth birthday. The sum of money required to launch the great medical undertaking on Longwood Avenue had been secured by March of that year, and preparations were under way to break ground in the summer of the following year. In recognition of Dr. Warren's approaching birthday, James C. White composed an extraordinary vote of appreciation which was read at the April (1902) meeting of the Medical Faculty.

Mr. President: I rise to propose an extraordinary vote. It is unnecessary for me to make the preliminary statement to this body that it may be truly said without boasting that all its members perform their work as teachers, and other duties connected with the administration of the school, and exercise any influence they may possess with governing bodies and the community at large in relations touching its interests, with the single purpose of advancing these, and without a thought of, or desire for, any special recognition of such services. I do not recall in my long connection with the Faculty any occasion which has called for a formal expression of its sentiments with regard to services rendered by any of its members. But I believe it to be the unanimous opinion of my colleagues here that such an occasion has now arisen and that they desire to place upon record their feelings of appreciation and gratitude towards two members of this body. There has been given to few, if any, teachers of Harvard University the ability and influence to render such extraordinary services as these we would commemorate, — services which shall stretch onward through unlimited generations for the promotion of medical science and the good of humanity.

A pressing necessity had come upon this school for greatly enlarged accommodations in consequence of the demands of its new system of instruction, and for a great increase in its endowment funds; for the support of its laboratories, and the encouragement of medical research, which were only possible by the acquisition of a great tract of land and the erection on it of many new buildings sufficient for the future needs of the school.

To fulfill these purposes it became necessary to raise the sum of three million dollars.

To accomplish this seemingly hopeless and unparalleled task, Professor John Collins Warren and Professor Henry Pickering Bowditch devoted themselves with the greatest confidence and energy. Through their instrumentality a syndicate of wealthy friends secured many acres of land, to hold until the school might want it; many of whom subsequently contributed largely to the fund. Through the great respect in which they are held by this community, and the eminent professional reputation borne by them throughout the country, they were able to induce persons of vast wealth to contribute great sums of money individually to the building and endowment funds:— from Mr. J. P. Morgan $1,185,000, Mr. J. D. Rockefeller $1,000,000, Mrs. C. P.

Huntington $250,000, and from many of the most generous habitual givers
to the school they obtained other large amounts sufficient to make up the
desired sum, in all, $3,011,825.

All this was accomplished by a few months of inspiring devotion. Thus
through their instrumentality has our school become the best endowed in
this country. It remains for its teachers to make it deserving of this high
position.

Therefore we the colleagues in the Faculty of Medicine of Harvard University tender to Doctor Bowditch and Doctor Warren our sincere thanks for
the great and lasting benefits they have secured for this school, and for the
advancement which medical science has received through their noble efforts.
[As quoted in T. F. Harrington, *The Harvard Medical School* (New York,
1905), III, 1197f.]

Dr. Warren was the recipient of many citations, but none could have
touched him more deeply than this honor coming from lifelong associates. This resolution and other personal honors and achievements
were not mentioned by Dr. Warren when he dictated his Reminiscences, or were carefully snipped out with scissors as he read the
typescript. It is to fill in some of the more important omissions that
these biographical notes are added.

A major endeavor in authorship was his book on *Surgical Pathology
and Therapeutics,* published by Saunders in 1895. A review written
by David W. Cheever for the *Boston Medical and Surgical Journal*
[*132*, 310 (March 28, 1895)] measures this volume against the surgical
knowledge of the period. Cheever wrote:

Accordingly bacteriology and the changes bacteria impose on the blood
must form the leading features of any new work on surgical pathology; and
they properly occupy all the primary chapters of Dr. Warren's book. Only in
morbid growths do we find the cell changes described by Virchow untouched
by the newer germ theories. Here, all must admit, that hitherto no causal
connection has been established between a spore, a germ or a bacillus, and
the occurrence of a morbid neoplasm. Misplaced cells illustrate the anatomical tissues of tumors, but fail to explain the reason of their growth;
and reversion to the embryonic type must be a vagary of vital force. Vitiation of the blood by fungi; fermentation of the vital fluids by their multiplication and decay; preventive inoculation by the products of bacterial culture,
all play the chief part in pathological changes . . . Here is the true road for
research; here the great hope of bacterial pathology . . .

The practitioner, the investigator, the advanced inquirer will enjoy and
profit by this conscientious and broad survey of modern pathology, in which
the author has brought discoveries well down to the present moment and
presented everything new, freshly and fully. We older practitioners admire
the universal seeking for truth, the balancing of theories, the endless, if
sometimes contradictory, experiments, which are admirably collected and
verified by the author . . . The writer's classical experiments and illustrations
of the microscopic anatomy of repair are all to be found here . . . The
chapters on tumors contain the author's investigations on rodent ulcer, and
on cancer . . . Amid this sea of inquiries and generalizations, wave after wave
of theory rolls in, depositing finally grains of truth, to form a solid land.

The *Boston Medical and Surgical Journal* reviewed the second edition of the book with the comment that "it filled a position formerly occupied by Billroth's *Surgical Pathology*" [*143*, 243 (September 6, 1900)].

Eighteen ninety-seven was Dr. Warren's presidential year in the American Surgical Association, and his address was entitled "The Influence of Anaesthesia on the Surgery of the Nineteenth Century."

On April 11, 1898 it was voted by the Harvard Corporation "that the bequest of William Oxnard Moseley be appropriated to the endowment of the professorship of surgery in the Medical School to be hereafter known as the Moseley Professorship of Surgery." On June 28, 1899 Dr. Warren, whose professorship dated from May 29, 1893, was designated Moseley professor of surgery. On his retirement in 1907 Maurice H. Richardson was elected to this named chair in his place.

Subsequent events pertaining to the Moseley professorship will be mentioned briefly at this point. They reveal Dr. Warren's concept of the department of surgery at the Harvard Medical School, and also point up the differences between his concept — one which prevailed in American universities up to that time — and a new pattern of academic organization derived from the Continent of Europe. The pressure for change to this new pattern was a by-product of the developments that followed the building of the new school in 1906.

After Dr. Maurice Richardson's death in 1912, which came at the end of a busy operating day at the MGH, the Moseley professorship went to Harvey Cushing, who had accepted an invitation to take up the duties of surgeon-in-chief at the new Peter Bent Brigham Hospital. Dr. Cushing received his medical degree from Harvard in 1895 and served a year as house pupil on the old South Surgical Service at the MGH. Transplanted to Baltimore, he soon began to flourish in the heady atmosphere of the new Johns Hopkins Hospital. Osler, in referring to the organization of this hospital, once said: "For the first time in an English-speaking country a hospital was organized in units, each one in charge of a head or chief." This statement would have been modified had Osler recalled that in 1821 John C. Warren and James Jackson took the position that each professional service at the MGH should be headed by a chief with continuous service. Actually, such an organization was maintained until 1835 (see note 4, Chapter XIX). But irrespective of this omission, Osler was correct in emphasizing the fact that the Continental type of clinic structure introduced in Baltimore was new to the American medicine of that period. The form — a hospital teaching service with a professor at the apex — was customary in the university centers of German-speaking countries. This structure was adopted wholeheartedly at the Hopkins as preferable to the older institutional patterns, originally derived from England and Scotland and still prevailing in one form or another in Philadelphia, New York, and Boston. The essential feature of the old pattern was distribution of the responsibility for ward patients among a number of practitioners, each of whom conducted a "service" during from two to six months a year as a side line to his private practice in the community.

The German conception of a university, which strongly influenced The Johns Hopkins University and was projected into the organization of The Johns Hopkins Hospital, placed greater weight on the extension of knowledge through research than on the transmission of knowledge by instruction. This conception was almost twice removed from that of such beloved institutions as the Pennsylvania Hospital, the New York Hospital, and the Massachusetts General Hospital, all patterned after British voluntary hospitals and supported by a philanthropy which directed them in their Good Samaritan missions. Cushing had ample opportunity to become familiar with the Continental type of department in his travels, and during his stay in Bern worked close to the surgical department organized in the German manner under Theodor Kocher.

It is not surprising, therefore, to find that Dr. Cushing, in his negotiations with President Lowell before accepting the Harvard invitation, pressed for recognition as "head of the surgical department" in the Medical School instead of being satisfied with one of several professorships of surgery. Lowell remained noncommittal on this point, however, and in a terse sentence informed Cushing that the professorship Harvard was offering him "would be a professorship of surgery, and would involve surgical teaching in the Medical School." The fact that other great hospitals had been partners in the teaching of Harvard medical students, long before the Brigham, made the Boston situation quite different from that at the Hopkins.

At an earlier date (1907), when Cushing had taken the opportunity provided by an offer from Yale to feel out the Harvard situation, Dr. James G. Mumford had written:

Dear Harvey: Here's a confidential word regarding plans: It must have been evident to you that your friends here, Dr. Warren, Allie Porter [Charles Allen Porter, son of Dr. Warren's contemporary, Charles Burnham Porter] and your humble servant, have long been striving to bring about an arrangement by which you might be called to a Chair of Surgery at Harvard . . . Allie and I have worked out a rather simple plan, which is now being considered by the authorities, but before pressing it further I am writing to you, without other authority than my own, to ask your opinion of it. Essentially it is this:

That on Dr. Warren's present retirement, there be continued the three professors, Bradford, Richardson, and Burrell, and that you be added — making four; that the 4 hold equal rank; that they choose from among themselves a Chairman or Dean; that Richardson continue in charge of M. G. H. teaching and Burrell of B. C. H. [Boston City Hospital]; that the four reorganize the general teaching scheme — especially the didactic work, laboratory work, animal work, neurological surgery etc., with reference to your interests; that pending the erection of the Brigham, in which you should have a hand, the Brigham people might open a surgical dispensary somewhere; and that you be given beds at the M. G. H. until your own hospital is completed. [As quoted in John F. Fulton, *Harvey Cushing: A Biography* (Thomas, Springfield, Ill., 1946), p. 336.]

But such egalitarian ideals did not satisfy Harvey Cushing. After receiving Mr. Lowell's letter with its definition of the post being offered, he drafted a letter pressing the point by a direct question but on second thought decided not to drop it in the mail. He did, however, express to the president a desire that in due time he be given the title of Moseley professor. The letter in which this was done (not included in the Fulton biography) was not well received in Boston, where it was read by Dr. Maurice Richardson among others. Apparently it carried the suggestion that Dr. Richardson might be ready to hand over the Moseley title in about two years. At any rate, Dr. Warren's pupil and assistant, Dr. Robert B. Greenough, thought it timely to warn Cushing that he was treading on sensitive and important toes. As events happened, Maurice Richardson died on the last day of July 1912; Cushing's election as Moseley professor was confirmed as from the first of September, and shortly thereafter he returned to Boston to take up the surgical portfolio at the Brigham.

President Lowell was fond of saying that power in this world is never conferred, it is always seized. The Moseley professorship soon became known as the senior chair of surgery, although it had been in existence only fourteen years; it also became identified in the minds of many as synonymous with the position of head of the surgical department at Harvard, which did not exist. The vision cherished by Warren, Porter, and Mumford of a federation in which decisions were to rest on the common sense of most after the consultation of all, faded away. Before long, by some ingenious extrapolation, the academic lineage of the third Moseley professor was projected back beyond Maurice Richardson and J. Collins Warren, through Henry J. Bigelow, George Hayward, and John C. Warren (a founder of the MGH) to the first John Warren, Hersey Professor of Anatomy and Surgery! When Dr. Cushing retired, President Lowell and Dean Edsall made it clear that the large clinical departments are made up of separate budgetary units corresponding to the major teaching hospital services and that professors in a department are of equal rank.

At the centenary celebration of the Royal College of Surgeons of England in 1900 Dr. Warren was one of the four Americans on whom honorary fellowship was conferred. Harvey Cushing, then thirty-one, was in London that summer. "Drs. Halsted, Weir, 'Col' Warren and Keen," he wrote home, "have been elected honorary members or fellows of the R.C.S. . . . Dr. Warren must be walking on air."

In 1905 Dr. Warren retired from the active staff of the Massachusetts General Hospital, which he had entered as a house pupil in May 1865, and where he had been a visiting surgeon since 1876. On January 31 of the year of his retirement Dr. Warren made the last formal visit of his long service at the Hospital. The members of his house staff presented him with an inscribed silver punch bowl, and from the nurses he received a huge wreath of laurel. Retirement from the Hospital did not end his consultation practice, which continued for another five years.

Appropriately timed came the degree of Doctor of Laws, conferred upon Dr. Warren in 1905 by the Jefferson Medical School, the institution in which he had enrolled for studies under Dr. Samuel D. Gross during the Civil War. Also in that year he was elected an honorary fellow of the Royal College of Surgeons of Edinburgh.

In 1906 came the dedication of the new buildings of the Harvard Medical School, and at the formal ceremonies his lifework and personal contribution to this great undertaking were recognized by conferral of the degree of Doctor of Laws. The citation read as follows:

JOHN COLLINS WARREN, Instructor and Professor of Surgery in Harvard University for thirty-five years; author, and eminent practitioner in surgery; the enthusiastic, winning, and indefatigable promoter of the great undertaking of the Medical School, who knew how to inspire others with his own well-grounded hopefulness and ardor.

In 1907 Dr. Warren became professor emeritus but continued to serve the University as a member of the Board of Overseers when elected to that body in 1908. For many years he was the active and vigorous chairman of the Harvard Cancer Commission, and his achievements in this position are set forth in Appendix II. The honorary degree of LL.D. came from McGill University in 1911.

The American College of Surgeons was organized in 1913, and in that year honorary membership was conferred on Dr. Warren. It is more than a coincidence that companions in this honor were Halsted of Baltimore, Keen of Philadelphia, and Weir of New York, comprising the same group of American surgeons similarly honored by the Royal College of Surgeons of England over a decade previously.

On June 18, 1913 Dr. Warren presided at the fiftieth anniversary dinner of the Class of 1863, Harvard College. Thirty-one members assembled at the Parker House. Francis Lee Higginson contributed two fine, large salmon from the Ristigouche Club for the occasion, notable in those days as a "feast of reason and flow of soul." With his labors in the vineyard of surgery drawing to a close, Dr. Warren had discontinued his undertakings in operative surgery, but his wisdom remained available to School and Hospital as he assumed the role of elder statesman.

The likening of surgery to a vineyard by old William Clowes is an apt metaphor. The vineyard of the Old Testament is the symbol of man's activity and work, and surgery is but an activity of medicine in which the physician uses the hand. Like the surgical operation, the vineyard is the work of the hand — "the vineyard that thy right hand hath planted" (Ps. 80:15). As in surgery, skill requires the guidance of wisdom if a vineyard is to bear fruit — "the vineyard of the man void of understanding" was overgrown with thorns and nettles (Prov. 24:30).

The omission of reference to personal honors and achievements in the Reminiscences is perhaps not as striking a feature as the absence of any recounting of personal exploits at the operating table. It was to fill this gap that a chapter was introduced to transcribe the Hospital record of the story of one of his patients, William Young, mechanic. And yet Dr. Warren is remembered as a greatly respected clinical surgeon, competent at the operating table and in the consulting room alike. It is extraordinary to find a surgeon making no reference to the tasks which have occupied the full and busy days of the years of life.

But most surgeons are messiahs, not prophets; Dr. Warren was a prophet. That he envisioned himself as such is revealed in a letter written to Harvey Cushing in April 1910. This letter was kindly supplied by Dr. John F. Fulton, literary executor of the estate of Dr. Harvey Cushing; it is mentioned but not included in his biography of Cushing.

We have . . . the material for building up a great and ideal medical university. Attached as it is to one of the greatest universities in the country I do not think it is an idle boast to claim that this can be accomplished.

I have been a sort of John the Baptist, preaching in the wilderness, and I am counting on you as the surgical Messiah.

The written word of history is largely a record of the doings and teachings of the messiahs of this world. They are the men of action, burning with the importance of the message they carry. They surround themselves with disciples and, like actors, have a flair for the dramatic. The prophet, on the other hand, is the man of thought and reflection, who looks upon the needs and shortcomings in the social order and upon its institutions rather than upon himself. The prophet does not seek to elevate himself above the level of his peers; and, although they may come to regard him with great respect, they are equally prone to turn a deaf ear to his admonitions. The prophet seems never to immerse himself wholly in the events of his time but looks to the future and prepares the way for greater undertakings; the messiah is the very quintessence of his time.

Dr. Warren was not ordained to be a messiah, working miracles with the new surgery created by Lord Lister. This privilege passed to men such as Halsted at the Hopkins and Cushing at the Brigham. Happy circumstances gave them new institutions responsive to their slightest wish and manned by eager disciples. Dr. Warren tells how the opportunity to introduce heat sterilization into this country was lost to his hospital because of his discontinuous periods of service as a staff surgeon. Halsted was known as "the Professor" and Cushing as "the Chief." Dr. Warren was "Coll," content to be one among equals, and without desire to stand alone. And yet at the end of his life he was privileged to say with Ecclesiastes, "I made me great works; I builded me houses; I planted me vineyards."

Dr. Warren died on November 3, 1927.

The Start on the Cancer Problem

The months Dr. Warren spent in Vienna with Biesiadecki and in Berlin with Virchow and Cohnheim studying pathological histology awakened a scholarly interest in cancers and other tumors which he maintained throughout life. It might be said that this interest came naturally to him because his grandfather, Dr. John C. Warren, had published in 1837 the first treatise on this subject produced in America, *Surgical Observations on Tumours with Cases and Operations*. The first published paper of Dr. J. Collins Warren, completed while still in Vienna, was on the development of keloid, an abnormal growth of scar tissue. After his return from Europe his essay entitled "The Anatomy and Development of Rodent Ulcer" was awarded the Boylston Medical Prize for 1872.

It is not surprising, therefore, to find that in 1899, when Mrs. Caroline Brewer Croft made a bequest to the University for the study of cancer, the committee of investigators organized to make use of the fund had Dr. Warren as its chairman. The study was not concentrated but work was carried on in the Sears Pathological Laboratory of the Medical School on Boylston Street and to some extent at the new Clinico-Pathological Laboratory of the Massachusetts General Hospital. The *First Annual Report of the Cancer Committee to the Surgical Department of the Harvard Medical School* was issued on October 23, 1900. In his introductory remarks Dr. Warren took pleasure in noting that the surgical department was now able "to undertake a systematic investigation into the origin of cancer," and also used the report as tangible evidence of "the policy of this department in devoting its energies, not only to the teaching of surgery, but to original research in some of the many inviting fields which are offered to well-trained and well-organized bands of scientific investigators."

This was a period in which the parasitic origin of cancer was being debated and both histological and bacteriological techniques were being applied to cancer tissue to identify some specific infecting microörganism.

A *Second Annual Report* appeared in February 1902, also addressed to the surgical department. The *Third Report*, in 1905, was from "The Caroline Brewer Croft Cancer Commission of the Harvard Medical School" and contained a listing of the members of the commission on the title page. Dr. Warren is listed twice, as chairman of the commission and with Dr. Henry K. Oliver as representing the Croft Fund. Doctors Henry P. Walcott and Arthur T. Cabot are listed "For the Corporation of Harvard College" and the name of Dr. Robert B. Greenough appears as secretary. In the *Fourth Report* (1907) an introduction by Dr. Warren gives a review of the previous annual reports and refers to the experiments of Professor C. O. Jensen of Copenhagen with the inoculable tumors of mice, a subject which was extended by the investigations included in the body of this report. Dr. Warren then continued his introduction as follows:

The Commission recognized the importance of approaching the subject of cancer research from an etiological point of view in the early stages of their investigations, but does not wish to be regarded as considering lightly the importance of the study of the disease from a clinical standpoint. To carry on clinical investigations on a scale which would bring out new and valuable data would require resources far beyond what most commissions have at their disposal. It is along these lines of investigation that large endowments would enable us to place the clinical and the laboratory work in close juxtaposition in such a way as to produce results which it is not possible to obtain either at the hospitals, or with the material of private practice which practitioners of the present day have at their disposal. Special wards for the study of cancer involve a large expenditure of money. The disease should be studied not only in its incurable stages, but at its very inception, when it is most susceptible to the action of remedial measures. Such institutions should be planned also to train men especially for cancer work. The Commission feels that the investigation of cancer has now reached a point where it is possible to take a new departure in this direction on a far more extended scale than has ever been attempted, and on lines even broader than those which have been laid down for the study and control of tuberculosis. Such institutions would not only be productive of valuable scientific data, but would train men who would be of the greatest value to the public health of the community from a protective standpoint. A moderate portion of the vast sums of money which are being used in the crusade against tuberculosis would be of the greatest value at the present moment in the attack upon perhaps the next most dreaded disease of modern times.

In 1909 the President and Fellows redesignated the Caroline Brewer Croft Fund Cancer Commission as the Cancer Commission of Harvard University, and it was this body which issued the *Fifth Report* of the series. This commission in 1910 decided on an extension of the field of investigation to include the study of living cancer in the human being. On April 13, 1910 a meeting of the Cancer Commission was held with invited guests. Acting as chairman, Dr. Warren opened the meeting as follows:

Ladies and Gentlemen: We have asked you to come here this afternoon to hear something about the work in which the Harvard Cancer Commission is engaged. And first I would make a brief statement in regard to its history. It is indebted to the generosity of a Boston lady, Mrs. Caroline

Brewer Croft, the daughter of the late Gardiner Brewer, who gave $100,000, the income of which was to be devoted to the study of the disease which we are considering to-day. We felt that it was important that we should first take up the scientific side of the study, inquiring into the cause and nature of cancer. We started our work here in the Medical School rather than in the hospitals, and devoted ourselves principally to studies in the laboratory; using our funds as salaries for the payment of investigators who were qualified to make a microscopic and experimental study of the question. At the same time, occasionally we attempted to inquire into certain clinical features of the disease as they developed incidentally from time to time in some one of the different hospitals. During this period, which is now ten years, we have been working along these lines principally, and have issued five biennial reports. Although we have not been able to discover the actual cause of the disease, as has been the case in many other diseases recently under investigation, we have got to this point in the course of study,— that, so far as we can see, the disease is not due to a germ; that it is due to some organic action of the cells of the body, by which they accumulate in enormous numbers and become a parasitic organism, a germ-like organism, which preys upon the body from the original site from which the disease was developed. By using mice for this purpose (a mouse becomes old at the age of two), we are able to determine a good many interesting questions, showing that certain breeds of mice are susceptible to disease, while others are not. And finally, we have found that the principle of vaccination can in certain cases be applied to tumors. That is, taking one mouse in which a tumor is growing, and inoculating him with another tumor of the same strain, the original tumor has disappeared while the transferred portion has failed to grow. In other words, we have used that small fragment as a vaccine; by some peculiar action of its own it has stimulated the antagonistic properties of the body, which were acting to a certain extent already against the original tumor, so that they act more strongly, and the tumor has actually disappeared. Now that point was brought out a year ago in our Report which has recently been distributed; and that turned our thoughts, of course, immediately towards the question of treatment. We felt that the time had arrived when we ought to take up this part of our inquiry, and we were considering the question of employing an official to keep us in touch with the hospital clinics, when, as you all know, a case occurred of spontaneous cure of cancer in New York. That is not an unknown thing. Physicians and pathologists are familiar with such isolated cases. In this case the patient had a peculiar dropsical affection by means of which a fluid was obtained. It was necessary to withdraw this fluid for the purpose of relieving the patient; and then it occurred to the physicians in charge that the presence of this fluid might have some connection with the disappearance of the tumors which were spread about in different parts of the body; and so they thought if they introduced that into the tissue of other patients afflicted in the same way, their tumors might disappear; and it has been found that in many cases the tumors are affected, as in the case of the mice to which I have just referred.

This has emphasized the importance of the necessity of turning our thoughts to the clinical side of the question. It seems as if the critical moment had arrived when we must take up that side of the question much more actively. Meanwhile, we have been training scientific men in our laboratories, who have become experts in the work to which we have referred. We wish now to place these experts in intimate contact with living cancer in human beings. Naturally, under those circumstances, we shall have conditions not obtained before. It is only the surgeon and the physician who have been in contact with the cancer patient; but the time has now come when the Commission feels that it would be most important and advantageous for them to have a small hospital on these grounds, in close proximity to the laboratories and under the control of the Commission.

It might be asked if, among all the hospitals that are going up, it would not be perfectly easy to obtain permission from the trustees for accomodations for the patients in some of their wards. The answer is that we want to have this little hospital entirely under our own control, independent of any other organization, so that we can study the cases to the greatest possible advantage; and if we work out some new problem of treatment we shall be in a position to be of service to them. Another answer is that such patients are not taken into the hospitals. The trustees are not inclined to take incurable cases. In the "Good Samaritan" there are no such cases, nor in the Channing Home — I might multiply instances of such hospitals at this time. So that we should be offering a home to a class which has none now; and we should be offering opportunities for special treatment which might be gladly availed of by people who are perhaps unable to provide it for themselves.

Dr. Warren's introduction was followed by an address by Professor William T. Councilman, largely devoted to an explanation of the problem of cancer in terms understandable to laymen. In his concluding remarks, Dr. Councilman spoke as follows:

As to the cause of cancer we are very much in the dark. Cancers undoubtedly do arise in connection with certain antecedent unusual conditions which are apt to be looked upon as active causes. Thus they may arise after injuries, particularly injuries which are long continued in their action, but it is more probable that the injury calls into activity some underlying predisposition to the disease. Nor have we much warrant in regarding some undiscovered parasite as a cause. Cancer does not act as a parasitic disease; the active agent is not a parasite, but a cell of the body which in some way is excited to a growth which has no limitation. Certain cancers undoubtedly arise from tissues which in the course of embryonic development have become separated from their normal relations, but this fact neither explains the growth nor can it apply to but a small class of tumors. What expectation is there that we may obtain in the future such knowledge of the disease that it may be controlled as are the infectious diseases? I think an expectation which the past justifies. Already the knowledge of the mode of growth and extension of the disease which has come from investigation has been applied to the surgical treatment. We know better now how the disease can be recognized in its very beginning. It is due to this knowledge that the surgeon now undertakes an operation in the early stages of the disease with the expectation of a definite cure. That in itself is a great advance. But there must be much more. We must ascertain just what change has taken place in the body of an individual with cancer which enables such an unlimited growth of cells to take place. In what way the tissues, the cells, the fluids, the nutrition, of such an individual differ from a normal individual. The problems presented are of general biological interest and closely related to those of normal growth. There must be full opportunity given for the study of the disease in man, combined with the study of tumors in animals and the study of the very closely related processes in plants. Every resource of physiology, of chemistry, of pathology, must be brought to bear upon this problem . . . We can frankly say at the outset that we do not know by what method of attack success is to be anticipated. The disease must be attacked by the same methods which have led to success in other fields. There must be opportunity; the complex problem must be broken up into its simpler components, and these must be followed out.

In the plan which has been presented by Dr. Warren, there will not only be given opportunity for the study of the disease, but all the resources of science can be brought to bear on the treatment of the patients . . . The disease cancer is one in which we have an intense personal interest. We cannot fly from it, cannot avoid it, as we can certain other diseases. We are in the position of soldiers exposed to a very deadly fire, and the most dangerous battery against us is the one which gives out not death alone, but a lingering death with pain.

Mr. Frederick P. Fish then made some brief remarks, bringing out the practical economic point of view.

It is largely because of . . . definite and precise scientific effort that the cost of production has been so greatly reduced and that wealth undreamed of in any stage of the history of the world has come to us of to-day. It is only a fair reciprocity that this wealth, which is due to the scientific work which characterizes our time, should be appropriated to an adequate extent to support the scientific aspirations and scientific effort on the part of men who are working for us in this field of research.

Mr. Fish spoke of the incessant appeals for funds and the need to exercise discrimination in dealing with demands. He gave whole-hearted endorsement, however, to a

scientific effort to control this disease — this cancer — one of the most malicious and malevolent of all that attack human life. It comes like a murderer in the night, like a venomous serpent, striking suddenly, and especially launching its deadly blows at those who are in good health and who might well have before them years of satisfaction, years in which they would bring comfort and aid and help to those who are about them. It does not kill quickly, as does the murderer or the serpent. The victims live a life of pain and agony, with hope crushed into despair on their own part and on the part of their friends and family.

Further frightening words about cancer led Mr. Fish to the optimistic conclusion:

I firmly believe we are near the end of the investigation, and near the dawning of great results. I have no expert knowledge on the subject and cannot speak as an expert; but I have had some experience in following scientific investigation generally, and I firmly believe these great physicians have now laid the foundations of success; they have determined the lines upon which to work, the lines upon which not to work; and what they need now — and their need is great beyond expression — is the opportunity to deal definitely and directly, in practice, with the disease as it appears in the human frame, the opportunity to study and apply what they have learned and will learn from day to day as the work goes on.

The concluding remarks of President Charles W. Eliot, given in his deep and vibrant voice, were dignified and forceful:

Among all the benevolent or philanthropic measures of to-day a distinction is to be observed, to which I wish to call attention in this case. As Mr. Fish has said, a multitude of good objects for the expenditure of private money in the hope of great public advantage is presented to public-spirited people in these days. We can, however, classify these efforts into two groups. The first group contains the efforts to palliate suffering, visible, evident, plainly before us, the efforts for the alleviation of miseries, sufferings, diseases in individuals. The Christian Church has almost from the beginning exerted itself strongly in this direction, not always wisely, but it has exerted itself for the palliation of misery established and visible. The second group of philanthropic efforts are palliative in part, but they are something better — they are efforts to build defences, to contrive and put into execution preventive measures and remedies. This second group I may call constructive measures. They resemble the educational effort, which is largely constructive in its nature, building up mental capacity and moral character as means of efficiency, as means of protection against evil.

Now, this particular effort to which our attention is called by Dr. Warren and his associates this afternoon is both palliative and constructive — palliative for the patients to be treated in this hospital — peculiarly unfortunate people, because there are so few refuges for such sufferers; but much more than palliative, for this effort is constructive: it aims to build up medical research and to bring it to an issue of defence, prevention, and cure. That is great construction. That is what has been going on in medical research for more than one hundred years, with extraordinary success. And here is a new effort in a direction much needed — desperately needed, I may say, by the human race.

I do not know how any call could be clearer or more ringing to a good man or woman of means. I do not know how any proposal could be made to stir more vividly hope, faith, confidence, in a happy issue. How happy would that issue be! Cancer is a disease which invades, or may invade, every class, every family. It makes no distinction between rich and poor, between educated and uneducated, between the fortunate and the unfortunate. It is everywhere. It arrives suddenly. It is one of the greatest miseries to which mankind is subject. The plan which Dr. Warren and his associates have put before us is practical. It is wise, well conceived, and full of hope; and if rewarded with success, what a blessing will its promoters have brought into the world!

The efforts of Dr. Warren and his colleagues secured $292,885 [*Harvard Graduates' Magazine* 21, 257 (December 1912)], and the generous gift of Mrs. Huntington led to the name given the new institution, The Collis P. Huntington Memorial Hospital for Cancer Research. The building was erected on the corner of Huntington Avenue and Van Dyke Street (now Shattuck Street), and the hospital was opened for the reception of patients in March 1912. In the words of Dr. Frederick C. Shattuck, this hospital stands to Dr. Warren's credit alone. "He was the father and mother. He begat it and bore it, nursed and fed it through its early years" [*ibid. 36,* 380 (March 1928)].

The construction and organization of the Huntington Memorial Hospital were designed primarily for the study of the cancer problem by the available methods of modern scientific research. It was operated under the control of the Cancer Commission and the directorship of Dr. E. E. Tyzzer, who had general supervision of the research work of the commission.

It is not without interest to call attention to an item in the *First Annual Report of the Collis P. Huntington Memorial Hospital for Cancer Research* (for the year ending June 30, 1913). In the report of the chairman of the Cancer Commission, Dr. Warren wrote:

It is much to be desired that a laboratory building should be constructed in close physical relation with the Hospital, where investigations along different lines of science can be pursued. At a cost of about $50,000.00 such a building could be provided, with ample accommodation for laboratory work in pathology, chemistry, physics, and other sciences . . .

A certain amount of chemical research on cancer problems has already been carried on in the laboratories of the Huntington Hospital, and in the Department of Biochemistry in the Medical School. Much more could be done if better facilities were provided in a chemical laboratory in close relation with the Hospital.

The laboratory building became a reality in 1922, largely through the fund-raising efforts of Dr. Warren; and by action of the Harvard Corporation it was given the name of The J. Collins Warren Laboratory. "This recognition of his services to the University was so appreciated by him," wrote Dr. Robert B. Greenough in the Huntington *Annual Report* for 1926–27, "that among all the many honors conferred upon him at home and abroad, he held this to be supreme."

Two Cycles of Medicine at Harvard: 1846–1906, 1906–

THE CYCLIC NATURE OF PROFESSIONAL ACTIVITIES

In the long evolution of surgery from an ancient useful art toward an applied biological science, Dr. Warren's generation saw the end of the pain of cutting, the dark decades of sepsis, and at long last the light of healing without suppuration. Dr. Warren thus explains that he witnessed "three great eras" of surgery and only in the third was surgery set free to develop its power to perform the miraculous. It is also possible to consider Dr. Warren's life span in terms of a single cycle in medicine as a whole. The cycle started in the 1840's, and concerning this decade Dr. Warren has given a penetrating sentence:

Suddenly a time arrived when it seemed as though medical science had reached a point where new activities were in order.

The recurrent nature of such a turning point within a learned profession and the fact that it heralds a new outlook and period of intense activity have been made a subject of comment by Sir Harold Himsworth. Suddenly a time arrives when the existing organization of the profession and its activities are no longer adequate to fulfill the terms of the unwritten contract between the profession and the society it serves. Himsworth believes that the accrual of new knowledge at a rapid rate and the accumulation of a mass of apparently unrelated data are the events which precede a turning point. The piling up of unsorted and unused information ultimately culminates in a profound sense of disorder and confusion; then, suddenly, hidden likenesses become revealed, new groupings of activities take place, order and meaning are restored, and unity is recognized in what but a short time before was disparity. The realignment of the structure and activities of the profession follows. A new outlook is acquired and under its influence a surge of enthusiasm and vigor pervades the field. A major crisis of integration and reorganization was encountered in the early sixteenth century by Linacre, physician to Henry VIII, and a similar situation, Himsworth suggests, confronts medicine today.

Dr. Warren's professional memoirs may be said to cover a cycle in medicine, far shorter, it is true, than the example selected by Himsworth, and bracketed by a turning point in the 1840's and another turning point in the first decade of the twentieth century. This cycle can be identified as the second in the history of the medicine centered on Harvard, the first having started with the foundation of the Medical School. A third cycle beginning early in this century may be nearing completion at the present time. This interpretation provides a useful framework for a grouping of events, and it may be noted that each of these three cycles in the professional activities of the physicians associated with Harvard occupies approximately sixty years.

THE BEGINNING OF DR. WARREN'S CYCLE

The new outlook and period of activity in Boston medicine which appeared in the 1840's, as recognized by Dr. Warren in his quoted sentence,[1] can be ascribed to the influence of young men returning from Paris. Many had been the pupils of Pierre Alexandre Louis. They were stirred by the new knowledge whereby disease could be defined in terms of morbid anatomy; they had glimpsed the effort of Louis to introduce the numerical method into the evaluation of clinical observation; they were thrilled by the invention of an instrument of precision for use at the bedside in the detection of disease — the stethoscope of Laennec.

These young men were so excited about the stethoscope that Oliver Wendell Holmes, one of the pupils of Louis, could not resist poking fun at their preoccupation with this new gadget. He wrote the "Stethoscope Song," in which his young man in Boston town bought himself a nice and new stethoscope.

> Now being from Paris but recently,
>   This fine young man would show his skill;
> And so they gave him, his hand to try,
>   A hospital patient extremely ill.

> . . . . . .

> This fine young man then up stepped he,
>   And all the doctors made a pause;
> Said he, The man must die, you see,
>   By the fifty-seventh of Louis's laws.

> . . . . . .

[1] Also, in remarks at the semicentennial anniversary meeting of the Suffolk District Medical Society in 1900, Dr. Warren referred to the fact that "there was at the middle of this century [nineteenth] a period of restlessness which found vent in organization, and which was worked out afterwards by the great development of the profession in this country." [*Boston Med. and Surg. J. 143*, 533 (1900).]

> Then out his stethoscope he took,
>   And on it placed his curious ear;
> *Mon Dieu!* said he, with a knowing look,
>   Why, here is a sound that's mighty queer!

And so the young doctor fresh from his training in Paris was led into one pitfall after another, and all because a spider had spun a web inside the stethoscope and entangled two buzzing flies!

In the 1840's Boston medicine was challenged by the rapid importation of knowledge and skills, and began to readjust itself. As Dr. Warren stated, new activities were in order. Hitherto it had made little difference where the professor might store his collection of bones or under what conditions students might assemble to study and dissect bodies. These impious activities had departed Holden Chapel in 1810 to be carried on first in old Marlborough Street, Boston and then in the Massachusetts Medical College on Mason Street. In the 1840's it became apparent that a new school was needed, and for the first time it was clearly seen that it would be advantageous to build close to sick patients so that they might be examined as Laennec and Louis had examined their patients. Hitherto American physicians had simply observed their patients.

And so in 1846 a new medical school was built at the foot of North Grove Street in Boston next to the Hospital. About the same time, wings were added to the Bulfinch Building, bringing more sick people under the observation of clinicians and their student apprentices. The Boston Society for Medical Observation was revived and, nationally, the American Medical Association came into being. Abroad, the old proprietary schools of London were being taken over by hospitals to bring order into the medical education of England. The University of London was not to become an effective influence in medical education for several decades; and at Harvard, following the resignation of President Josiah Quincy in the summer of 1845, the College was destined to slumber through the presidencies of five worthy gentlemen whom Samuel E. Morison has called the "minor prophets," awaiting the genius of Charles W. Eliot to awaken its interest in the education of the doctor.

Medicine was but one of many fields stirred by the ferment of activity in science and technology. Novel and significant events were taking place in all American centers of learning. In New England the Lowell Institute of Boston was inaugurated early in 1840 with a course of lectures on geology by Benjamin Silliman of Yale. Over a hundred lyceums were busy in Massachusetts bringing science and allied topics to the people. Dr. Samuel L. Dana had given up a medical practice in Waltham to apply chemistry to textiles and agriculture. Photochemistry had already come to America; in 1839 two Harvard College seniors, Edward Everett Hale and Samuel Longfellow, made experimental photographs of Harvard Hall and other local subjects, using Talbot's process. The United States Exploring Expedition under Commander Charles Wilkes returned in 1842 from a four-year "Southern Seas" cruise with voluminous scientific data that required years to sort and classify. At Harvard College two new chairs were founded, the Perkins professorship of astronomy and mathematics with Benjamin Peirce as incumbent, and the Fisher professorship of natural history with Asa Gray. The appearance of the Great Comet in 1843 stirred the public to donote funds for the 15-inch "Great Refractor" telescope at Harvard's new observatory, directed by the instrument maker William Bond. Samuel Morse's electromagnetic telegraph was put to public use in 1844, and soon Dr. William F. Channing and Moses Farmer developed a telegraphic fire-alarm system for Boston, the first in the country. Charles Goodyear of Woburn vulcanized India rubber. Uriah Boyden of Boston and James Francis invented water turbines for the mills of Lowell.

Bernard De Voto has referred to 1846 as the Year of Decision in the history of the United States because so many of the events with which it was crowded proved crucial in the development of the nation. On March 13, 1846 William B. Rogers wrote out a plan for a polytechnic school, the basic document that led eventually to the founding of M.I.T. ("Boston Tech") at No. 18 Summer Street. Elias Howe, Jr., of Cambridge patented his sewing machine. The Association of American Geologists met in Boston on September 20, 1847 and took the first step toward the organization of the American Association for the Advancement of Science. The Lawrence Scientific School was founded at Harvard, with Louis Agassiz as its professor of zoölogy and geology; and Yale started a school of applied chemistry, which developed later into the Sheffield Scientific School. Dr. Jeffries Wyman of Harvard published the first scientific paper on the gorilla; his studies were later utilized in Darwin's *Descent of Man.* The expanding Boston Society of Natural History, with Dr. John C. Warren as president, bought the vacated medical school building on Mason Street, and in 1849 Warren's private museum of natural history, with its famous skeleton of *Mastodon giganteus,* was erected at No. 92 Chestnut Street. George Corliss invented a new steam engine. Lemuel Shattuck applied statistical techniques to mass phenomena in the field of public health. And when Congress established the *American Ephemeris and Nautical Almanac* as a governmental enterprise, it was set up in Cambridge close to Harvard's mathematicians and astronomers.

Into this period, already crowded with exciting happenings, came

the announcement that sulphuric ether could be used to abolish the
the pain of surgery. This event may be taken as a marker of the
turning point at which the new cycle in medicine began, and the
major emphasis of the new cycle for American medicine was forecast
by the very nature of this discovery. Dr. Warren was to come of age
in this cycle and play an important part in its happenings.

In looking upon the event of October 16, 1846, everyone has been
moved by the great humanitarian appeal of the release of man from
pain and suffering. This appeal remains undiminished today, when
the methods of alleviating pain have been multiplied and made both
safe and kindly. In contrast to present-day insistence on experiment
design and programmatic research, the circumstances surrounding the
discovery of the use of ether were crude and amateurish; in fact,
scientists are somewhat apologetic that so important a finding could
have been made in such a direct and simple way by a practicing dentist. Morton happened upon it just as a Danish peasant, while plow-
ing his field, stumbled on an ancient Viking horn richly embossed and
made of pure gold.

But be that as it may, it was immediately obvious that sulphuric
ether was a product derived from materia *chemica* and not a con-
coction derived from medicinal plants. Ether had been known for
three centuries and had been employed medicinally for more than
half a century, but had never won a secure place for itself in therapy.
Now it had been shown that this product of the chemist could be put
to such direct and practical use! It is true that useful alkaloids had
been isolated from crude drugs by chemical methods, but these compounds were active principles of well-known materia *medica* and as
such understandable. A few aperients and purgatives had found their
way directly from the chemist to practical medicine, and potassium
iodide had been introduced a decade before for the treatment of
syphilis. Despite these predecessors, the abolition of the cruel pain
of surgery was so complete and so striking that it is by no means an
exaggeration to say that ether was the first compound produced by
the chemist to find a major place in the therapy that was so dear to
the heart of the American doctor. The event was the beginning of his
acceptance of science in medicine.

Surely, as the inscription in the old operating theatre states, the
knowledge that ether brings insensibility to pain spread throughout
the civilized world; but also to those with vision to see came an awareness that the ancient art of alchemy had come into its own. As a science
applied to the relief of human suffering, chemistry had yielded the
miraculous. It is true, as the inscription states, that a new era for
surgery began, but in perspective it can be seen that a new era was

beginning for all of medicine — an era in which the healing art was to be armed and guided by science.

The happenings in which Dr. Warren participated occupied a single cycle in medicine and led toward the new outlook and burst of activity in which President Eliot and his Medical Faculty were to find themselves early in the twentieth century. The dedication of the new Harvard Medical School, with which Dr. Warren's Reminiscences are concluded, can be taken as the turning point at the close of this second cycle in Harvard medicine (1846–1906).

In searching for the significant events in Dr. Warren's cycle it will be recalled that shortly after mid-nineteenth century the young men seeking to complete their medical education abroad turned toward the German-speaking countries of Europe. They went beyond Edinburgh and London, where their grandfathers had studied with Syme and Astley Cooper; they went beyond Paris with its crowded hospitals, where their fathers had walked the wards with Louis and learned to use the stethoscope of Laennec; they went to Vienna and Berlin and the other university centers of Germany and Austria, where they sought out Oppolzer, Hebra, Billroth, Ludwig, Virchow, Langenbeck, and other apostles of the new order in the science of medicine. James C. White, Calvin Ellis, and Charles W. Eliot himself (as a student of chemistry) were in the vanguard of this pilgrimage. So were young Warren and Henry P. Bowditch. On their return these and other young men brought a mature outlook to American universities, and it was through such efforts that these institutions were led out of their adolescence and into the full vigor of youth.

In Boston the new order in medicine first found expression by the addition in 1871 of three small laboratories to the attic of the North Grove Street School. Two were for Bowditch, just back from Carl Ludwig and Claude Bernard; the other was called the "microscope room" and in it Oliver Wendell Holmes taught histology. The windows of these laboratories looked out across the Hospital lawn to the dome of the Bulfinch Building, where just twenty-five years before it had been demonstrated that a product of the new science could be put to direct and practical use in the control of pain. Dr. Bowditch was the first professional medical scientist in the faculty, the first to devote his full working day to investigation and instruction in the newly formed department of physiology, the first teacher in the Medical School who did not choose to practice medicine.

The Boylston Street building, so well described by Dr. Warren, was ready for occupancy in 1883. It provided more ample laboratory space, but was merely a temporary easement of the growing needs of the School. This building was recognized as inadequate even before construction was complete. In the same year Dr. Bowditch became the first dean who was not identified primarily as a practitioner.

Midway in the cycle that extended from the 1840's into the first decade of the new century came the beginning of the reformation in medical education, which started at Harvard and prepared the way for the reforms that were to be instituted at Johns Hopkins. The need was urgent to educate doctors of greater competence than hitherto in order that they might develop and use the new tools that were on the way, for, as the nineteenth century advanced, medical science swept forward with ever-increasing momentum.

Boston cannot claim the most brilliant single experiment of this period — certainly the one with the greatest significance to medicine. This came with the emergence of the Johns Hopkins University and Hospital between 1875 and 1895. At the Hopkins the vocational blinders were lifted from professional education and, for the first time in America, medicine sought to attain the status of a university school of graduate studies.

The endeavor of President Eliot to stimulate graduate education at Harvard met with indifferent response until the example of the Hopkins forced the faculties to face the problem in a wholehearted manner. By 1881 Eliot was able to write in King's *Harvard Register:*

In 1865 the exclusion of the graduates of the Schools of Divinity, Law, Medicine, and Science from all participation in the election of the Overseers could be readily explained and justified. The College was the only department which refused to admit uneducated persons, enforced upon its students a long residence in common, and offered some reasonable guarantee that most of its graduates were educated men . . . Within the past ten years, however, the professional schools have undergone such transformations, that many of the differences between them and the College, which were so striking in 1865, no longer exist.

Dr. Warren has given an intimate story of how the present Medical School quadrangle was planned and built. The designers laid out and named Avenue Louis Pasteur, and when all was complete placed a bronze bust of this French savant within the main entrance, where to this day it stands alone. The measure of this tribute can be taken if it is recalled that on the façade of the building erected for the school in 1883 were inscribed the names Hippocrates, Celsus, Galen, Vesalius, Paré, Haller, Harvey, Sydenham, Hunter, and Bichat. Each of these men represented an epoch in the progress of medicine. The choice of Pasteur alone for the 1906 buildings was a happy one, for if a single scientific activity were to be pointed out as the most powerful stimulus to the design and building of the quadrangle, it would be the rapid growth of that knowledge initiated by his work. Elaboration of the germ theory of disease and its application to human problems pervaded medical thought for decades, and the doctrine of specific etiology held first place in the minds of hundreds of scientists. This development of bacteriology and immunology led ultimately to the specific therapy of infectious disease. The surgery of today came into being with Lister and his achievement of aseptic healing of the surgical incision.

Not merely the surgery of today but the hospitals in which it is done became possible only with the prevention of the passage of infection from one patient to another by simple measures of individual isolation. In the 1860's, as described by Dr. Warren, the great evil of infection had swollen to a magnitude which threatened the very existence of hospitals. When numbers of injured or wounded persons were collected together under one roof, pyemia, erysipelas, hospital gangrene, and other septic diseases developed in epidemic proportions. The cause was then far from clear. The construction of compact granite buildings such as the Bulfinch was abandoned, and at the MGH the space extending to water's edge was given over to one- and two-story pavilion wards made of brick and wood. Great importance was ascribed to ventilation, and these wards were set widely apart so that in walking from one to another it was necessary to pass out of doors. The plan, when one of these buildings became permeated with infection — "pyemia-stricken" — was to demolish its fabric and destroy the materials. A fresh structure would then be built. The operating room for abdominal surgery, opened by Dr. Warren on February 21, 1889, was of this temporary construction and purposely set apart from other buildings of the Hospital. It was never demolished because of infection, however, and was used for one purpose after another for sixty-five years until removed in 1954 to clear the site for the Warren Building.

It is easy to overlook the fact that the great hospitals of today are newcomers to the social order, contemporaries of the motion-picture theater, the automobile, the airplane, and other noisy developments of the present century. The Peter Bent Brigham Hospital was constructed as recently as 1912–13, and yet its architectural design shows the influence of the old nightmare of pre-Listerian hospital infection: one- or two-story ward buildings with access through corridors open originally to the outdoors. No provision was made for private patients because even at that time people of means were reluctant to enter large hospitals.

Once it is recognized that the hospital of today is an acquisition of the present century, it is not surprising to find that its emergence has disrupted many older relations in the social order and that its mission, specifically its function in education, is as yet not clearly delineated. In 1889 the functions of university and hospital could be defined without overlap by President Daniel Coit Gilman of the new Johns Hopkins:

Permit me state in a sentence the principle which should govern both boards of trustees [University and Hospital]. All that belongs to medical instruction should be under the control of the University; all that belongs to the care of the sick and suffering, and all that concerns admission to clinical opportunities, or to residence within the walls of the Hospital, belongs to the Hospital. A joint Committee can easily adjust all questionable points if the fundamental principle is agreed upon.[2]

The difference was thought to be clear and obvious, but at the time of the Gilman enunciation few American hospitals had done more than assent reluctantly to a passive part in education. For decades medical students had been coming to the hospitals in droves, but only to follow some teacher on a ward visit or perch on narrow benches and crane their necks to see the operation going on in the pit below. Individual teachers had from time to time made intensive efforts to improve instruction. Thus in 1887 Dr. C. B. Porter was appointed professor of clinical surgery in recognition of his custom of instructing small groups of students at the bedside. This bedside teaching supplemented the formal lectures and was an early step toward the clinical clerkship.

While the hospitals were absolved from educational responsibilities by the Gilman statement of 1889, it must be remembered that before this time very few universities in this country had shown an inclination to take seriously their own efforts toward the education of the doctor. In fact, while certain individual institutions such as the University of Michigan, the Chicago Medical College, Harvard, and Johns Hopkins made noteworthy contributions, American universities as a group cannot be given credit for leading medical education to its present standards. The major effort came from the profession itself.

On September 6, 1893 Dr. Warren delivered an address entitled "Medical Education in the United States" before the First Pan-American Medical Congress in Washington, D. C. At this time he outlined the steps taken by the profession:

At a meeting of the Medical Society of the State of New York in 1839, when the subject of medical education was brought forward, it was pro-

[2] Fabian Franklin, *The Life of Daniel Coit Gilman* (New York, 1910), p. 266; reprinted by permission of Dodd, Mead & Company, Inc.

posed to hold a national medical convention the following year in Philadelphia, consisting of representatives from the different schools and State
societies. No response was made to the action of this society, but in 1845
Dr. N. S. Davis, then a delegate from Broome county, New York, offered
a resolution that a national convention be called in 1846; and the American
Medical Association thus was formed. The fundamental idea which brought
about the formation of the Association was the improvement of our system
of medical education.

It was high time that some such movement should take place, as the
rapid increase of the number of medical schools brought with it a constant
increase in the laxity of methods of teaching . . . The American Medical
Association . . . put on record its opinion, "that the abuses which exist in the
modes of medical education pursued in this country demand the serious
consideration of the profession," and at each meeting it continued to sound
a note of warning on this all-important subject. One of the principal reforms
which it proposed to bring about was the lengthening of the term . . . from
four to six months . . . At the second [annual] meeting of the Association,
which was held in Boston [1849], a paper was presented from the faculty
of Harvard University opposing this proposal . . . If Harvard was unwilling
to lead in the matter of reform at that time, it is not surprising that the
other schools should not have been persuaded to change their customs. To
the Chicago Medical College — which was founded in 1859 — must be
given the credit of having been the first to attempt to lengthen the college
course and to establish the system of teaching upon the so-called graded
plan. The school was in fact organized for this express purpose.

Little change was, however, effected by the Association in the methods
of teaching at that time, although the discussions which were constantly held
were destined eventually to bring forth good fruit.

Thus, in the words of Dr. Warren, the fundamental idea which
brought about the formation of the American Medical Association
was to improve the system of medical education. In 1902 the Association set up its Council on Medical Education. This body inspected
and classified all medical schools then existing and in 1907 pointed
out the urgent need for change in our casual way of training doctors.
In the autumn of 1908 the Carnegie Foundation appropriated money
for a more detailed appraisal of medical schools and assigned this
difficult task to Mr. Abraham Flexner. His report in 1910 was one
more event among the many happenings which showed that this
nation wanted better doctors, and served notice on its universities to
set about producing them.

The introduction of scientific thinking into the education of the
American doctor began by underlaying the old-time clinical lectures
and demonstrations with the teaching of laboratory science. At first
there was little integration of the new science with the old useful art,
and for a generation the flavor of pedantry lingered on in clinical instruction. As scientific concepts developed and methods of diagnosis and
treatment ready for use at the bedside appeared with quickening pace,

it became more and more apparent that a different type of emphasis was advisable for the student pursuing clinical studies. Symptoms and signs of disease required translation into physiological and chemical terms if the rapidly increasing knowledge was to yield improved clinical procedures. The crucial change desired by the farseeing members of the Harvard Medical Faculty was a hospital ward service under the continuous direction of a physician chosen jointly by hospital and university, who would be entrusted with the responsibility for shaping clinical instruction. The successful consultant then in control of a ward service was often a virtuoso in the art of healing but by no means always an adequate teacher. Not only did the demands of a large practice leave too few hours to spend with students, but, as has been said more frankly, these demands required a pretense of omniscience that at last deceived even the pretender.

It was at the Hopkins that formal and significant changes started in clinical instruction. Medical students were brought into the wards and assigned duties which permitted them an intimate share in the doctor-patient relations that are prized so highly in learning to become a doctor. Also at the Hopkins, the young surgeon was called in from the sidelines to share the responsibilities of the surgeon-patient relation under exacting supervision. The widespread emulation of these forward steps in education has led to the appearance of the present-day "teaching hospital," an institution whose very name gives evidence that it has committed itself to an active and supporting part in medical education. Only a very few hospitals can be teaching hospitals; the others remain workshops for practicing doctors.

In the face of the need for a change in the methods of instruction of medical students and with the example of the Hopkins at hand, it seemed to Dr. Warren that the MGH moved with exasperating slowness toward any change in the organization of its professional services that might bring them into accord with the hopes of the Medical Faculty. This attitude was maintained despite the fact that the two missions of the Hospital of that time — patient care and teaching — had been set forth clearly in the documents that surrounded its charter in 1811 and in the often-quoted circular letter of John C. Warren and James Jackson (1810) which indicated joint action with a medical school.

Dr. Joseph Garland has described in the following passage the seemingly casual way in which Medical School and Hospital were related. The parenthesis contains the key.

The relations between the Massachusetts General Hospital and the Harvard Medical School have been based, like the government of England, on certain unwritten conventions. By a tacit gentlemen's agreement both parties recognize their interdependence, and the representatives of both parties being gentlemen (frequently the same gentlemen!), mutual good will usually prevails. Other good hospitals have come into the field to serve the growing population — just as other good medical schools have been founded in the community — but the Massachusetts General Hospital and the Medical School of Harvard University stand unique as the still robust pioneers.[3]

For a long time neither the Hospital nor the University accepted medical education as a prime institutional responsibility. This responsibility rested on a few members of the profession who constituted themselves as the Medical Faculty and also held Hospital staff positions. Harvard showed little interest in, and certainly exerted no effective control over, medical instruction until after the accession of President Eliot in 1869. It is not too surprising, therefore, to find the Hospital lagging when the School wished suddenly to move ahead.

The Hospital was by no means asleep, however, or, as so often is said of old institutions, wrapped in self-satisfied complacency. With great vigor it pursued a course which by placing first things first led unerringly toward its important mission in the coming years. In carrying out the twofold mission of its charter, the MGH at no time relinquished the principle that the care of the patient was the first concern of a hospital. Time has shown that by hewing to this line a hospital can best fulfill its obligations to education and make contributions to the advance of medical knowledge. Patient care in the broad sense is not limited to the mobilization of technical skills to aid the sick man within the gates, but looks outward into the community and anticipates the needs and hopes of the people for health and well-being. Dr. Garland has also expressed this admirably. The Massachusetts General Hospital, he wrote, "has been generously supported by the community that it has helped to safeguard through so many years. This is the basis of its present greatness, and the foundation on which its future will rest."

So with literal adherence to the Gilman idiom, which defined the sphere of the hospital as "all that belongs to the care of the sick and suffering," the Massachusetts General Hospital during the critical decades in which modern hospitals were taking form concentrated its energies on girding itself to meet the ever-growing demands of the community. This remains today its primary, absorbing task. Dr. Washburn has described its growth as a process of "tearing down and building, and tearing down and building again." The brick-and-mortar shell of a hospital has far more in common with the structural framework of an industrial plant than with an academic cloister.

[3] *Harvard Alumni Bulletin* 48, 757 (July 6, 1946).

Constant remodeling is called for while the industry retools and realigns itself to meet needs that were unforeseen a decade previously.

The stalemate in academic reform perpetuated by adherence to the old order within the MGH staff organization, blocked the most vigorous and creative phase of Dr. Warren's professional life. His strong loyalties forbade an open reference to this state of affairs while dictating his Reminiscences, for any comment might have reflected unfavorably on his close friends and colleagues. From the vantage point of this present restless and dynamic period one can only marvel at the apparent lack of bitterness and frustration in the description of his return from Europe, a young man exuberant with an awareness that it was time "to cast off much that was old and prepare ourselves for the dawn of a science which was to revolutionize medicine" — only to take his place on the benches and maintain a respectful silence while his elders performed the Saturday morning operations in the same old way.

There can be little doubt, however, that the ultraconservatism exhibited at the MGH during this critical period rankled and that it was a very significant factor in shaping the pattern of the new Medical School on Longwood Avenue. Dr. Warren, in addressing the First Pan-American Medical Congress in 1893, thus referred to

the old-fashioned prejudice which resented the intrusion of students into the hospital wards. The theory of the trustee of that time was: This money was given for the cure of patients and not for the education of physicians. They could not be persuaded that the two interests were identical.

In 1906 Dr. Frederick C. Shattuck found it still timely to observe: "The humanitarian and the educational duties of a hospital do not conflict, they are indissolubly bound together if, indeed, they are not identical."

PRESIDENT ELIOT SEES A NEW CYCLE AHEAD

On the evening of the first of May 1909, President Eliot met for the last time with his Medical Faculty. In a brief glance backward over the decades spent together he dismissed the years of disorder and confusion within the profession on a generous note of understanding. Then raising his eyes to the future, Eliot saw that medicine as of that day had passed a turning point and that new activities were in order. Harvard had prepared itself for these activities by building the new quadrangle of institutes of medical science, which extended on both sides of the Faculty Room in which he was seated. The president continued:

It seems to me that the coming years have in them more possibilities of progress in medical education than any of the past years have had. Money is going to be poured out for the promotion of medicine and especially of preventive medicine. I congratulate you, as members of this fortunate and strong body, on your prospects of happy productive work.[4]

Within a few weeks President Eliot was to receive from his University the degree of Doctor of Medicine, *honoris causa,* with the citation, "He found our Medical School brick and left it marble." Harvard was ready to enter upon another cycle of even greater productivity in American medicine.

NEW ACTIVITIES BEGIN

It is not within the purview of this epilogue to set down, much less to interpret, the events of the busy decades which followed those happenings in medicine recorded by Dr. Warren. A few items that obviously postdate the Reminiscences already have been noted in order to round out some significant sequence of events. With the same thought in mind, it is tempting to look for evidence to support the estimate of Sir Harold Himsworth that medicine is once again confronted with a situation in which a new outlook is imperative and that once again activities are in order which will reaffirm the unity of the profession and integrate its widely scattered undertakings. Among straws in the wind pointing in this general direction is the uneasy soul-searching that is stirring medical faculties throughout the nation. In a few instances efforts to allay a growing sense of disorder and confusion have brought the introduction of more rigid administrative techniques; also, that unmistakable symptom of faculty unrest — the turning over of the curriculum — is under way in many places. Another symptom of unrest, which might be alarming if not understood, has been the reappearance of the priest-physician with his appeal to the ancient god of healing through faith, carefully concealed, as would be necessary in the present century, by what are said to be the swaddling clothes of a new science.

Even a casual inventory of the present state of medicine discloses that certain trends are the inevitable outgrowths of the decisions and activities of Dr. Warren's period. A somewhat more extended effort to connect current happenings with the groundwork laid by our predecessors may therefore be excusable both as a confirmation of Himsworth's thesis and as a base line for what may lie ahead. It is obvious that the formulation of a new outlook calls for evaluation of change in terms of such a unidirectional and continuous flow of human experience; change need not be a sudden threat to the stability of cherished customs and institutions.

Within two years from the opening of the new Medical School

[4] *Harvard Medical Alumni Bulletin* (October 1935).

quadrangle at the head of Avenue Louis Pasteur came the first break in the tight pattern of staff organization at the Massachusetts General Hospital. For some seventy years the Hospital had adhered to a system of divided services and divided responsibility which, in the appraisal of its director-historian, Dr. Frederic A. Washburn, had been both ineffective and harmful. In 1908 the first step was taken to revert to the form of organization originally instituted by Drs. John C. Warren and James Jackson. ("There should be a head to everything," Warren had said in 1828. "A divided responsibility is a doubtful one.") Two vacancies appeared simultaneously on the Board of Visiting Physicians, giving opportunity to provide Dr. Frederick C. Shattuck a continuous service as visiting physician, with Dr. Richard C. Cabot as assistant. The Board of Visiting Surgeons were more hesitant in making up their minds, but three years later created the post of surgeon-in-chief with a continuous service for Dr. Maurice H. Richardson. In 1912 the conduct of hospital professional affairs was reorganized and given over to the General Executive Committee.

In the same year came another noteworthy event: for the first time in the long history of the Hospital a physician was invited to come from outside the Boston area to join the clinical staff, as successor to Dr. Shattuck, and also to assume the Jackson professorship of clinical medicine at the School. This man was Dr. David L. Edsall, called from Washington University in St. Louis, where he had been a professor of preventive medicine. A search for a surgical head on a full-time basis to succeed Dr. Richardson following his death was interrupted by the First World War, but in 1919 Dr. John M. T. Finney of Baltimore was offered the position of chief of the surgical division together with the John Homans professorship in the University. Dr. Finney declined to accept, and it was not until 1923 that Dr. Edward P. Richardson was selected for a full-time continuous service, and subsequently the Homans professorship.

THREE ADDRESSES IN 1912
Dr. Shattuck Speaks at a Dinner of the Medical Faculty

On April 24, 1912 the Medical Faculty gathered at a dinner commemorating an unusual event — a number of distinguished members were retiring or had already received the title emeritus. Following applause for Dr. James C. White, who had been an active teacher from 1863 to 1902, Dr. Frederick C. Shattuck, emeritus as of 1912, was introduced as a teacher and a student of disease who nevertheless was able to lighten the serious pursuit of his profession with rare wit and humor.

As the shadow of Dr. Shattuck lengthens, its profile is sometimes shaped by his talents as a raconteur and skills as a clinician of nimble wit. These attributes may enhance but should never dim the signifi-cance of his part in the 1906 recasting of the Harvard Medical School and in its subsequent developments. Although formal acknowledg-ments and honors were concentrated on President Eliot and Drs. Bowditch and Warren, the fine hand of Dr. Shattuck was ever visible. It was characteristic of Shattuck that he should poke fun at himself and pass lightly over his own accomplishments. His writings, however, leave no doubt about his clear grasp of the situation and the changes that were under way.

At the dinner of the Medical Faculty Dr. Shattuck paid special tribute to Dr. Warren and to the memory of Dr. Henry P. Bowditch:

It was, I think, in 1898 that an informal meeting was held at Dr. Warren's house, and there he and Bowditch, whose spirit watches over and abides with us, unfolded their prophetic dream. They saw this spot with its beauti-ful and ample school buildings, set about, as it soon will be, by a group of affiliated institutions for the relief, study and the prevention of disease. I, doubting Thomas that I was, confess to having classed them as general paretics, typical megalomaniacs. Rarely have the visions of youth and the dreams of age been so united, so fully and quickly realized in fact. May we not read a deep meaning into the fact that the court of the school buildings is opened to the east, and, through the Avenue Louis Pasteur, is flooded by the rays of the rising sun? . . . The clinical facilities of the Harvard Medical School are unrivalled in this country. The contracts for the new Children's Hospital are signed, ground is breaking, and within two years we shall see the whole twenty-two [twenty-six] acres of the original purchase actively serving the purpose for which it was secured. The Peter Bent Brigham Hospital, the Infants' Hospital, the Children's Hospital, the Collis P. Hunting-ton Memorial Hospital and the Nutrition Laboratory of the Carnegie Insti-tution of Washington are levers of human uplift. Immediately adjoining are the House of the Good Samaritan, the Dental School, a monument to the devotion and chronic self-denial of its faculty; and it is whispered that an animal hospital [Angell Memorial Hospital] may come in the immediate neighborhood . . . Never have the sources of inspiration been so overflowing as they are to-day. The irrigating channels are well laid; the ground is ready; the laborers are keen and skilled; the crop is assured.[5]

Thus, after the completion of its great undertaking, the faculty, like the God of the Old Testament, looked upon its work and saw that it was good.

The concept that clinical teachers might voluntarily limit their practice to better serve university functions was not yet known to Boston. In fact there were some who gave the name "Medical Center" to the new development, suggesting thereby that one of its primary functions was the practice of medicine by the faculty and introducing a somewhat different meaning than had been implied in the planning

[5] *Boston Med. and Surg. J. 166,* 684 (May 2, 1912).

of Dr. Warren and his colleagues. An editorial writer in the June 13, 1912 issue of the *Boston Medical and Surgical Journal,* under the heading "The Development of a Medical Center," referred to a "remarkable center of medical education, practice and research." Although the first half of this century was to see many medical centers spring up throughout the country, Harvard had already formulated a policy of much broader scope and, as subsequent events have disclosed, this policy was to safeguard the "great and ideal medical university" envisioned by Dr. Warren.

President Lowell Addresses the Medical Alumni Association

The triennial meeting and dinner of the Harvard Medical Alumni Association were held on May 22, 1912 under the presidency of Dr. Warren. In the afternoon at the Medical School a program was arranged by Drs. Ernst and Rosenau. Several speakers with the aid of lantern slides described the new clinical facilities that were clustering about the quadrangle of the institutes of medical science. The dinner at the Hotel Somerset that evening was attended by over three hundred graduates and guests, and Dr. Warren occupied the chair. His own address deplored the lack of social activities in medical student life and challenged the alumni to devise means of providing a dormitory for the undergraduates. This address was an important step toward the achievement of Vanderbilt Hall in 1927.

The need for a medical school dormitory had been recognized by President Eliot in his 1894–95 Report and by a committee on university education in medicine in 1903. The *Harvard Bulletin* of March 25, 1908 had stated:

Largely through the efforts of J. Collins Warren '63 . . . the project for meeting this need has already advanced so far that sketch plans have been prepared for a dormitory fronting on one corner of the Avenue Louis Pasteur and facing a Harvard Medical School Union on the opposite corner . . . One important feature of such a building would be a hall sufficiently large to seat from five hundred to one thousand persons.

The majority of those present at the triennial meeting saw in Dr. Warren's renewal of the proposal merely a project to house the medical students. A few may have recognized the hand of the new president of the University, Abbott Lawrence Lowell.

Mr. Lowell had taken up the duties of the presidency on May 19, 1909 with the firm conviction of a need for further development and change. There was more to be done at Harvard than merely hold the ground gained by Mr. Eliot. When introduced by Dr. Warren, Mr. Lowell spoke of the present as a time of sowing rather than of harvest. By no means was "the crop assured."

Despite present improvements, we have still much progress to make in the art of medical as well as of collegiate teaching.

We are too apt to treat students as freight rather than passengers, as things to be instructed rather than human beings. I feel we are too fond of treating the student as if he were . . . a goose to be stuffed.

We fail to think the opinions of students about their education are of any value. Yet their opinions are just as good as ours and besides, theirs are fresh, while ours are canned.[6]

Mr. Lowell placed high value on intellectual prowess and believed that excellence is not won by students or by faculty merely from being afforded an opportunity to develop, or from instructing and being instructed. In his mind, productive scholarship was distilled from the struggle of competitive effort and could best be encouraged by having men live and work together in small groups within which they would mature by a process of attrition in an atmosphere of good fellowship. With this conviction foremost in his mind, it is not surprising that the new president did not allow his vision to be confined by the restricted concept of a medical center; he saw the opiate of complacency in the insular isolation which might overtake the Medical Faculty. At the triennial dinner Mr. Lowell broke through the centripetal thinking which was beginning to bind the imagination of the doctors:

We want an opportunity to have clinics with all the hospitals in the city. We are calling men from other parts of the country as educators. We have two eminent ones here to-night. One is a professor of surgery and the other of medicine.

The president was referring to Dr. Harvey Cushing, who was to take up his work at the Peter Bent Brigham Hospital in the autumn, and to Dr. David L. Edsall, newly appointed Jackson professor of clinical medicine and physician-in-chief of a continuous medical service at the Massachusetts General Hospital.

Dr. Edsall is Guest Speaker at the Aesculapian Club

Mr. Lowell's was not the first introduction of Dr. Edsall to alumni of the Harvard Medical School. On January 20th of the same year he had come from St. Louis as the guest speaker at the midwinter meeting of the Aesculapian Club. His address on that occasion, entitled "The Clinician, the Hospital and the Medical School," was carefully prepared, and was published in the February 29, 1912 issue of the *Boston Medical and Surgical Journal.*

Dr. Edsall had minced no words in speaking to the group of important practitioners in the Boston area. Difficulties that interfered

---

[6] *Ibid.*, 896 (June 13, 1912).

with proper relations between medical schools and hospitals were, he believed, products of misunderstandings rather than anything else, and it was obvious that these misunderstandings centered about the role of the clinical teacher. In the past, he said, when demands upon a teacher were relatively slight, it was possible to combine the career of the teacher with that of the practitioner; today, however, the academic clinical career could not be followed as an agreeable adjunct to a career as a practitioner.

There was great need, Dr. Edsall continued, for large hospital services generously equipped for teaching and research, and freely used for these purposes. He placed great emphasis on the choice and training of junior men and on the establishment of conditions favorable to their further development. The success of the play is not assured merely by having the principals of the cast all stars.

And then, in the guise of an incident said to have taken place in Great Britain, came the following passage:

Owing to its having recently acquired new facilities, a prominent university school recently reduced the amount of clinical teaching in the hospital where it had been previously carried on, in order to make good use of the new. The older hospital immediately asked the medical school to compensate it for the loss of prestige that this involved. The reply of the medical school was both satisfactory to the hospital and interesting evidence of the enlightenment that recent years have brought. They built the hospital a clinical and research laboratory.

And so the two men who were to shape Medical School policy during the next quarter of a century — President Lowell and Dr. Edsall, soon to become dean of the Medical Faculty — were not content merely to irrigate and till the ground at the head of Avenue Louis Pasteur, but turned their thoughts toward developing the Massachusetts General and the Boston City Hospital as essential parts of the Harvard undertaking. These two leaders saw an accrual of strength to the University and an extension of its influence in the community through a reasonable dispersion of Medical School activities.

The making of doctors calls for constant shifting of instructional activities between laboratory bench, classroom, dispensary, and hospital. To envision the "university medical school" desired by Dr. Warren requires that emphasis be placed on the total body of teachers and scholars that makes up a medical school, rather than on some one geographical site with its particular group of buildings. The latter idea of a university lingers erroneously in contemporary usage, although the broader concept conveys the true meaning of the medieval Latin *universitas*. A university activity may be housed in a single group of buildings, or for convenience the teachers and scholars may be housed in separate parts of a city or, indeed, in separate cities.

The noble group of buildings on Avenue Louis Pasteur, with laboratories, museums, and lecture halls, developed into a focal center from which the advanced students made daily pilgrimages to the hospitals. In the same manner, medical students had visited the homes of the patients of their preceptors during the days of instruction by apprenticeship, or spent months abroad in the great hospitals of Europe, as did Dr. Warren. Under Mr. Lowell and Dr. Edsall the Medical School of Harvard University actually extended into the great teaching hospitals of metropolitan Boston.

THE RISE OF THE TEACHING HOSPITAL

Even after the introduction of measures for controlling the passage of infection from patient to patient had made the present-day hospital possible, several decades passed before people relinquished their fear of hospital infection and were more willing to become hospital patients. Real headway in this respect was not gained until about the time of the 1914–1918 war. Since then, hospitals have become amazingly complex organizations — so complex, indeed, that their primary purpose is sometimes lost to sight.

The Peter Bent Brigham Hospital, a welcome and needed addition to the list of institutions academically related to the Harvard Medical School, celebrated its Founders' Day on November 12, 1914. Dr. Warren was present at the ceremonies and spoke words of congratulation on behalf of the Boston profession. Dr. Cushing liked to refer to him as the guardian spirit of the new hospital.

On May 17, 1917 Dr. Warren crossed the threshold of the new Phillips House of the MGH and was escorted to a room on the sixth floor as its first patient. The Phillips House was one of the first multi-storied buildings to replace the spread-out pavilion hospitals of the decades of infection, and also the second major building for private patients in this country, antedated only by Mt. Sinai in New York City. It soon replaced the small and outmoded nursing homes such as St. Margaret's Infirmary in old Louisburg Square on Beacon Hill, which surgeons had used for their private patients when for one reason or another it was not possible to set the stage in a private house for the complex ritual of an operation.

The Phillips House was one more step in the growth of the MGH from a small and thrifty agency which cared for the poor of the community into a general hospital of world-wide reputation. During the first three decades of this century its destiny as the General Hospital envisioned by its founders was achieved, for there is much evidence to show that the adjective "General" in its title refers, not to a wide range of human ills and ailments, as commonly supposed, but to the principle that there shall be no racial, religious, social, or economic restrictions applicable to the people it serves.

The steady development of the MGH has greatly increased its resources as a teaching hospital, and for decades the academic relation with the University has been prized as a stimulating and constructive force. Teaching hospitals throughout the country are moving forward with universities in full confidence that partnership in the educational undertaking will enhance their usefulness and also add to their stature.

Alan Gregg has likened the ideal relation between university and hospital to the human arm. The usefulness of the arm comes from the joints, from having one part articulated with another, rather than two rigid parts ankylosed into a single stick. Hospital and medical school "work better apart, with freedom, individuality and independence." Gregg warned against attempts to build relations that take on the flavor of rigidity. Particularly he deplored agreements that might connote prohibition of action.[7]

In facing up to educational responsibilities, hospitals have, among other changes, converted the old brief internship, which was nothing more than on-the-job training, to a prolonged period of intramural practice under supervision. During these years a young doctor may acquire skills and go a long way toward an understanding of the practical art of medicine. To prepare himself in surgery the young man embarks upon hospital intramural practice that lasts five or more years, and only then is he admitted to the qualifying examinations of a specialty board.

The hospital, under university leadership, has met with far more than indifferent success in its own educational undertakings for the recent graduate. Alan Gregg, whose judgment in educational matters is worthy of great respect, has said that "the teaching and supervision given an intern or resident in a teaching hospital involves an intimacy with his teacher that surpasses anything he has experienced in the previous 20 years of his education." [8]

THE RISE OF CLINICAL INVESTIGATION

In close linkage with the emergence of the teaching hospital came the development and rise of clinical investigation — the analysis of disease processes in the living human patient. Clinical investigation became formally established when in the spring of 1908 a group of young physicians, bored with the dull programs of the Association of

---

[7] *Harvard Medical Alumni Bulletin* (October 1939).
[8] *Bull. Am. Coll. Surgeons* 40, 65 (1955).

American Physicians, staged a walkout. The new organization that came into being was officially christened the American Society for Clinical Investigation and colloquially known as the Young Turks. Among the founders were Henry Christian, Joseph Pratt, and Edwin Locke — all becoming important figures in the Harvard Medical School — and David Edsall, who ten years later was to become its dean. Clinical investigation by the methods of physiology also received a great impetus from the American Society for the Advancement of Clinical Investigation, founded in 1909 by Dr. S. J. Meltzer and known affectionately as the "Meltzer Verein."

The intellectual restlessness shown by the young physicians also pervaded the ranks of the surgeons. Young Dr. John Homans spent the winter of 1908–09 in Baltimore working with Harvey Cushing. Dr. Maurice Richardson had written to Dr. Cushing on July 31, 1908:

> I feel that my men, although they make splendid practitioners of surgery, fail to get from me any inspiration toward so-called research work. Of course we are seeking all the time — and hoping that we shall find — knowledge in the fields of practical surgery; but it seems that the coming generation needs a broader field in which to work; that the men should be more than purely clinical observers.[9]

The desire of the doctor to increase his understanding of the patient was nothing new; all systematic knowledge in medicine has been built up by the contributions of keen observers. But to utilize to the full the controlled methods of experimental science and the precise measurements of observational science meant that, in addition to being master of many skills of the clinic, the investigator must possess a well-grounded competence in some science related to medicine. A physician equipped in this manner called himself a clinical investigator, and he may be looked upon as a direct descendant of the seventeenth-century physician who retained the title of "natural philosopher" as an indication that his interests were not entirely absorbed by the technical and commercial aspects of practice. Whenever clinical investigation of a major order has been achieved it almost always can be traced to such a bivalent person. At times, however, a brave start has been halted by a heavy burden of teaching or a failure to confine clinical responsibilities within reasonable limits or merely the lack of a flair for sustained research effort, and under these circumstances the investigative activities of a well-intentioned physician have occupied but a brief part of his career. On the broad front of scientific endeavor, however, the summation of many small gains means a steady forward movement, and it may be said that not only has the effectiveness of the healing arts been furthered by the contributions

[9] J. F. Fulton, *Harvey Cushing* (Thomas, Springfield, Ill., 1946), p. 281.

from the natural and medical sciences but also this effectiveness has increased parallel with the rise of clinical investigation.

The Medical School quadrangle, dedicated in 1906, just two years before the Society for Clinical Investigation was formed, contained meager provision for studies by the clinicians of the faculty, and of course to this day there are no facilities for keeping a patient or a healthy volunteer overnight. Apparently it was thought that, if investigations were contemplated by clinicians, either the work could be carried on for them (or even by them) in the departmental institutes of medical science, or else their efforts would find more congenial surroundings in the pathological laboratories of the associated hospitals, where, for example, Richard Cabot worked on ring bodies in the red blood cells and Henry Christian studied the pathology of fat and fatty degeneration. To have school and hospital close together was convenient, as this provided classrooms and lecture halls for the instruction of all classes and brought to the laboratories a handy source of human secretions, excretions, and autopsy material. But this proximity had been sought primarily as a means of bringing control of clinical instruction into the hands of the Medical Faculty. All evidence at the time indicated that disease would be elucidated by the researches of medical scientists in the institutes of medical science.

Planning, however, is never better than the assumptions upon which it is based. The new Medical School buildings had been occupied less than a decade when unprecedented happenings began to take place in the hospitals. Instead of wearing the frock coat traditional to the morning rounds on the medical service at the MGH, Dr. Edsall appeared in a surgeon's gown as if to show that to be a good physician one must be a surgeon as well and use the hands to uncover knowledge. The therapeutic nihilism of Richard Cabot caught the fancy of young physicians and led them to walk in the narrow path of scientific pharmacology. Strychnine, caffein, camphor in oil, calomel, "nux and gentian," and many other time-honored familiars from the depths of the ward medicine closet were put aside.[10] When the first ward for medical patients at the Peter Bent Brigham was opened on March 31, 1913, Francis W. Peabody was on hand as chief resident physician, sampling alveolar air with Walter Boothby. This technique was soon projected into studies on acidosis and dyspnea in renal and cardiac disease. James Howard Means, then Henry P. Walcott Fellow in clinical medicine at the MGH, measured the basal metabolism with his subjects on various diets and undergoing starvation.[11] In a corner of

[10] For example, D. L. Edsall and J. H. Means, "The effect of strychnin, caffein, atropin and camphor on the respiration . . ." *Arch. Int. Med. 14*, 897 (1914).
[11] *J. Med. Research 27*, 121 (1915).

the chemical laboratory of the MGH, Walter W. Palmer, J. H. Means, and James L. Gamble, all of the medical service, studied creatinine elimination simultaneously with basal metabolism and secured publication of their results in the erudite *Journal of Biological Chemistry*.[12] This team offers an early example of what will be described as the "task force" approach, with Walter Palmer bridging the gap to Professor Lawrence J. Henderson of the Division of Chemistry in the University. George R. Minot, with Channing Frothingham, Jr., watched the effects of the injection of bovine bile into rabbits in the laboratory of the Department of Theory and Practice of Physic,[13] and with L. H. Newburgh he recorded blood pressure in patients with pneumonia on the East Medical Service of the MGH.[14] Following a sojourn at Johns Hopkins, Minot wrote on the nitrogen metabolism before and after splenectomy in a case of pernicious anemia.[15]

These men are mentioned as examples of the many clinical investigators of the period; their enthusiasms soon began to reach the medical students, at least those who were willing to put forth some special effort. It no longer sufficed for a student to read Osler's textbook of medicine, a work that was perpetuating the old approach in edition after edition. Students turned to current periodical literature and small monographs such as the one on acidosis prepared by Watson Sellards. By the 1920's the senior medical student enjoyed the same thrills and excitements in walking the wards and gathering in the laboratories with Peabody, Means, Cecil Drinker, or George Minot that James Jackson, Jr. and his contemporaries had found in Paris with Louis nearly a century before. Oliver Wendell Holmes had said of Louis:

Louis taught us who followed him the love of truth, the habit of passionless listening to the teachings of nature, the most careful and searching methods of observation, and the sure means of getting at the results to be obtained from them in constant employment of accurate tabulation.[16]

It was this same attraction that caused the study of disease to swerve from the institutes of medical science back into the hospitals. The bedside of the patient once again became a frontier of medicine.

In 1923 David L. Edsall, having built laboratories of clinical investigation at the MGH, gave up his hospital portfolio to become full-time dean of the Medical School. From the dean's chair Dr. Edsall built new budgets and strengthened departments with the

---

12 *19*, 239 (1914).
13 *J. Med. Research 22*, 79 (1912).
14 *Arch. Int. Med. 14*, 48 (1914).
15 *Johns Hopkins Hosp. Bull. 25*, 338 (1914).
16 O. W. Holmes, "Some of My Early Teachers," in *Medical Essays, 1842–1882* [Riverside Edition of Holmes's Works, IX; Boston, 1891], p. 436.

swelling tide of donations that poured into the school, and his greatest satisfaction came from making places for the supporting cast of junior men, who in his mind determined the success of the play. A tutorial plan manned by junior instructors brought small groups of the more imaginative undergraduates into intimate contact with the laboratories of medical science and with clinical investigation. The era of memorizing facts from textbooks and regurgitating them in quiz classes had come to an end.

The research strategy of the clinical investigator is to start with a problem and then find a productive way to study it. An example of what happened when this approach was introduced is found in the development of the Collis P. Huntington Memorial Hospital for Cancer Research. The charter of this hospital as envisioned by Dr. Warren was a broad and frontal attack on the cancer problem presented by human sufferers from the disease. Originally the scientific work was to be farmed out to the institutes of medical science, and for this reason the hospital was built right on the Medical School grounds. The first investigative project which merited high priority in the mind of Dr. Warren was an appraisal of the effects of radium on cancer, but in the design of the quadrangle of institutes no provision had been made for physics. Physics was not a "medical science." To meet this situation Dr. Warren in the *First Annual Report* of the hospital (1912–13) requested funds for a research laboratory that would be a part of the hospital. Money was forthcoming, laboratory space was made available, and two physicists were installed. Thus as early as 1913 it became evident that the planned study of a disease (in this instance cancer) is different from the analysis of some problem in biology or chemistry which may be pertinent to disease and by chance lies in the pathway of workers in a medical science department. To work directly toward the understanding of a disease requires the assembly of a task force in which are represented those scientific methods and skills requisite to the approach chosen by the investigator. In such a task force clinicians and laboratory investigators must work shoulder to shoulder.

Dr. Warren had recognized the need for such a combined approach in his oration on surgery delivered at the annual session of the American Medical Association in 1905. Specifically, he was pleading for the more rational approach to the management of breast tumors which would come from a closer association of pathologist and surgeon:

The laboratory workers' range of vision, however, is often at best but microscopic, and it is no wonder that, unaided, he sometimes misinterprets the changes rung by nature on some simple theme. Without the laboratory worker's aid, however, the clinician becomes swamped in a mass of clinical detail from which alone he has again and again been unable to extricate himself. There can be little question that the combination of energies which accomplishes most in surgical progress is that obtained by the coöperation of the laboratory investigator with the surgeon of clinical experience. Too long have these two departments of medicine conducted themselves independently and, as I feel, greatly to the disadvantage of them both. The clinician and the laboratory man, however, in these days of specialism seem sometimes in danger of drifting even further apart, and we find some of the modern problems sadly in need of a pathologic "clearing-house" to put things on a more practical basis.[17]

By 1919 it became apparent that the rise of clinical investigation was having an unforeseen effect on the institutes of medical science that had been placed in the marble quadrangle built by Bowditch and Warren. In his first statement of policy as dean of the Medical Faculty on the 7th of April of that year, Dr. Edsall deplored the fact that a career in clinical investigation was attracting so many of the young men of scientific training and interest away from medical science as a profession. This trend was attributed to a disparity in financial rewards favoring the clinical research career, and for over thirty years the same reason has been invoked, but this is by no means the entire difficulty. A lessened recruitment of first-rate young men to any field, scientific or clinical, is early evidence of a diminished intensity of activity within that field relative to other areas which have gained the ascendancy.

The fact is that the approach to the study of disease in man by the task force of the clinical investigator has proved more attractive to the young physician than the tactics of the medical scientist. At the mid-point of the twentieth century, those engaged in the biological study of man in health and in disease appear to be seeking a new unity. The strategy of our predecessors was to divide this study into a number of separate departments or disciplines — anatomy, physiology, biochemistry, pathology, pharmacology, bacteriology, and the rest — and look to each unit for discoveries which might be useful in or at least pertinent to the healing art. In addition to giving students an introduction to the concepts and principles of biological science, these departments were assigned the task of instructing them in the basic skills and information required to practice medicine. Despite this strong vocational slant, the research activities of the medical sciences have been carried on within the broad context of human biology. President Conant spoke of the medical sciences as applied research, and undoubtedly their organizational position within the Faculty of

[17] "The Surgeon and the Pathologist: A Plea for Reciprocity," *J. A. M. A. 45*, 149 (1905).

Medicine may have indirectly influenced their investigations. To maintain their vitality, the medical sciences require the same freedom of research and prestige enjoyed by their university counterparts in the natural and biological sciences, irrespective of whether they are called "medical sciences" and placed organizationally within the Medical Faculty or, under some other name, lie within the Faculty of Arts and Sciences.

It is impossible to deny that the vocational pull of clinical medicine has exerted an influence on the teaching activities assigned to the medical sciences and thus indirectly on their research. This influence has been felt through the voice of the clinicians in the selection of departmental heads. A vocationally minded faculty inevitably shies away from the intense and brilliant analytical scholar who is perforce a specialist, and favors the "generalist" who is thought to be less theoretical and therefore a "sounder teacher," and who in other subtle ways bears a resemblance to the idealized and legendary family doctor — this despite the universal recognition that the scholar is the very man who brings forth the new and revolutionary concepts which reshape the traditional procedures of the healing art.

The bringing together of men from several disciplines in clinical investigation, a tactic which has been called the task-force approach, cannot be transferred to instructional methods solely on a priori grounds. Current efforts are being made at Harvard and elsewhere to revitalize the medical sciences by some rearrangement of the curriculum that will bring together or "integrate" the teaching activities of the departments. These efforts often reflect the patterns of directed superorganization visible in so many trends in contemporary society. Without doubt the student, a hardy fellow, will derive some immediate benefit from the resulting burst of enthusiasm for instruction. In the long run, however, one of two things is likely to happen: either there will be a conscious selection of coöperative generalists who submerge themselves willingly in the "integrated" teaching corps; or, if strong professors who retain the capacity of nomads to roam in unexplored places are appointed, these individualists will delegate their interdisciplinary teaching duties to more docile technicians and assistants. Either event will seriously cripple the contribution of the university to medicine as a science.

A third possibility, but one that calls for long-range vision, is that the emerging academic organism, in its present state already labeled *preclinical science*, will be subjected to shrinkage after the manner of a Jivaran head as new and vigorous areas of science, such as biophysics, molecular biology, enzyme chemistry, and whatever may come next, lend their support to medicine by literally or figuratively moving into the quadrangle of medical science.

While President Conant classified the worker in medical science as an applied scientist, the clinical investigator more nearly qualifies for this designation. At least in his own mind his investigations have a bearing on some aspect of normal or abnormal human biology. But the effort of a decade ago to compare and define the activities of scientists is really not worth reviving. It was a mischievous pastime, to say the least.

In his research strategy the clinical investigator first stakes out the problem and then chooses the particular method with which to press for its solution. This strategy substitutes the siege for the opportunistic and therefore more random method of approach. It may be true that this is a different form of scientific activity from that identified as "pure science" and said to deal with ideas or concepts arising from experiment and observation, which in their turn lead to further experiment and observation, and so on. A worker in a science as thus defined is free to study the scroll as it unrolls itself before him, and is content to contribute fresh concepts and methods to his particular science in its dynamic and helicoid course. His genius need never pause before a specific problem of disease.

Francis Peabody saw most of this very clearly and did not drop into the tempting pitfall of analogy. During the latter days of his life he set down certain thoughts and reflections in a letter to Dr. Warfield Longcope. This letter was dictated from a reclining chair and carried his last message to the profession. Among other things he said:

The clinical investigator, with his knowledge of disease in man, thus finds the problem first and determines the practical way to study it, turning to his colleagues in the fundamental sciences especially for technical experience . . . The medical clinic should encourage its staff to use methods of any sort, no matter how difficult or specialized, that are needed for the solution of their immediate problems; but their first interest should center about the general subject of disease in man. The first interest of the "scientist," on the other hand, is in the development of his own particular field.[18]

The use of difficult and specialized methods today may mean adding an expert familiar with them to the task force. The departmental identification and long-range career planning of such an individual are pressing problems at the moment, for these matters, naturally important to a young man, have been measured on the Procrustean academic pattern of yesterday. All too frequently the expert who joins the task force is viewed as a pariah by his parent department and looked upon as a temporary resident by those in

[18] Quoted in F. W. Peabody, "The Soul of the Clinic," *J. A. M. A. 90,* 1193 (1928).

the area in which he is working. This situation offers a striking example of the immediate confusion brought about by the emergence of new intellectual relations that transcend departmentalized science, and of the disturbance that comes about when habits of organizational thinking are conditioned by rigid departmental boundaries.

A few years ago President Conant recognized the need for "roving professors," individuals free to move from department to department and even from faculty to faculty, wherever they might find the most congenial circumstances for productive scholarship. It can be submitted that the need today is for instructors and assistant professors who are free to "rove" without prejudice to their academic future. A step in this direction was made by President Lowell in the formation of the Society of Fellows. As will be recognized, this comparison is far from being a precise one, but there are some elements in common. In writing of President Gilman's conception of a small body of scholars satisfied to trust to themselves and their own achievements for success, President Lowell referred to the Society of Fellows at Harvard as a revival of this idea. As envisioned by Mr. Lowell, the Fellows were a carefully selected group of promising young scholars living under conditions of complete academic freedom. In addition, the Fellows enjoyed social contact with one another and with older scholars. Complete academic freedom provided an opportunity to cross interdepartmental or interfaculty lines; also, the individual trusted to his achievements for academic recognition, instead of looking for security in a position on some departmental promotion ladder. Firm identification with a specific department may offer short-range advantages for reappointment and promotion, but the work load of routine teaching and examinations can leave little time for creative effort.[19]

The present time also seems out of joint for the departmentalized medical scientist because his colleague, the clinical investigator, seeks knowledge and methods pertinent to his problem from any point on the wide circle of university science. His quest for consultation and assistance can no longer be limited to the panel of medical sciences in the quadrangle of the Medical School. This trend, started in 1914 by bringing physicists into the cancer problem, has increased, and lines of communication have been cast by clinical investigators into every sacred temple of academic learning. Neurologists have torn the veil from cybernetics; the anesthetist has joined the entomologist in recording the wing beat of *Drosophila* with a stroboscope; and psychiatrists walk with anthropologists. The linear

[19] See A. Lawrence Lowell, *What A University President Has Learned* (Macmillan, New York, 1938), p. 31 and footnote.

scale on which scientists were placed a decade ago is now perceived as a four-dimensional network. Francis Peabody also saw this very clearly in 1923 when he delivered an address before the American Association for the Advancement of Science. He said:

It is only a few years . . . since the medical investigator seemed well prepared to attack the problems of metabolism if he were fortified by a background of general biological chemistry, but his successor of to-day often finds it necessary to turn to physical chemistry, to electrochemistry, to photochemistry and to the various branches of physics. In the use of these sciences the medical investigator may be forced to go entirely outside of the ranks of his own profession and seek the coöperation of experts whose experience has never brought them into contact with the field of medicine. Many of the possible linkings between medicine and what a comparatively short time ago seemed to be wholly unrelated sciences are already becoming evident to us; and no one can foretell what other unexpected affiliations may soon become desirable.[20]

The laboratories of the clinical investigators have grown up in the hospitals, adjacent to the floors on which are lodged the patients under study. Recourse to animal experimentation is had only to piece in gaps of evidence when it would be inappropriate or possibly not without risk to carry out certain procedures on patients. Not infrequently the investigator and his associates use their own bodies for tests of safety. With the development of clinical investigation new responsibilities have descended on the teaching hospital. Along with fulfilling its manifold duties to the people of the community it has been called upon to build and operate laboratories for clinical investigation, arrange special wards for metabolic studies, and provide space for investigators, research fellows, and special students not only from the medical school but from other departments of the university with which it is related and from other universities throughout the world.

PRESIDENT CONANT SEES DISORDER AND CONFUSION

The Faculty of Medicine assembled in a special meeting on January 21, 1953. Once again a Harvard president was meeting for the last time with his Medical Faculty. The flag was flying over the Administration Building in recognition of the importance of the day. Mr. Lowell had been followed by James Bryant Conant, and now Mr. Conant had come from Cambridge to say good-bye.

The president gallantly spoke of his great confidence in the future of the Medical School, but there were notes of reservation and qualification in his address. The future was by no means as clear to Mr. Conant in 1953 as it had appeared to Mr. Eliot in 1909, nor

[20] *Science 59*, 136 (February 8, 1924).

did his voice have the same ring of confidence. To anyone who carries heavy responsibility in the decade of the 1950's, the future is less clear than it was to a predecessor in the first decade of the century. Also, it was characteristic of Mr. Eliot that he should speak with the "certitude of finality."

"After the War," Mr. Conant said, "it appeared as though Medicine were about to enter new phases of activity, for which the School was not wholly prepared." Concern was expressed about the action of hospitals in taking up "problems of research which heretofore they had not attempted to attack." Viewing this trend as "potentially dangerous," Mr. Conant thought it timely to warn against the "development of 'hospital schools' like those of Great Britain." It was obvious that Mr. Conant believed that the growth of teaching hospitals and the increase of research in hospitals, particularly that research he identified as "pure science," were draining strength away from the University toward the periphery. A natural scientist in his own right, Mr. Conant in a previous address before the New York Academy of Medicine, on March 11, 1948, had seen the clinical investigator only as a man who was "treating patients or studying by pathological methods the effect of disease on the human organisms." Clinical investigators as a group, he had said, "may be considered the medical equivalent of what are called development engineers in industry." In their laboratories "projects are to be reworked and if promising are handed on to the manufacturer for production."

At the special meeting the president continued with a brief account of his negotiations conducted between the school and its academically related hospitals. He spoke of the need for coöperation and restraint, but in no way suggested the desirability of agreements such as Alan Gregg had deplored as possibly prohibitive to freedom of action.

Finally, Mr. Conant expressed his confidence in medical schools in general because of "the tremendous advances in the application of science to medicine," and specifically in the future of the Harvard Medical School, "located in a great medical center which as yet has not reached its full potentialities."

With the same *"Ave sed non vale"* given to Mr. Eliot on May 1st, 1909, the special meeting of 1953 came to an end.

AIDE-MEMOIRE FOR THE COMING CYCLE

The limits that define university responsibility and professional responsibility in medical education are far from absolute. These limits have changed in the past, and change may be expected in the future. The educational activity of the profession was at one time carried on in the office of the practitioner, as Dr. Warren so well described, and now is conducted largely through the hospital, an agency which can be sensitive to professional needs without deviation from other more vital functions. American universities became saddled with a heavy burden of vocational training at a time when the hospitals of our new and rapidly developing society could not possibly have coped with the task. Until the final decades of the nineteenth century, most hospitals were little more than almshouses. Over the years it has become an unquestioned assumption that a four-year course of instruction in medicine directed toward the degree of M.D. is a natural university function. This assumption is held despite the fact that a considerable part of the undergraduate course of study is concerned with the acquirement of information and skills that qualify the student to go forth and practice medicine. Much of this information and many of these skills are ephemeral and of no significance to the broad subjects and fields of learning that rightfully find position in a university. There is little wonder that medical faculties are accused of being out of touch with other faculties, and although the world of sick folk and their kin within which a doctor spends his working day cannot be said to be unreal, it is indeed a world apart. From a practical standpoint, however, so long as instructional training of the doctor is not a burden which prevents a university from accomplishing its more basic tasks, there can be no doubt that medical education will remain and prosper under direct university guidance.

It should be held in mind, however, that university interest in professional education cannot be taken for granted; from 1782 until 1869 Harvard gave only nominal sponsorship to the instruction of the doctor. Then came the opportunity to foster his scientific education and by so doing strip away his caul of medieval ignorance and superstition. The old-time practitioners were actually antiscientific, not merely unscientific, and it has been university leadership that has armed their successors with the tools and the powers of the new science. The doctor of today is not making full use of his university privilege and fellowship if he is content merely to develop his facility as a healing artisan and fails to grow in the understanding of men, which is found not only in science and in practice but also in the intimate sharing of "the common human adventure" with university colleagues.

The only agency sensitive to professional needs and now in a position to lighten the burden of the university is the hospital. In the Harvard undertaking the hospital traditionally assumes full responsibility for the years of graduate training that follow after the course of undergraduate studies. These years in the hospital were for a long time dedicated overtly to the acquirement of techniques and practical experience; only recently, throughout the country and chiefly in teaching hospitals, is this period approaching an educational experience. The hospitals which have led in this movement have utilized members of a medical faculty in their training programs.

By a careful examination of the subject matter of the present undergraduate medical curriculum, it is not unlikely that those portions specifically intended to qualify one for practice could be identified and that they might be transferred to the graduate period already under the aegis of the hospital. Replacement of such material from the university-wide courses of study might be made with advantage, or possibly the undergraduate educational period in the university could be shortened.

Changes in patterns of university and hospital participation in medical education must mean greater rather than less acceptance of university standards by the hospital and the profession. Medicine, now more than ever before, is dependent on broad knowledge — not only on the concepts and methods coming from the natural and medical sciences, but on all knowledge that may arise from the "passionless listening to the teachings of nature" by man and about man. Medicine is dependent upon a continuation of the methodical search for knowledge by all methods, but especially by careful experiment, observation, and the "constant employment of accurate tabulation." The exigencies which attend the care of the sick in hospital and the alert watch which the hospital must maintain to help safeguard the health of the community are likely, except under the most favorable circumstances, to interrupt or distract the endeavor of science and serious scholarship. This can be as true today as it was when James Jackson wrote:

It is a novelty to pursue the method of Bacon thoroughly and truly in the study of medicine; though it is not new to talk of it and to laud it . . . Many no doubt thought of [keeping accurate tabulation of observations] . . . I myself thought seriously of it more than thirty years ago, and had blanks printed for my cases . . . But the difficulties attending the plan in private practice discouraged me too soon. So far as I have known, M. Louis is the only physician who has devoted himself for years together, at a mature age and after a sufficient education, to simple observation, without the distraction of medical practice, and without having any share in the treatment of the cases under his observation.[21]

[21] From Jackson's preface to the American edition of Louis's *Researches on the Effects of Bloodletting* (Boston, 1836).

Despite such a handicap there is good reason to believe that the distractions of the hospital milieu can be controlled, or rather that insulation can protect against them. The hazard of flagging or spurious scholarship is not peculiar to any particular institution as such; it threatens university and hospital alike in a strongly materialistic society in which education is often dominated by a vocational or trade-school approach. In a glance over the country at large one sees hospitals which by favorable academic relations have achieved standards of scholarship that rise above those prevailing in many institutions labeled as universities.

So long as the scientific frontier of medicine maintains its communication with science as a whole, it makes little difference whether this frontier lies in a hospital or in a university laboratory, or in some other institution unrelated to either. For the hospital to assume ascendancy in the schooling of the doctor, however, would be quite a different matter. Consider, for example, its helplessness in the face of the threat of increasing specialization. The intensive exploitation of skills and specialties by the profession is but the natural result of its responsibility to bring expert care to the sick. As the variety and complexity of these skills and specialties have increased, there has resulted a piling up of training requirements and an insistence upon rigid conformity to existing types of careers. Specialties have become deeply entrenched in hospital departments and services, with the inevitable result that the clinical years of the medical undergraduate curriculum have been espaliered to conform with the organizational pattern of the hospital rather than shaped primarily by the educational needs of the student. The university remains the only institution which can exert an effective counterforce to specialism; only by making its broadening influence felt in the hospital can further disintegration and fragmentation be countered.

The pull toward vocational training in medical education is a powerful one and by no means confined to hospital influences. Organizations of specialists have shown little hesitancy about dipping into the subject matter presented to undergraduates — usually with the recommendation that instruction in this or that set of skills be increased. Charles Morris has suggested: "If the particular medical school does not suit the budding obstetrician, urologist or practitioner of any sort, then the conclusion should be that the would-be obstetrician, the urologist and the practitioner should not go there — not that the school should cease to be a university school." [22]

There can be no question that the profession should continue to look to the university for leadership in medical education, and that

[22] *Universities Quarterly 9*, 254 (1955).

the medical faculty in turn must think, not solely as doctors, but also as members of a university faculty. The hospital will have ample place as an essential and supporting partner in the joint undertaking. Medicine cannot afford to go it alone in the iatrocentric isolation of a hospital or on some island of hospitals called a medical center. If "caring for the whole man" is to express more than an abstraction in the coming decades, a greater breadth of understanding will be required of the doctor than he is developing at the present time. This need in his education is not something that can be satisfied by halfway measures. It can be met only by striving for a better integration within the young doctor himself. It will require a "whole doctor" to care for the "whole man," and the making of whole men is a true university function.

The approach to such a goal may well begin with a further loosening of the rigid vocational curriculum, much of which has been handed down from the time when it was the sole purpose of the school to graduate a general practitioner of medicine. In a talk before a medical alumni group in 1895, President Eliot proposed a logical criterion by which a medical school that aspires to qualify as a department of a university may be distinguished from an enterprise conducted at the vocational level. Expressed in mathematical terms, this "Eliot index" would be the ratio between the educational opportunities a faculty spreads before its students and the sequence of courses that can be encompassed by an average student in four years. No department of a university, he said, can be extended and improved under the restriction that it shall teach no more than a fair student can learn.

With an increase in the number and variety of courses offered in the medical curriculum and with the full educational resources of the university laid before the medical student, his choice would be limited only by the confines of fields of concentration selected in accord with his personal desires and with tutorial guidance. Required instruction in skills and specialties, which hounds the conscientious student today, can with advantage be converted to an elective status or postponed to the graduate period. In common purpose with mature students of other ancient arts and new fields of learning, the young doctor could then work toward a broader, fuller, and riper understanding of the whole man he is to serve. In this direction lies the great and ideal medical university sought by Dr. Warren.

THE NEXT HARVARD

It may well be that once again a time has arrived for a new outlook in the thinking of the profession. If so, it is heartening to believe that with new activities in order, the Medical Faculty may set its course by the words of still another Harvard president — Nathan M. Pusey:

The University's mission is to lead individuals with joy and understanding into an informed and thoughtful commitment to their lifetime enterprise within the common human adventure.[23]

The great undertaking of the new Medical School as organized and built by Dr. Warren and his colleagues in 1906 has served us well. During the past fifty years it has undergone many changes. The opportunity for leadership in even greater change lies ahead if those who have followed after have courage to undertake the new activities that are in order. Change is but adjustment to the ebb and flow of human experience, and the success of the boldest plans will be assured when they unite the visions of youth with the dreams of age. For, as Archibald MacLeish wrote in *The Next Harvard:*

From the beginning of its history the next Harvard has been in process of evolution, and the next Harvard is in process of evolution now. Harvard, like other universities, is committed to one time and one time only — the future toward which the American Republic moves.

[23] *President's Report,* 1954–55.

Sources

Three known manuscripts of his recollections or reminiscences were prepared by Dr. J. Collins Warren. In subject matter these manuscripts are essentially alike.

Manuscript 1 (on deposit at the Massachusetts Historical Society) is a ribbon typescript entitled "Recollections of Three Eras in Surgery" and held in four of a series of five numbered, gray, ring-binder covers each of which bears the stamp imprint "J. Collins Warren 58 Beacon St. Boston Mass." Clipped inside the cover of binder number one is the following note in Dr. Warren's handwriting:

Note

A copy of these Recollections has been placed in the keeping of the Massachusetts Historical Society. There are many changes and corrections in this original MS., made from time to time which have not been reproduced in the copy, — but should be.

J. COLLINS WARREN

This manuscript, thus designated by Dr. Warren as the "original MS.," occupies 253 pages of text on standard typewriter paper. There is no separate title page. Each of the first four binders has a separate table of contents, and that in the first binder is headed "Recollections of Three Eras in Surgery." The text is followed by "Appendix I. History of the Harvard Cancer Commission" (pp. 254–258 and 258A–258E); "Appendix II. Need of Student Dormitories" (pp. 259–260); "Appendix III. Nélaton and Garibaldi" (pp. 261–264); a section entitled "Recollections of Dr. Holmes" (pp. 265–267); and a list of publications of Dr. J. Collins Warren from 1868 to 1910 inclusive (numbered pp. 1–4).

Judging from the note attached to the first binder and the fact that the text is distributed among four well-worn loose-leaf binders, it seems probable that Manuscript 1 is the "original" with respect to changes and corrections. There is nothing within it to indicate the date of preparation or when it was deposited in the Historical Society.

This typescript bears many corrections in pencil and in typewriting; also, numerous excisions of words, phrases, and sentences appear to have been made with a sharp penknife (or surgical scalpel).

The fifth binder contains miscellaneous papers relating to Park Street and to General Joseph Warren. Under the front cover is a

loose note reading: "See chapter in book entitled *Old Park Street* —
by Dr. Robert M. Lawrence." This book (*Old Park Street and Its
Vicinity*) included contributions by Dr. Warren and was published
by the Houghton Mifflin Company in 1922.

Manuscript 2 (on deposit by Mr. Joseph Warren at the Massachusetts Historical Society) is a ribbon typescript identified on the
title page as "Medical Recollections" by J. Collins Warren, but in
its table of contents as "Recollections of Three Eras in Surgery"
(the same title found in Manuscript 1). Also noted on the title page
are "Written 1913–1915" (in type) and "Corrected June 1916" and
"Corrected again April 1927" (the latter two in pencil). The pages,
which are unbound, are contained in a cardboard stationery box
tied with cord. Within the box is a memorandum typed on a Massachusetts Historical Society letterhead under date of February 7, 1927:

Recollections of Three Eras in Surgery and other Medical Recollections,
deposited by Dr. J. Collins Warren, March 26, 1919, subject to his recall or
that of his legal representative.
Copy of the original in possession of Dr. Warren.

In Volume 45 of the Warren Papers (Massachusetts Historical
Society) there is the same memorandum, followed by a notation (in
ink) over the signature of J. Collins Warren that this copy and other
material on deposit were "received . . . in return" on May 9, 1927.

The cardboard box container carries three notations, the first two
of which are in ink:

[1] Medical Recollections by J. Collins Warren. (Original in Dr. Warren's
possession.) — Deposited by Dr. J. Collins Warren, March 26, 1919. Subject
to his recall, or that of his legal representative.

[2] Recollections by Dr. J. Collins Warren. Redeposited by Prof. Joseph
Warren March 27, 1929. Subject to recall by him or his legal representative.

Typed on a pasted label is the note:

[3] Deposited by Joseph Warren (born 1906) — Sept. 26, 1955.

The text of Manuscript 2 occupies 261 pages of typewriter paper,
and in addition there are appendices and a table of contents, which
is headed "Recollections of Three Eras in Surgery." The typescript
bears many corrections (in pencil, ink, and typewriting) and excisions generally duplicating those in Manuscript 1. This is presumably the copy referred to in the note attached to Manuscript 1 as the
"copy of these Recollections . . . placed in the keeping of the Massachusetts Historical Society." Apparently, in 1927 the changes and
corrections which had accrued in Manuscript 1 were reproduced

in Manuscript 2. Manuscript 2 and probably Manuscript 1 (no date can be established for deposit of the latter) were withdrawn by Dr. Warren from the archives of the Historical Society on May 9, 1927. Further editing of the Recollections was terminated by Dr. Warren's death on November 3, 1927. His son Professor Joseph Warren re-deposited Manuscript 2 with the Historical Society on March 27, 1929.

Professor Warren died in 1942, and his son Mr. Joseph Warren (born 1906) formally redeposited Manuscript 2 in the Historical Society on September 26, 1955.

Manuscript 3 (property of Dr. Richard Warren). A ribbon type-script bearing the title "Reminiscences of J. Collins Warren, M.D." was found among the effects of Professor Joseph Warren after his death and became the property of his son Dr. Richard Warren. This manuscript was the sole basis for the present edited and an-notated version.

The date at which Manuscript 3 was made has not been established. Possibly it was 1926, when Dr. J. Collins Warren was working on his material with the assistance of A. M. Pickering. Many of the ex-cisions which mar Manuscripts 1 and 2 are indicated in Manuscript 3 by conventional ellipses or by such phrases as "small portion cut out here"; or an excised word is merely omitted without comment. A number of excisions and corrections appear in Manuscripts 1 and 2 that are not found in Manuscript 3; thus the latter preserves the passages in their original form. Such passages have, in the main, been carried through (with or without editorial change) into the present version.

The typescript entitled "Reminiscences of J. Collins Warren, M.D.," as preserved in Manuscript 3, contains a title page but no table of con-tents. The text ends on page 253, and an appendix on the need for a medical-school dormitory begins on the same page and extends through page 255. Following page 127 the manuscript is divided between two cardboard binders, but there is no break in continuity of text. A few notations in the manuscript have been made in pencil by the present editor and by previous readers of the script. A blue pencil has been used on pages 1–4 to indicate wherein this copy differs from Manuscript 1.

INDEX

Abajian, John, 153n
Abbott, Gilbert, 1n
Abdominal surgery, 81, 84, 106, 132, 168–170
Abernethy, John, 13
Adams, Samuel, 24n
Aesculapian Club, 253
Agassiz, Louis, 182, 239
Agnew, D. Hayes, 49
Alexander, Czar, 106
Alexander, Mr., 190
Allgemeines Krankenhaus, 93–98, 102–104, 106–110
Ambulance, 151n
American Association for the Advancement of Science, 239, 265
American College of Surgeons, 66, 226
American Medical Association, 32n, 217, 238, 244–245, 260
American Society for the Advancement of Clinical Investigation, 257
American Society for Clinical Investigation, 257
American Surgical Association, 49, 153n, 157n, 223
Amodeo, Prince, 101
Amory, C. W., 207n
Amory, Robert, 177n
Amputation without anesthesia, 37
Anatomic corrosion specimens, 103n
Ancient and Honorable Artillery Company, 7n
Andrew, Gov. John A., 56
Anesthesia (ether), 18, 31, 80n, 82n, 85, 100n, 177n, 240
    at Bromfield House, 33n
    complications, 32, 34, 121n, 134, 153n
    daguerreotype, 31n
    demonstration before Massachusetts Medical Society, 35, 36n
    first MGH demonstration, 1–2, 33, 153n, 241
    in obstetrics, 43n
    semicentennial, 36, 152–153
    as turning point in medicine, 240
Antisepsis, 130, 134, 171, 243
    at Billroth's clinic, 108n

debate in American Surgical Association, 157n
    at Lister's clinic, 128, 135–139
    at MGH, 138n, 145–146, 146n, 156–162
    modern appraisal of Listerism, 149n–150n
    in ovariotomy, 167n, 168n
    semantics of, 3n, 149n
    spray, carbolized, 159–160
    Warren's letter on Listerian method, 146n
Antiseptics in Civil War, 125n
Appendicitis, 84, 172
Appleton, Nathan, 24n, 101
Arlt, Carl Ferdinand von, 69, 97, 109
Arnold, Benedict, 12
Arnold, Howard Payson, 33n
Artificial respiration, 9n, 33n
Asepsis
    early development of, 161–162
    at Johns Hopkins, 171
    at MGH, 169–170, 228
    semantics of, 3n
Associated Charities, Boston, 202n
Association of American Physicians, 256–257
Atlee, John L., 71, 132
Atlee, Washington L., 71, 132

Babington, Dr., 13
Back Bay, 21n, 207
Bacon, Francis, 268
Bacon, John, 179n
Bacon, Robert, 210
Bacteriology. See Germ theory of disease
Barker, Lewellys F., 205n
Barnes, James K., 57
Barrett, Dr., 25n
Bartlett, Paul, 6n
Bartlett, W. Francis, 101
Beach, Henry H. A., 146n, 151, 159n, 161n, 167
Beebe, Lucius, 92n
Beecher, Henry K., 153n
Begg, Alexander S., 143n
Bell, Alexander Graham, 178n

Date Due

Library Bureau Cat. No. 1137